PSYCHOSOCIAL PROBLEMS OF COLLEGE MEN

PSYCHOSOCIAL PROBLEMS

OF COLLEGE MEN *by the Staff*

of the Division of Student Mental Hygiene,

Department of University Health, Yale

University

EDITED BY BRYANT M. WEDGE, M.D.

New Haven: YALE UNIVERSITY PRESS, 1958

to Dr. Clements C. Fry (1892–1955)
who devoted his life to his
student friends and patients
and who initiated and inspired
the work reported here

CONTRIBUTORS

ROBERT L. ARNSTEIN, M.D.
Psychiatrist, Department of University Health; clinical instructor, Department of Psychiatry, Yale University

JAMES S. DAVIE, Ph.D.
Sociologist, Department of University Health, Yale University

ROBERT W. HARRISON, M.S.
Psychiatric Social Worker, Department of University Health, Yale University

HENRY HARPER HART, M.D.
Consultant in Psychiatry, Department of University Health, Yale University; member, American Psychoanalytic Association

WALTER W. IGERSHEIMER, M.D.
Psychiatrist, Department of University Health; assistant clinical professor, Department of Psychiatry, Yale University

ALFREDO NAMNUM, M.D.
Psychiatrist, Department of University Health; assistant clinical professor, Department of Psychiatry, Yale University; member, Western New England Psychoanalytic Society

BERNARD NEUGEBOREN, M.S.
Psychiatric Social Worker, Department of University Health, Yale University

ERNST PRELINGER, Ph.D.
Psychologist, Department of University Health, Yale University

RALPH M. RUST, Ph.D.
Psychologist, Department of University Health, Yale University

FRANCIS J. RYAN, Ph.D.
Research Assistant, Department of University Health, Yale University

BRYANT M. WEDGE, M.D.
Chief Psychiatrist, Department of University Health; associate clinical professor, Department of Psychiatry, Yale University

PREFACE

THE COLLEGE AGE, second only to early childhood in personality development, may be a decisive epoch in the formation of healthy adult personalities. It is a distinct period in psychological development and one strikingly subject to the influence of social experience. Yet there has been little scientific scrutiny of personality development in college and certainly no accepted general theory has been developed. This volume reports on studies which are part of a sustained effort to explore and describe this age period. It is addressed to those behavioral scientists (sociologists, psychologists, psychiatrists, and psychoanalysts) who are interested in personality development, as well as, and even more primarily, to college educators, whose understanding of students is of such importance for the outcome of a significant life period.

The work reported here has been carried out by staff members of the Division of Student Mental Hygiene of the Department of University Health at Yale University.* The Division offers psychotherapeutic assistance to students of the University and carries on research and training in college psychiatry. This work has been generously supported by a gift from the Old Dominion Foundation, founded by Paul Mellon, for whose interest we have been grateful.

The chapters of this book are written by several authors using various methods of approach to the problem of personality development. This is necessitated by the belief that no single scientific discipline is yet able, methodologically or theoretically, to present comprehensively a subject so complex. The studies are integrated by the viewpoint that growth of the personality is a dynamic process resulting from interaction of biological, interpersonal and social forces. The authors have made only minimal concessions to the reader from other disciplines, believing that the methods and language used should convey meaning within the framework of each approach. Consequently some chapters, even

* The history of the Division is reported by C. C. Fry in *Mental Health in College,* New York, Commonwealth Fund, 1942. Its present structure is described by B. Wedge in "Developing a College Mental Hygiene Service," *Mental Hygiene, 41*:3, July 1957.

though they represent essential contributions to understanding of the whole subject, may require sturdy effort to comprehend.

It is suggested that each reader might start with the approach most familiar to him and work to other chapters from these, perhaps skimming quickly over difficult passages to get the flavor of each approach.

The chapters are so organized that the reader approaches the development of college students from "outside in," from the social milieu to the internal organization of the personality. Clinical studies are included, in the firm belief that intensive study of individual cases is a basic methodological approach to the study of the personality. Instances of disturbed development or of failure to adjust are particularly instructive in throwing light on processes which might otherwise be overlooked.

When cases have been reported here they have been disguised so that they cannot be identified, except perhaps by some of the patients themselves. Nevertheless, accuracy of reporting facts essential to the case has been strictly observed. The observations on Yale University and its students in general, on the other hand, have not been softened in any way. It is a University with its own characteristics, one of which is its capacity for critical self-evaluation. Consequently, since an essential thesis of these studies is the effect of the meeting of persons in transition with a relatively stable institution, the nature of the University is described as objectively as possible.

We wish to thank Dr. Ralph W. Alexander for permission to republish Chapter 8 and part of Chapter 5, both of which originally appeared in *Student Medicine,* and to Dr. John Frosch, editor of the *Journal of the American Psychoanalytic Association,* for releasing the paper presented in Chapter 13 for this publication. The members of our devoted secretarial staff deserve praise for their patience in preparing the manuscript.

It is with deep regret that we record the absence of Dr. Alfred Gross, who was Consultant to the Division, from the list of contributors. He was preparing a paper on the application of psychoanalytic ego psychology to treatment of the college student before his sudden death.

B. M. W.

New Haven, Conn.
March 1958

CONTENTS

CHAPTER 1

The Psychosocial Position of the College Man

BY BRYANT M. WEDGE AND JAMES S. DAVIE

This introduction outlines the theoretical framework of the studies to follow and specifies social characteristics of the scene in which they have been conducted.

1

IN INTRODUCING a course on the evolution and role of secondary education in France in 1905, Emile Durkheim (4) remarked:

> I think that the science of human affairs can serve to guide human behavior usefully. To behave well, says an old adage, one must know one's self well. But we know today that in order to know ourselves well, it is not enough to direct our attention to the superficial portion of our consciousness; for the sentiments, the ideas which come to the surface are not, by far, those which have the most influence on our conduct. What must be reached are the habits, the tendencies which have been established gradually in the course of our past life or which heredity has bequeathed to us; these are the real forces which govern us. Now, they are concealed in the unconscious. We can, then, succeed in discovering them only by reconstructing our personal history and the history of our family. In the same way, in order to be able profitably to fulfill our function in a scholastic system, whatever it may be, it must be known, not from the outside, but from within, that is to say, through history.

Durkheim's suggestion that the effects of education can be understood and modified through knowledge *in depth* of the nature of individuals using educational institutions *and* of the nature of the institutions to which these individuals are exposed is as germane today as at the turn of the century. Many systematic studies bearing on these effects have since appeared in relation to lower education at all levels, adding considerably to the effectiveness of lower educational institutions. It may suffice here to mention the proliferation of courses in child development in preparing teachers, and the use of such concepts as "readiness" to undertake specific learning tasks. At higher educational levels, however, remarkably little systematic attention has been paid to personality development or to the effects of scholastic systems on this. Such a dearth of studies is all the more notable because intellectual productivity, presumably a desideratum in persons undertaking higher education, has been repeatedly shown to be delicately dependent on personality factors.

Nevitt Sanford has suggested that the reason for neglect in this area may be the "notion among psychologists that the personality is well formed by seventeen or thereabouts, and that what happens after that is merely an expression or an unfolding, of what has previously been established" (8). It is true that only recently has dynamic psychological theory begun to offer an adequate conceptual framework in terms of which the changes taking place in the college years can be studied, that is, ego-psychological theory. This theory makes it possible to study the processes of reorganization of the personality in terms of current experience in college, this reorganization being, perhaps, a distinctive characteristic of the college years.

There may also be some reluctance to treat a special segment of the population, based on attendance at college, as a distinct group showing distinct developmental characteristics. It is a thesis of the studies in this volume that the college student represents a special and relatively important case of psychosocial development within the range of possibilities encompassed in the age period of roughly 17 to 22 years. Fry, in 1942, called college students "a special group of adolescents" (6). While by no means exempt from general laws of personality development, such special cases deserve to be studied in their own right, especially when the outcome of the period appears to be decisive for the continued life course.

A number of writers have pointed out that the college student has postponed the attainment of the full status of adulthood. Blos states that "the artificial prolongation of a maturational period (adolescence) affects almost every student at one point of his college career" (1). Clothier (2) also speaks of a protracted adolescence and suggests that this prolongation *may* lead to a more certain and dependable maturity. In a recent and highly significant contribution to the psychology of adolescence Erikson refers to the "more or less sanctioned intermediary periods between childhood and adulthood" as *psychosocial moratoria* "during which a lasting pattern of 'inner identity' is scheduled for relative completion." He also points out that the development of a satisfactory "inner identity" requires a reconciliation of the growing person's conception of himself and his community's recognition of him, again emphasizing the significance of the society for psychological development at this level.

In earlier adolescence, roughly between 12 and 17 years of age, there is a relative increase in the strength of the instincts and a relative weakening and fatigue of the controlling mechanism, the ego (7). This accounts for the turmoil and flightiness of that period. Later adolescence, approximately from 17 to 22 years, presents a considerably different dynamic picture. It is our general view that, in the college student at least, the ego is relatively strong in relation to the instincts but has definite tasks in bringing itself in relation to social reality. It is interesting that although we have no distinct word for this period, it was recognized by the ancient Greeks in the term *ephebic*, referring to the period of garrison duty and training of the citizen-to-be from the ages of 18 to 20. Thus the adolescence of persons who go to college or utilize other psychosocial moratoria seems to fall into two distinct phases. In the first, adolescence proper, the ego is mainly concerned with mastery of the instincts; in the second, the ephebic stage, the ego is concerned with establishing the relation of the person to reality.

The impetus to processes of self-definition is furnished not only by anticipation of adulthood but by the impact of leaving the family. This throws upon the student the necessity to gain recognition and take positions for himself as distinct from those which depended on the family. This process of individuation or identity formation requires the achievement of a stable organization or synthesis by the ego of diverse impulses, roles, values, and interests into a coherent whole.

Self-definition requires the establishment of occupational, sexual, social, and ideational syntheses. The details of the processes by which such hierarchical organization is achieved, the conditions which facilitate or retard this process in various individuals, and the effects of the particular college experience on the more or less final organization are issues of considerable importance for the understanding of the meaning of college in personality growth. Since it is apparent that these processes sometimes go awry, such detailed knowledge can be expected to influence corrective action, both in the college psychiatric clinic and in the teaching and administration of college programs. The studies reported here represent preliminary explorations of several aspects of this process. In order to view the processes of reorganization at all levels of personality function, a variety of methods are necessary. Sociological methods can best specify the characteristics of the community in relation to which the person must define himself, while only psychoanalytic research methods can define the mechanisms by which new synthesis is achieved at deeper levels of the personality, i.e. in relation to the distribution of instinctual energy. Hence, comprehensive understanding of the psychosocial development of the college student requires approaches at levels from the environmental to the instinctual, by methods from the statistical to the intensive study of individual cases. The present studies represent but samplings of these levels, and perhaps hint at the interlocking nature of the processes, but it is not yet possible to construct more than a skeletal model of the whole.

As mentioned earlier, Erikson has convincingly shown that the formation of a satisfactory sense of personal identity depends on the willingness of the society to recognize the identity which the individual is attempting to achieve. It follows from this that studies of the personality development of the college student must specify the social qualities of the college scene in which the studies are conducted and, by implication, the type and range of role which that section of the larger society is willing to recognize. Surprisingly few investigations have taken this into account, perhaps because of some reluctance to expose colleges to objective critique. Exceptions are to be found in the studies at Vassar College by Sanford and his associates (9), in the series of publications by the staff of Sarah Lawrence College (10), and from the study of student life at Princeton (3). Research of this type should eventually make comparison possible which can illuminate still further the accuracy of general models.

The second section of this Chapter describes salient features of the Yale College culture which impinge on the student.

2

As any visitor to a number of colleges can attest, there is a great variation among colleges in the United States. Some insist on a rigid code of behavior and require their student to sign pledges concerning smoking, drinking, movie attendance, dancing, and so forth, while others are ultraprogressive and proudly proclaim they have practically no rules at all. Some have large departments of physical education and place a premium on muscle, while in others intellectuality rules the day and athletic participation is considered rather crude. Some pride themselves on the immediate pragmatic usefulness of their curriculum, while others tend to stress pure knowledge, theoretical exposition, and an aesthetic appreciation of life and the universe. Some devote themselves to a philosophy of individual, tailor-made courses with intense tutorship, while in others hundreds of students are herded together and exposed to knowledge through loudspeaker systems. Some boast of their "all-round education" and exert subtle pressures against one-sided activities, while others emphasize the development of special talents.

One could continue to list many *separate* ways in which colleges differ, and if one considered colleges in terms of the *totality* of their individual characteristics, the range would be even greater. As with individuals, each college creates its own impression on the observer. The impression it creates is a function of its particular combination of characteristics. It is this unique configuration which most differentiates a college from other colleges and gives to it its own special character.

Since the chapters to follow are based exclusively on Yale students, it is advisable at the outset of this volume to sketch briefly some of the more salient aspects of undergraduate Yale. While an adequate treatment of the topic would entail a volume in itself, the following remarks should serve as a reasonably accurate introduction to the Yale that is inevitably an intimate part of our subjects' lives.

Yale is both a college and a university. It is a college in that general education is offered to secondary-school graduates in its undergraduate schools of Yale College and the School of Engineering. It is a university in that graduate training is offered in its graduate and professional schools. Until recently it has been a college-centered university. It has been so in two senses. First, historically, Yale was founded (in 1701) as a college devoted to general instruction in the arts and sciences whereby young men might be more fit for service "both in Church and Civil State." It was not until over a century later that the first professional school was founded under Yale's name. During the ensuing years Yale gradually became a university as its various other professional schools were founded and developed. Second, and more important, although Yale grew from a college to a university, the College remained the focal point or the heart of the University until the twentieth century.

During the past three or four decades the university aspects of Yale have been increasingly emphasized, with the result that graduate, undergraduate, and professional schools now tend to be regarded as separate but integral parts of the whole that is contemporary Yale. Although the position of the college has changed within the university, its basic educational philosophy has remained essentially unchanged. Here one finds expressed in many ways the idea that the task of education is to educate the whole man, to help him to develop spiritually, socially, physically, morally, and intellectually, so that as an adult member of society he many conduct himself as a gentleman and as an intelligent citizen.

With the above as a general background, we may quickly sketch in some of the more striking characteristics of contemporary undergraduate Yale. Located in a city that is rich in historical tradition, Yale is a private male residential college which annually admits about 1,000 students. To them it offers a four-year course of instruction culminating in the award of a bachelor's degree. Organizationally, undergraduate Yale consists of the Freshman Year,

Yale College, and the undergraduate program of the School of Engineering.

The "Common Freshman Year" is organized under its own Dean and advisory council and conducts its own disciplinary, counseling, housing, and feeding operations. In its curriculum it serves as a subordinate unit of both upper schools (Yale College and the School of Engineering). Its intended function is to prepare first-year students for the more advanced work of the upper schools and to help them become oriented in their new environment. As one means toward the attainment of these ends, each freshman is assigned to a resident counselor to whom he can go for information and advice. He also consults with designated faculty members about his choice of courses. The normal freshman program consists of five year-courses or the equivalent which must show a reasonable distribution among the various fields of study.

After Freshman Year the students move to one of the ten residential colleges, where they remain until graduation. Each of the residential colleges has its own recreational, social, and boarding facilities plus limited athletic facilities such as squash courts. It is presided over by a resident master and a group of faculty members known as fellows, several of whom reside in the college. The college system was established to enhance the social and educational values inherent in small-group life. In theory, it affords each student an opportunity for membership in a social unit and greater opportunities for contact with the faculty than he might otherwise find.

When students move from the freshman campus into the residential colleges, they enroll in Yale College or the undergraduate program of the School of Engineering. In both, the normal course program is five year-courses or the equivalent for each of the upperclass years. Yale College offers the B.A. or B.S. degree in the liberal arts and sciences. The B.A. degree is awarded to those who pursue a course of study which provides for a liberal breadth in the arts and sciences and for concentration in one of the humanistic fields of work during the junior and senior years. The B.S. degree differs in that students major in mathematics or in one of the natural sciences during their last two years. Those entering the Engineering School may enroll for the B.E. or B.S. degree.

The former is awarded for work in one of the several fields of engineering; the latter, for work in an industrial administration program which seeks to develop both administrative and technical skills. Students in both programs are strongly encouraged to give careful thought to their choice of electives and to balance their technical training with a judicious selection of courses from the arts and humanities.

While most students follow one of the course programs sketched above, some enroll in special programs such as the Directed Studies program and the Scholar of the House program. Directed Studies is designed for the first two years of college work and features a carefully organized and integrated combination of courses which are intended to provide students with a common intellectual basis for the work of the last two years. The Scholar of the House program is designed to give a handful of seniors of demonstrated ability an opportunity for truly individual work. Excused from regular course requirements, they are free to devote their senior year to the execution of a project of their own choosing.

Implicit in all of the above is the assumption that the graduating Yale senior, regardless of his school affiliation, program of study, or degree received, should be a man who is educated in breadth and depth, a man who can think and express himself clearly, is appreciative of the world around him, and who is sensitive to his responsibilities as a citizen. To achieve these ends Yale tries many means. It is simultaneously conservative and self-critical. It holds to its fundamental beliefs about the purpose of a college education and eyes with suspicion any fanciful but unproven proposal for altering the *status quo*. Yet it is ever aware that there is room for constructive improvement. Therefore, the familiar question of the best ratio of breadth to depth—required to elective courses, discussion groups to lecture courses—and many other similar questions are constantly under consideration.

The combination of firm devotion to ends and questioning of the best means to attain such ends is a healthy state of affairs but not without its inherent difficulties. While it is desirable that an institution clearly state what it stands for and believes in, the espousal of a liberal arts education inevitably alienates somewhat those faculty members and students who are more pragmatically minded and vocationally oriented. Similarly, while it is desirable to be open-minded and self-critical, a certain amount of discomfort is engendered by the vacillation and apparent indecision which tend to accompany such an attitude. Like many other colleges, Yale experiments with various means to achieve its particular ends, and the vigorous discussion of alternate means on the part of students, faculty, and administration has at times its divisive rather than unifying effects. Like all colleges, Yale is faced with the fundamental question of whether to treat its undergraduates as somewhat irresponsible adolescents or as responsible young adults. Although it leans toward the latter, it tends to vacillate between these two poles because of the nature of the age group. It sees a natural progression of maturity from freshman to senior year but recognizes that at any point in this progression student behavior has both adolescent and adult aspects, each of which must be treated differently. Although student government is virtually nonexistent, college regulation of student affairs is kept at a minimum. However, the watchful parental eye of the college is ever open and ready to intervene if necessary. By declining to take an arbitrary and consistent stand on the question of best means and by its attempts to remain open-minded about it, Yale tends to complicate the question of the proper means for attainment of its own educational ends. Despite periodic disagreement on particulars, however, most students and college officials would express the feeling that the solutions Yale has achieved to date are good ones and that even better ones will gradually emerge over the coming years.

No description of the character of an educational institution would be complete without consideration of its student body. The student body is important in sheer numerical terms because it usually outnumbers the faculty and administrative personnel. It is important because it represents the raw material with which the college must work and from which it hopes to fashion its conception of an educated man. It is important because students become alumni and, as such, rightly or wrongly, are walking advertisements of their alma mater. As alumni they are frequently called upon for moral and financial support of their college's current educational practices and future plans and often contribute their share, fair or not, of both constructive and reactionary criticism. The student body is also important because it represents another major world within college walls, the world of peer culture, the patterned behavior and values of which may diverge from that desired by the official culture of the faculty and administration and which may often serve as obstacles to the attainment of official ends.

Traditionally, the Yale student body has tended to come from the upper levels of the social and economic strata of American society, particularly from these levels on the eastern seaboard of the United States, and has exhibited the characteristics thereof. In keeping with the values and circumstances of their families, most of the students (traditionally) have been educated in private secondary schools. Their parents have been native-born, Republican, Protestant, and well educated. Their fathers have been top-level proprietors, executives, or professionals, and the family income, often bulwarked by inherited funds, has permitted a comfortable mode of life. This tradition is still reflected in contemporary Yale but to a much smaller degree than formerly. It has been modified in the last few decades by raising of academic standards for admissions, by successful efforts to draw students from as wide a geographic area as possible, by extensive granting of scholarships to able students, by offering other means of financial support such as student employment and loans, and by an increasing tendency to admit students of public high-school background. Some of these changes Yale has consciously effected. Others reflect changing conditions in the society at large as wealth has become more evenly distributed, as educational costs have mounted, and as the quality and quantity of competition for admission to college has increased.

Today Yale accepts approximately one out of every four applicants. Acceptance is determined by multiple criteria. A prediction based on secondary-school record and on aptitude and performance test scores is used to determine the degree of capacity the student has for doing the academic work at Yale. Also, since the college is not interested in brain power alone, other subjective criteria are employed. These fall under the general heading of "personal qualifications" or "promise as a person" and involve such considerations as good character, good citizenship, and leadership ability. The presence of these intangible qualities is inferred from data gathered through such devices as personal interviews with alumni and admissions officials, letters of recommendation, personality appraisals by secondary-school principals and headmasters, secondary-school extracurricular records, and so forth. An outstanding record on any one of these criteria is generally not sufficient to insure admission. Rather many different criteria are weighed and balanced in an effort to evaluate the total person in terms of his accomplishments and potentialities. On the outcome of this intricate and often nebulous process will depend the student's acceptance or rejection.

It is thus not surprising to find that the class which has been created by the admissions process is, as an entity, a group of intelligent, capable young men of good character who have demonstrated their abilities in academic and extracurricular pursuits and show considerable promise of continuing good performance in college and of becoming good citizens and influential leaders in the adult world. It is also not surprising to find that the general values of the student body concentrate around the concept of the all-around man. At Yale, this type of person is characterized by a reasonable level of scholarship, a good degree of social competence, and an active involvement in campus activities. Much of this is represented and influenced by the system of senior societies to which approximately ten per cent of a class is elected in the spring term of junior year. Election to a society is the highest honor that a student can receive from his fellow undergraduates. Such an honor is generally reserved for those who most closely approximate the Yale ideal, particularly for those who have been outstandingly successful in extracurricular and athletic pursuits.

While the above configuration represents a general ideal, one can distinguish several alternate types of adjustment to campus life which have been effected by different groups within the student body. These types are presented not as an exhaustive categorization of the student body but rather as an illustration of the variety of types that can and do exist on the Yale campus. They are: (1) the intellectual or scholarly type, consisting of persons whose interests are primarily intellectual and who are regarded somewhat askance by their fellow students; (2) athletes who, while respected for their athletic prowess, are regarded as a special type until they have demonstrated they have something more than muscle to contribute to Yale life; (3) a rather large group of the vocationally oriented, frequently found as premedical or engineering students; often they come to Yale on scholarship and are anxious for professional or vocational training and advancement; these tend to be more concerned with post-college status in adult society than with in-college status in the campus society; (4) a relatively small but prominent group who have great business ambitions and are socially mobile individuals; usually from the middle class, these quite often participate actively in campus activities, tend to show a modest academic achievement, and are heading for the world of business; (5) perhaps the largest group, an intermediate one composed of individuals who show good achievement without strong goals or drives but who are intellectually competent and who seem to be fairly well-rounded individuals without being deeply committed to anything.

Since extracurricular participation and achievement is an avenue to campus acceptance and prestige and since it consumes vast quantities of the time that is not spent on course work (and occasionally at the expense of course work), some mention should be made of the vast array of facilities for such activities. In the realm of athletics, Yale has gymnasium and field facilities for almost all sports. The usual team sports of football, basketball, and baseball are played, along with other well-known but less popular sports, such as hockey, soccer, swimming, and track. There are facilities for the "individual" sports, such as tennis, squash, and golf. In addition, there are facilities for some of the lesser-known athletic activities, such as crew, polo, fencing, lacrosse, and rugby.

The many athletic activities are organized on several levels. Freshman Year boasts an extensive intramural program in addition to its intercollegiate teams. This is paralleled on the upperclass levels by an extensive intramural "residential college" program of athletic competition as well as by the "official" college teams which represent the college in intercollegiate competition. In keeping with its emphasis on the whole man, Yale firmly believes that athletic participation or at least physical exercise is a necessary ingredient of the college experience. However, it also believes that athletics should be kept in proper perspective, as evidenced by its membership in the Ivy League and its subscription to the principles thereof.

In the realm of nonathletic activities there also exists a wide variety of "things to do." Most of these activities take place on the upperclass levels. One locus of activity is the residential college, which often has its own newspaper, interest groups, social committees, and so forth. As with athletics, the other locus of activities is the campus itself. Here a great variety of groups is found. They range from small, somewhat evanescent clusterings of the alumni of some preparatory school to large, well-established, and prestigeful organizations like the college newspaper, the chairmanship of which has been one of the prize extracurricular plums for many decades. It is unnecessary to list the many separate organizations that exist on campus. Rather it is sufficient to point out that as in athletics where a student can find a contact or non-contact sport, a team sport or an individual sport, which interests him, so can he find something of interest in nonathletic activities. He can involve himself in publications of various kinds or in radio or TV work. There is debating and student dramatic production. There are political and religious groups. In the realm of music, there are instrumental and choral groups and a host of informal singing groups. There are also special interest groups such as model railroading, sailing, and premedical clubs. A nonresidential fraternity system exists to supplement the students' social lives. Finally, there are two honor societies and the senior society system. In brief, there are many opportunities for participation in athletic and nonathletic extracurricular activities. Actual participation in activities is encouraged by the campus value that it is good to participate, that one should be outstanding if possible in some area of his participation, and that if one can succeed in one of the more prestigeful activities such as a major sport or a major activity like work on the college newspaper, then so much the better as evidence of the man's intrinsic worth.

As with athletics, Yale feels that these other types of extracurricular activities have their proper place in the scheme of things educational. They are judged to have a broadening and enriching influence on student development. Through them the student experiences the joys of comradeship and a sense of group identification and loyalty. He develops his special skills and interests and accumulates valuable experience in encountering and solving problems, and in meeting and dealing with other people in various situations. However, here too the question is one of proper perspective. One frequently hears complaints from the faculty and administration that the average undergraduate spends most of his time lurching from crisis to crisis and that campus life is too distressingly faithful a reproduction of the intense competitiveness of American business life. This verdict distresses college officials, for it detracts from the cherished conviction that the college years should be devoted to a life of quiet contemplation rather than one of frenetic activity. In their eyes this is not the most fruitful way in which a student might prepare himself for adult life. In the students' eyes, however, such activity tends to be viewed as a practical preparation for later life. They observe the adult world with all of its competitiveness, commercialism, and emphasis on action rather than thought, form their own conceptions of what constitutes success in adult life, and busy themselves accordingly. How to combat these tendencies which are a reflection of the larger society is one of the chief problems of the liberal educator at Yale.

REFERENCES

1. Blos, Peter, Psychological counseling of college students, *American Journal of Orthopsychiatry, 14*:571–80. 1946.

2. Clothier, F., The challenge of a protracted adolescence, *Vassar Alumnae Magazine*. Oct. 1947.

3. Davie, J. S., and Hare, A. P., Button-down collar culture, *Human Organization, 14*(4):13–20. 1956.

4. Durkheim, Emile, *Education and Sociology* (Glencoe, Ill., Free Press, 1956), p. 152.

5. Erikson, E. H., The problem of ego identity, *Journal of the American Psychoanalytic Association, 4*:56–121. 1956.

6. Fry, C. C., *Mental Health in College*, New York, Commonwealth Fund, 1942.

7. Josselyn, Irene, The ego in adolescence, *American Journal of Orthopsychiatry, 24*:223–37. 1954.

8. Sanford, Nevitt, Personality development during the college years, *Personnel and Guidance Journal, 35*:74–80. 1956.

9. ——— ed., Personality development during the college years, *Journal of Social Issues, 12*(4):3–70. 1956.

10. Taylor, Harold, ed., *Essays in Teaching*, New York, Harper, 1950.

CHAPTER 2

Satisfaction and the College Experience

BY JAMES S. DAVIE

The author utilizes a sociological and statistical approach to the problem of satisfaction with college. He views satisfaction as a resultant of the interaction of the student and the college environment and tests the hypothesis that satisfaction is related to the student's success in handling internal and external pressures. The study demonstrates that satisfaction is related to social and personal background factors and to characteristics of the student's experience at Yale.

IN THE DAILY ROUTINE of a college one encounters many manifestations of the fact that all students are not equally satisfied with their total college experience and that what is satisfying to one student may be dissatisfying to another. In the conversation of students, for example, who has not heard statements like the following? "This place is the greatest!" "I don't feel happy here." "I'm getting the kind of education I want." "My roommates are grade-A stinkers!" "I guess this place is O.K." "I've got a terrific major!" "He's one of that damn fraternity crowd." "I don't belong here." "My classmates are a great bunch of guys." "The social setup on campus stinks!" "My courses are boring." "I can't think of a better college to attend than this one!" "I don't like this place."

In a gross way such statements indicate something of the student's feelings about himself and his college experience, but they do not enable one to assess with any reasonable degree of certainty either the true extent of the feelings or the reasons for them.

In the following pages we shall summarize a series of studies which were designed to yield a more comprehensive and meaningful picture of student satisfaction than that afforded by casual observation. We shall present a way of viewing and a method of studying the phenomenon of satisfaction, as well as the kind of results obtained when satisfaction is studied from this viewpoint with this method at Yale.

1. THE STUDIES

It is our thesis that "satisfaction with the college experience" is a resultant of the interaction process between the student and the college environment. It is a feeling tone which reflects the success with which the individual handles both internal needs and external pressures.

The interaction of a student and his environment is conceptualized as a dynamic on-going process. The student acts on the environment; the environment acts on the student; and the action of each is influenced by the reaction of the other. For analytical purposes, one may look at the interaction process from two viewpoints. If one focuses on the student and pictures him as trying to satisfy certain needs as he manipulates his environment, then satisfaction can be interpreted as a measure of drive reduction—of how successful the student has been in fulfilling his conscious or unconscious needs and achieving his goals in the college environment. If, however, one focuses on the environment and pictures it as posing certain requirements to which the student must adjust, then satisfaction can be interpreted as a measure of "fit"—of how successful the student has been in meeting requirements imposed on him from without.

In the latter approach the environment is conceptualized not as a mere aggregate of individuals pursuing their separate ends but rather as an organized entity exhibiting shared patterns of belief and behavior. In effect, the university environment exhibits two major "cultures," the official culture of the faculty and administration and the "peer culture" of the student body.* As with the larger society, each culture transcends the individual student. The official culture persists through the continued presence of faculty and administrative personnel. While individual students may come and go, the peer culture also persists, being

* See, for example, Edward Y. Hartshorne, "Undergraduate Society and the College Culture," *American Sociological Review, 8*(3):321–32, 1943; and James S. Davie and A. Paul Hare, "Button-down Collar Culture," *Human Organization, 14*(4):13–20, 1956.

transmitted from one generation of students to another in an un-broken sequence. As Hartshorne has commented (p. 322):

> The college "generation" is only four years. Actually, how-ever, the temporal horizon of any individual student spans seven annual class-groups: his own, the three ahead of him when he is a freshman, and the three behind him when he is a senior. Since every class-group inherits from its prede-cessors, by direct personal contact over three years, and in-directly over an indefinite period, there is ideal generational continuity to transmit the cultural heritage. No link is lost.

Both cultures impose requirements on the student. Many of the requirements of the official culture are formalized into rules and regulations about course selection, degree requirements, class attendance, athletic eligibility, entertainment of guests in dormi-tory rooms, and the like. Other requirements are less formalized but are equally present, as when a student is dismissed for "con-duct unbecoming a gentleman." Requirements are also imposed by the peer culture, although less obviously, for they are seldom specified in writing except for an occasional statement in campus publications such as the humor magazine or the editorial page of the student newspaper. Nevertheless, how much one should study, how one should behave on dates, how one should speak, eat, dress, and behave toward others are matters which are not left exclusively to the discretion of the individual. In brief, every educational institution tends to develop a unique character or *ethos* in terms of its prevailing educational philosophy and stand-ards and the kind of person it consciously or unconsciously selects, shapes, and finally produces as alumni. Thus, because students differ, at any given college some students will fit better than others, will experience less stress and strain in their adjustment efforts, and will feel more satisfied with their total experience at that college.

At the time the student is interacting with his college environ-ment, he is a young adult subject to the psychological and social pressures which tend to characterize this period in the life cycle. From a developmental and psychological viewpoint, perhaps the most striking thing occurring during this period is the individual's struggle to assume an identity, to develop a meaningful self-concept, to obtain an answer to the question: Who am I? * From a more social-psychological viewpoint, young adulthood is a period during which the individual is completing the process of emancipating himself from his family and preparing himself for that imminent point in time when society expects him to function as an emotionally independent, self-supporting, productive member of society.† The peer group assumes increasing importance at this age, for it affords the student additional support as he severs his emotional dependency on the family. It provides him with an anchor point as he experiments with various roles and attempts, from elements in his experience with his peers, parents, and others, to synthesize a life role which is tailored to his needs and to external circumstances as he perceives them. In addition, the imminence of adult life which centers chiefly around the job and marriage confronts the student with the important questions of vocational choice and heterosexual relations. All such aspects of young adulthood may influence greatly the nature of the interaction of the student with his college environment.

It was with the above orientation that the studies of satisfaction at Yale were begun. The questionnaire was selected as the basic research tool and detailed questionnaires were sent to random samples of the classes of 1953, 1954, 1955, and 1956 in the spring term of their senior years. The sample percentages for the studies were 20, 40, 25, and 25. The percentage of the samples returning completed questionnaires were 81, 75, 79, and 78.

The purpose of the initial study was twofold. From a practical viewpoint, it sought to obtain a clearer picture of the undergraduate scene against which one could better evaluate the complaints which students made about their college experiences during their visits to the Division of Mental Hygiene. From a more technical research viewpoint, it sought to determine whether one could measure satisfaction with the college experience through questionnaire methods and, if so, to identify some of the types of factors associated with different degrees of satisfaction. Results

* See Erik H. Erikson, "The Problem of Ego Identity," *Journal of the American Psychoanalytic Association,* 4(3):56–121, 1956.

† For elaboration of this point of view see James H. S. Bossard, *The Sociology of Child Development,* New York, Harper, 1948.

of the initial study were sufficiently favorable to encourage further work in this area.

Whereas the primary focus of the first study was on satisfaction as a resultant of the interaction process and on the question of whether it could be measured, the focus of subsequent studies shifted to the interaction process itself. Increasing attention was paid to the identification and measurement of both individual needs and environmental pressures and to their relation to satisfaction for both the study group as a whole and for specific types or categories of students within the study group. As the studies progressed, the questionnaires varied somewhat in length and content as useful questions were retained, apparently useless ones were eliminated or rephrased, and still others were added, the possible importance of which was indicated by the analysis of the data currently on hand. In general, however, each of the four questionnaires asked the student for his retrospective reaction to and evaluation of selected aspects of his undergraduate experience.

2. SOME GENERAL ASPECTS OF THE YALE EXPERIENCE

As we turn to the Yale undergraduate scene, it is desirable to indicate some of the major characteristics of the Yale student body. By so doing we may indicate something of the flavor or *ethos* of Yale as well as the types of variables which have been considered in the study of satisfaction with the Yale experience. We shall arbitrarily define as a major characteristic any attribute possessed by 60 per cent or more of the students in the study groups. It should be clearly understood that the following description is of *groups* of students, not of individual students. While each attribute mentioned is *separately* true of a majority of Yale students, any given student may possess any number of these attributes.

The majority of Yale undergraduates come from middle- or upper-class homes on the eastern seaboard. Their parents are native born, Protestant, alive, and living together. Their mothers are housewives. Their fathers, by United States census definitions, are professionals, proprietors, or executives. In secondary school the students were in reasonably good spirits most of the time and felt that they had a reasonably good time there. They participated in academic, athletic, social, and extracurricular activities and reported that their performance in each of these areas was not adversely affected by personal problems.

At Yale they spend their first year in a dormitory room on the freshman campus and have roommates. At the beginning of their sophomore year they move to one of the ten residential colleges, where they remain until graduation. During each of these latter years they have roommates. During their four years at Yale they participate in academic, extracurricular, athletic, and social activities. As in secondary school, their performance in each of these areas is not adversely affected by personal problems. Similarly, they are not bothered by insomnia, by nervousness, or by loneliness. They get along well with peers of both sexes, have little trouble making friends at Yale, and feel that they have a reasonably sufficient number of friends and dates while at Yale. They have their own cars or access to the cars of friends and have $25 or more pocket money available for pleasure each month.

At the beginning of the sophomore year they enter Yale College (as opposed to the Engineering School), where they enroll for the B.A. degree, which they receive three years later with a major in one of the humanities or the social sciences. They choose their major primarily on the basis of its intrinsic interest to them, and if they had it to do over would choose the same major again. They feel that a highly important function of college is to provide one with a basic general education and appreciation of ideas. They agree with the statement that the purpose of a college education is not to teach one how to earn a living but rather how to enjoy the living one will earn. Another highly important function of college is the development of one's ability to get along with different kinds of people. Vocational training is not considered highly important.

At time of entrance they have only a hazy idea of what Yale is "all about," both academically and nonacademically, but express a desire to compete and succeed in both academic and extracurricular activities. The level of grades received in college is seen as being positively related to success in later life, but the relationship is not perceived as being a large one.

At graduation they report that they feel satisfied with their total experience at Yale, that they have been successful in getting what they have wanted out of college and in adjusting to the various demands Yale has made of them in both academic and non-academic activities. In addition they feel they have been successful in living up to what their parents have expected of them both academically and nonacademically. During their college days they have seriously considered from one to three different occupational fields as a possible lifetime work and at time of graduation are fairly certain of the field which they will enter. They say that their family and/or friends will have little or nothing to do with obtaining their first permanent job. Highly important attributes of an ideal job are the chance to use their special abilities or aptitudes and the chance to be creative and original. On graduation day they are single and unattached (not engaged, married, or going steady) and anticipate that at some time they will take further course work at some graduate school.

With the above as a general background, we may now consider in greater detail the data gathered from the satisfaction questionnaires. Our first concern will be to portray what seem to be some of the "high" and "low" spots of the college experience for the study groups as a whole. We shall discuss in Section 3 the instrument used for measuring the individual student's satisfaction with his Yale experience, and in Section 4 the variables which are related to satisfaction within the study groups.

The four years. In an effort to crosscut the variety of undergraduate experience and to focus on one of the relatively few common denominators of undergraduate life, the subjects in the study groups were asked:

1. Which year at Yale have you enjoyed the most?
2. Which year have you enjoyed the least?
3. Considering the influence of all your studies, contacts, activities, etc., during which year did you develop the most?
4. During which year did you develop the least?

In a simultaneous effort to preserve the variety of individual experience, the students were encouraged to write in their reasons or explanations for their choice of a particular year. Table 1 presents the tabulation of the choices made. It shows that for the majority of the students senior year was the most enjoyable while freshman year was the least enjoyable. Junior and senior years were the most rewarding and freshman and sophomore years least rewarding.

TABLE *1*. PERCENTAGE DISTRIBUTION OF ANSWERS TO THE "YEAR" QUESTIONS, 1953–56

Year Enjoyed Most

	1953	*1954*	*1955*	*1956*
No answer	1	0	0	2
Freshman	6	3	4	11
Sophomore	4	5	7	11
Junior	22	21	17	21
Senior	65	69	70	53
Combination answers	3	2	1	2

Year Enjoyed Least

	1953	*1954*	*1955*	*1956*
No answer	1	2	1	1
Freshman	53	45	52	45
Sophomore	26	34	29	32
Junior	12	10	11	14
Senior	5	7	6	5
Combination answers	3	2	2	2

Year Developed Most

	1953	*1954*	*1955*	*1956*
No answer	1	1	1	2
Freshman	13	9	12	16
Sophomore	9	10	10	18
Junior	31	30	35	33
Senior	43	48	42	30
Combination answers	3	3	1	1

Year Developed Least

	1953	*1954*	*1955*	*1956*
No answer	4	1	2	2
Freshman	37	31	33	32
Sophomore	39	45	40	40
Junior	9	14	13	16
Senior	9	8	11	9
Combination answers	2	2	1	2

As might be expected, the reasons given by the respondents for their choices covered a wide range of factors. These are difficult to assess in a quantitative way, but one can describe certain themes which seem to run throughout. As the quotations below suggest, those who chose freshman year as least enjoyable and rewarding tended to stress the difficulty of adjustment to a new environment. In the academic area, the reasons offered stressed course work, which was pictured as difficult or as unstimulating and repetitious of secondary school work. In the nonacademic area, frequent mention was made of poor rooming situations and a general need for better "orientation."

> "Had a few unpleasant experiences with roommates, not yet adjusted and settled at Yale. I was enormously homesick. I didn't see much of my sweetheart and felt a bit out of things on the freshman campus."

> "Poor adjustment to scientific courses."

> "Unsuccessful in picking courses. Physics *and* calculus too much. *No* social life."

> "Nothing but study, little sleep and student employment."

> "Boring repetition of senior year prep school."

> "Poor teachers in poor required courses."

> "Incompatible roommates."

> "Poor roommates."

> "Didn't know my way around."

> "A big adjustment from a small country day school."

> "The totally unfamiliar feeling of being unsupervised."

> "Strangeness of the east and of college life (I come from California)."

> "I had disagreeable roommates, bad classes and a poor schedule."

> "I was immature in both actions and financial control."

> "Little social life, failed to get interested in my courses. Roommates not altogether my type."

> "Wasn't adequately prepared. Went to high school. Family problems."

"Difficulty in adjusting to Yale environment and studies."

"I suffered a severe ego shock by meeting competition with peers where I was unable to triumph, both scholastically and extracurricularly."

"Tremendous amount of repeat work."

"Repeat senior year high school."

"I spent second term heeling the *News,* merited election and failed. My marks fell. All very unrewarding."

"Perhaps because my courses duplicated those taken in high school."

"Like a post-grad in prep school."

"Too young to know what was going on around me."

"Did not know the ropes. Had to learn by experience."

"A great deal of adjustment and time catching on."

"Uncertain in friends and ambitions—lost."

"Lack of guidance and social contacts."

"Too rushed to know where I was or why."

"Too young and too much time devoted to athletics."

Those who chose sophomore year as least enjoyable and rewarding tended to stress the lack of natural progression of their college experience. This period seemed to be a lull between the stimulation of freshman year and that of the junior and senior years.

"Felt that classes were not very relevant and entered no new fields."

"Discouraged over grades and progress."

"Required no further adjustments than those made freshman year."

"Poor instructors and courses."

"Three roommates from Andover."

"I had to fill requirements, lack of interest; too much emphasis on meeting the right people, etc."

"Completely mixed up as to values socially and academically."

"It was sort of a leveling-off period."

"The challenges of freshman year diminished, yet the opportunities of junior year were not yet present."

"Certain required subjects uninteresting—athletically at the bottom of the pile—as in everything else."

"Pretty gloomy year. Nothing seemed to work. Bad marks."

"I hadn't gotten into my interesting courses yet and I had learned about myself the year before."

"Dull courses."

"I was mixed in a bunch of terribly poor courses."

"Least intellectual advance—a dead year."

"Poor set of roommates, fair academic year, socially very poor somehow."

"Marks low. Rushed a frat three times. Calculated attempt at mass popularity freshman year did not pay off sophomore year."

"Bad room. Not many friends."

"Had a hard time making friends in the college."

"Low grades—tension in room."

"Very little money—could hardly afford a movie—novelty had worn off."

Junior and senior years present a different picture. Those choosing junior year as most enjoyable and rewarding pictured it as a pleasant year marked by a full life and the stimulation of entering one's major field, and as a year unmarked by the worries of senior year such as theses to complete, comprehensive exams to take, and jobs to acquire.

"More social activities: Junior Prom, etc. Also each year progressively easier but in senior year uncomfortable obligation of thesis and comps."

"Not yet confronted with problems and worries of senior year but yet felt well adjusted to college life."

"No pressure of services, graduation, jobs, etc."

"Had most fun socially, not too much work as in senior year."

"The beginning of upperclass courses; enough but not too much work. Extracurricular activities."

"Very enjoyable social, athletic, and intellectual engagements."

"This is the year you are beginning to find yourself—your studies are shaping up as you take the subjects you like and you know where you stand socially and athletically."

For the group as a whole, senior year was the most enjoyable and rewarding. The students who so chose it tended to give one or both of two reasons. The first was a feeling which might best be described as a sense of fruition of previous efforts. Here frequent mention was made of the major as a source of intellectual stimulation and integration. Also mentioned was the feeling of successful culmination of efforts along nonacademic lines. The second reason may be described as a sense of "most complete" orientation variously expressed as "knowing the ropes" or being thoroughly "familiar" with the environment. In brief, senior year seemed to be a period during which the individual was enjoying the fruits of previous efforts and feeling most comfortable in his relations to the environment.

"Rewarding culmination of three years' work along several lines: athletic, academic, social."

"Meaningful work and courses in the field of my principal interests."

"Complete freedom to choose courses and synthesize results."

"Culmination of previous effort. Interrelationship of previous studies tied up."

"Fuller social life."

"Senior society."

"More responsibility and officership in different organizations."

"Membership in a senior society."

"More free time. I 'knew the ropes' better."

"A senior should be well-adjusted. He knows his way around, when to work and when to play. He's the big fish and as such has certain advantages. Also, the feeling of successful completion."

"More women and more English courses."

"Thorough familiarity with school and friends."

"Enjoyable subjects, increased number of friends, more permanent dating."

"Most interesting subjects and perfect roommates."

"Most familiar with the college."

"Adjustment good. I knew the 'ropes' and had the advantage of knowing how to think and study better. The love between my sweetheart and me was very strong and it gave us a great deal of confidence in each other. In this year all the things I have been studying began to jell and the insights I have had began to build up a more complete philosophy. Well-adjusted by this time. Began to appreciate more fully all that Yale is and has to offer. The threads of my major were tied together well by senior seminars. I also had the background of three previous years to build upon and refer to."

The themes presented above describe some of the common elements in the reasons advanced by the majority of students for their choice of the separate years. As such they help to illuminate the quantitative findings and to give one, in a highly generalized way, some of the flavor of the separate undergraduate years as experienced by the study groups as a whole. Because they are merely themes, however, they do not reflect the great variety of individual experience. As the quotations suggest, the reasons given are a complex mixture of factors of individual orientation, maturation, and motivation, on the one hand, and factors of formal structuring and basic characteristics of the college experience on the other.

Contributions to development. In another effort to explore some of the common denominators of undergraduate experience, seven of the more salient and universal features of undergraduate life were selected and presented to the study groups with request that they be ranked in order of the relative contribution each item had made to the student's over-all development and preparation for life after graduation. A mean rank was then computed for each item and a group profile constructed by listing the seven items in order of decreasing size of mean rank.

As Table 2 shows, junior and senior department courses and

TABLE 2. CONTRIBUTIONS TO DEVELOPMENT: RANK ORDER OF ITEMS
BY SIZE OF MEAN RANKING: 1953–56

	1953		*1954*		*1955*		*1956*	
Item	*Mean Rank*	*Rank Order*	*Mean Rank*	*Rank Order*	*Mean Rank*	*Rank Order*	*Mean Rank*	*Rank Order*
Junior and senior departmental courses	2.1	1	2.5	1.5	2.7	1.5	2.4	1
Roommates and friends	3.1	2	2.5	1.5	2.7	1.5	2.7	2
Other junior and senior courses	3.7	3	4.0	4	4.0	3.5	3.9	3
Social activities	4.2	4.5	3.8	3	4.0	3.5	4.3	4
Extracurricular activities	4.2	4.5	4.7	5	4.3	5	4.4	5
Courses taken freshman and sophomore years	5.2	6	5.0	6	4.6	6	4.5	6
Athletics and sports	5.5	7	5.4	7	5.7	7	5.8	7

roommates and friends are consistently regarded as contributing the most to the student's over-all development; junior and senior year electives, social activities, and extracurricular activities the next most; and freshman and sophomore year courses and athletics the least.

These findings reinforce the impressions one gets from the "Year" questions in Table 1—namely that for the group as a whole, the courses of the first two years are one of the low spots in the college experience; that the courses of the last two years are one of the high spots of the experience; and that interpersonal relationships are an important factor in the student's undergraduate experience.

These impressions are further reinforced by results obtained when the students in three of the samples were asked to rank the same items in terms of how enjoyable each was. As Table 3 indi-

TABLE 3. CONTRIBUTIONS TO ENJOYMENT: RANK ORDER OF ITEMS
BY SIZE OF MEAN RANKING: 1954–56

	1954		*1955*		*1956*	
Item	*Mean Rank*	*Rank Order*	*Mean Rank*	*Rank Order*	*Mean Rank*	*Rank Order*
Roommates and friends	2.0	1	2.1	1	2.1	1
Social activities	3.1	2	2.8	2	3.0	2
Junior and senior departmental courses	3.7	3	3.8	3	3.7	3
Extracurricular activities	4.4	4	4.0	4	4.3	4
Other junior and senior courses	4.5	5.5	4.7	5.5	4.6	5.5
Athletics and sports	4.5	5.5	4.7	5.5	4.6	5.5
Courses taken freshman and sophomore years	5.9	7	5.8	7	5.7	7

cates, the rank order of the items was invariant in all samples. Friendships were most enjoyable, social activities next, and so forth down to freshman-sophomore courses, which were least enjoyable.

Recommended changes. In still another effort to learn what the study groups felt to be some of the shortcomings of their experience at Yale, the question in Table 4 was asked of three samples, with the replies as indicated. The results indicate first that the Yale undergraduate seems reasonably satisfied with the character of his education. Only about 20 per cent would have preferred more occupational preparation and about 37 per cent more liberal arts emphasis. However, he expressed dissatisfaction with some aspects of that education. Specifically, the majority tended to favor changes in the direction of more personal contact with the faculty, more personal direction in studies and in course selection, and more discussions with fewer lectures.

TABLE *4*. RECOMMENDED CHANGES: 1953–55

As you see it now, would your college experience
have been more valuable to you if it had:

	Percentage Answering Yes		
	1953	*1954*	*1955*
provided more personal contacts with the faculty?	85	82	85
given you more personal direction in studies and in course selection?	65	55	56
contained fewer lectures, more discussions?	65	66	63
provided more personal contacts with your class-mates?	47	36	51
allowed more time for intellectual pursuits?	46	43	42
permitted greater freedom in course selection?	40	46	36
provided more personal contacts with other classes?	40	35	48
placed more emphasis on liberal studies not closely related to any occupation?	35	35	42
allowed more time for activities and social life?	25	*	*
allowed more time for extracurricular activities?	*	29	46
allowed more time for social activities?	*	19	31
required more work in courses?	25	29	28
placed more emphasis on occupational or professional preparation?	18	19	22

* Item not asked this year.

3. THE MEASUREMENT OF SATISFACTION

Before the initial questionnaire was composed, a hypothetical portrait of the satisfied student was sketched. It was thought that the satisfied student, one who had been successful in handling internal needs and external pressures, would have the following general characteristics: while in college, he would not have considered leaving; he would not have felt uncomfortable or "out of place"; and he would have been in good spirits most of the time. As he was about to graduate, he would feel that his experience at college had been pleasurable; he would not feel that his experience would have been more pleasurable had it occurred at another college which differed in basic characteristics, such as the size and sex composition of the student body; he would repeat his experience at the same college if given the opportunity; and if he could not rechoose the same college, he would choose one which was closely similar.

Accordingly, seven questions were included in the questionnaire and the following results, in percentage distribution, obtained:

1. Have you ever considered leaving Yale?

	'53	'54	'55	'56
No answer	1	0	1	0
1. No, never	72	70	70	72
2. Yes, but not seriously	21	22	20	20
3. Yes, seriously	6	8	9	8

2. Have you ever felt "out of place" at Yale?

	'53	'54	'55	'56
No answer	1	1	1	0
1. No, never	33	36	25	25
2. Yes, but only occasionally	57	55	60	62
3. Yes, frequently	8	6	11	10
4. Yes, most of the time	1	2	3	3

3. How would you say you have felt most of the time at Yale—in good spirits or in low spirits?

	'53	'54	'55	'56
No answer	0	1	1	1
1. Very good spirits	18	21	21	23
2. Fairly good spirits	55	48	61	54
3. Neither good nor bad	16	22	12	16
4. Fairly low	10	7	4	6
5. Very low spirits	1	1	1	0

4. All in all, what kind of time have you had
at Yale?

	'53	'54	'55	'56
No answer	1	1	1	0
1. Very good time	37	50	41	43
2. Fairly good time	46	39	44	44
3. OK	12	6	10	9
4. Fairly poor time	3	3	3	2
5. Very poor time	1	1	1	2

5. If you had it to do all over again, would
you again choose Yale?

	'53	'54	'55	'56
No answer	1	0	1	0
1. Definitely yes	71	62	55	61
2. Probably yes	23	31	35	24
3. Probably not	4	6	6	12
4. Definitely not	1	1	3	3

6. If for some reason you could not attend
Yale, what college would you choose instead? (write in)

	'53	'54	'55	'56
No answer	2	11	12	9
1. Harvard or Princeton	52	48	48	46
2. Other Ivy League	12	11	6	9
3. Other	34	30	34	36

7. As you see it now, would you have enjoyed
your college days more had you attended

	A Coeducational College?			
	'53	'54	'55	'56
No answer	2	1	2	2
1. No	62	65	61	63
2. Yes	36	34	37	35

	A Smaller College?			
	'53	'54	'55	'56
No answer	2	1	2	2
1. No	70	67	72	73
2. Yes	28	32	26	25

	A Larger College?			
	'53	'54	'55	'56
No answer	2	1	2	2
1. No	97	97	98	94
2. Yes	1	2	0	4

From the above results one must conclude immediately that, as measured by these questions, there is a high level of general satisfaction with the college experience for the groups as a whole. To each question the majority of students gave favorable responses. They had not considered leaving Yale, had not felt seriously out of place, had been in good spirits most of the time, and had had a good time. They did not feel that they would have enjoyed their college days more in a different type of college. They would have rechosen Yale and, as a second choice, would have chosen another Ivy League university, particularly Harvard or Princeton. Perhaps these results are to be expected, if only because of the finding of Havemann and West (in their nationwide study of college graduates) that the graduates of Ivy League schools are more loyal to their alma mater than any other group of graduates in the United States; when asked if they would attend the same college if they had it to do all over again, 98 per cent said yes.* The problem for the researcher interested in satisfaction in an Ivy League population thus becomes one of developing a more refined measurement of satisfaction than separate questions afford. One may presume, for example, that not all of the 98 per cent of Ivy League graduates in the Havemann and West study were equally satisfied with their college experience. Even when one breaks this "rechoose" group down by questioning the certainty of rechoice, as was done in our studies, one is still left with a majority of the subjects saying that they would definitely rechoose their alma mater. One may presume that in this group, too, there were some who were more satisfied than others. Accordingly, all but two of the several satisfaction questions were combined into a single measure which would "spread out" the study groups more than did the single questions.

The "prefer larger college" item was eliminated because almost no one would have preferred a college larger than Yale. The "second choice" question was eliminated because of the percentage of students who did not answer it in three of the samples and because analysis indicated that it was not a useful question. For some students, a choice of Harvard or Princeton was an expression of satisfaction with their Yale experience. For others it was an expression of dissatisfaction with their Yale experience. The

* Ernest Havemann and Patricia Salter West, *They Went to College* (New York, Harcourt, Brace, 1952), p. 215.

former group appeared to be one which felt at home in the Ivy League and, if they couldn't attend Yale, would attend the "next best," Harvard or Princeton. The latter group also felt at home in the Ivy League but thought that the Harvard or Princeton atmosphere would be better suited to them than that of Yale. This was particularly true of intellectually oriented students who would choose Harvard and explain their choice with remarks to the effect that one can get just as good an education if not a better one at Harvard without the pressures to engage in extracurricular and social activities which they felt were too strong at Yale.

Analysis of the remaining questions by chi-square and correlational techniques revealed that in each of the four samples each question was significantly * related to each other question and to a total score based on all the questions.† Thus the questions were interpreted as having a dimension in common beyond the conditions to which they ostensibly referred—a dimension we have labeled "satisfaction with the college experience." By arranging the students on a continuum in terms of their total scores on the questions, one could then proceed to determine what factors were related to this dimension. Section 4 presents the results obtained when the satisfaction continuum is cut at the median and the more satisfied half of the study groups is compared with the less satisfied half. A median split is employed because it is considered a more stringent test than other alternatives, such as comparing the extremes of the continuum. If a variable significantly differentiates one half of the class from the other and does so consistently from sample to sample, one can be fairly certain

* The term "significant" is used throughout this chapter in its statistical sense. Whenever it is used to describe a relationship, it indicates that the relationship under discussion could have occurred by chance alone less than five times in one hundred. In brief, the criterion of significance used in the present research is the $p < .05$ level of probability.

† The total score for each student was obtained by simply adding the numerical values of his responses to the questions. The mean correlation of each question with every other question in each of the four samples was $+.55$, $+.53$, $+.55$, and $+.52$. The mean correlation of the questions with total score was $+.80$, $+.82$, $+.79$, and $+.81$. When the four samples are combined into one, the mean intercorrelation of the questions is $+.54$, with all correlations $\geq .40$. The mean correlation with total score is $+.81$ with all correlations $\geq .74$.

that that variable is an important one for any consideration of the topic of satisfaction with the college experience or, at least, satisfaction with the Yale experience. Before turning to the results, however, it will be helpful to portray briefly the two halves of the study groups in terms of the average percentage of each half which gave the most favorable response to each of the satisfaction questions for the four samples.

Of the students in the top half, 93 per cent had never considered leaving Yale; 48 per cent had never felt out of place while at Yale; 40 per cent had been in very good spirits most of the time at Yale; 77 per cent had had a very good time at Yale; 93 per cent would definitely rechoose Yale; 89 per cent would not have enjoyed their college days more in a coeducational college; and 92 per cent would not have enjoyed their college days more in a smaller college. By contrast, of the students in the bottom half, only 52 per cent had never considered leaving; 10 per cent had never felt out of place; 3 per cent had been in very good spirits; 13 per cent had had a very good time; 36 per cent would definitely rechoose Yale; 46 per cent would not prefer a coeducational college; and 52 per cent would prefer a smaller college. In brief, as measured by these questions, the top half was definitely more satisfied than the bottom half. We shall hereafter refer to the top half as the more satisfied and designate it by the letters MS, and to the bottom half as the less satisfied and designate it by the letters LS.

4. RESULTS

In each sample the MS and the LS students were compared and differences tested for statistical significance. Since the content of the questionnaire varied somewhat from year to year and since the direction and significance of association of any single variable with the satisfaction measure also varied, the present summary is restricted to variables which were included in at least two of the four studies *and* which consistently separated the MS and LS groups. Accordingly, the following criteria of relationship are employed. A variable is said to be related to the satisfaction measurement if the direction of association is the same in all studies *and* the chi-square is significant at the $p < .05$ level in the majority of the studies. Thus, for variables appearing in two studies, both tests must be significant; for variables in three studies, at least two of the three tests must be significant; for variables in four studies, at least three of the four tests must be significant. Tables 5 and 6 present those variables which met the above criteria of relationship.

TABLE 5. VARIABLES RELATED TO SATISFACTION STATUS

(For each variable, the first line gives the percentage of MS and of LS students making the response indicated in the 1953 study; the second line, the same for the '54 study; the third line, the same for the '55 study; and the fourth line, the same for the '56 study.)

Variable	Response	% MS	% LS
Considered leaving Yale	Never	89	61
		92	47
		97	48
		94	53
Felt out of place at Yale	Never	60	11
		42	13
		46	6
		43	8
Spirits most of the time at Yale	Very good	39	1
		39	2
		40	4
		43	5
Kind of time at Yale	Very good	73	7
		84	17
		75	14
		77	13
Rechoose Yale	Definitely yes	99	51
		92	32
		87	28
		94	32
Prefer coeducational college	No	87	45
		83	48
		87	40
		92	41
Prefer smaller college	No	91	52
		92	49
		94	55
		92	59

TABLE 5. (cont.)

Variable	Response	% MS	% LS
Second choice college	Harvard or Princeton	62	43
		62	46
		68	43
		59	44
Satisfaction with total Yale experience	Very satisfied **	*	*
		*	*
		49	21
		39	12
In general, are you a satisfied person?	Yes **	*	*
		87	75
		80	56
		63	40
In general, are you a dissatisfied person?	No **	*	*
		61	23
		71	47
		79	51
Goal success	Very successful **	50	29
		54	31
		29	11
		78	58
Benefits received over expected	Received more than or equal to what expected from Yale	86	42
		84	54
		82	59
		*	*
Number of shortcomings of Yale experience	Few **	58	36
		52	34
		38	23
		77	38
How well adjusted to Yale life	Very well **	*	*
		*	*
		79	48
		73	49
Difficulty adjusting to Yale	Little or none **	*	*
		56	34
		55	27
		80	39

TABLE 5. (cont.)

Variable	Response	% MS	% LS
When felt adjusted to Yale: academically	Always	*	*
		*	*
		38	21
		31	15
When felt adjusted to Yale: nonacademically	Always	*	*
		*	*
		46	15
		44	22
Fulfill father's expectations	Very well **	*	*
		45	31
		45	27
		47	32
Fulfill mother's expectations	Very well **	*	*
		41	31
		53	35
		43	27
Type secondary school attended	Private school only	54	33
		54	40
		49	34
		46	34
Total annual family income	$10,000 or more	54	37
		50	33
		49	32
		46	36
Personal problems in secondary school adversely affecting performance in (a) athletic activities	No	*	*
		*	*
		60	50
		65	47
(b) extracurricular activities	No	*	*
		*	*
		86	75
		76	60
Perception of Yale at entrance	Very hazy	*	*
		*	*
		13	29
		14	28

TABLE 5. (cont.)

Variable	Response	% MS	% LS
Student employment	No	69	54
		68	54
		61	46
		62	45
Spending money per month	More than $25	*	*
		85	67
		87	71
		81	76
Campus prestige	High	62	31
		64	44
		*	*
		*	*
Personal problems adversely af- fecting performance at Yale in	Never or only slightly	*	*
		*	*
(a) academic activities		86	66
		85	54
(b) social activities	Never	*	*
		*	*
		47	25
		60	34
(c) extracurricular activities	Never	*	*
		*	*
		58	29
		62	42
At Yale bothered by feelings of (a) loneliness	No **	*	*
		48	20
		90	57
		84	54
(b) nervousness	No	*	*
		*	*
		76	61
		74	53
(c) insomnia	No	*	*
		*	*
		68	50
		73	57

TABLE 5. (cont.)

Variable	Response	% MS	% LS
Get along with boys	Very well	41	29
		57	40
		60	30
		61	45
Get along with girls	Very well	91	76
		55	40
		58	28
		58	40
Enough friends at Yale	Yes **	66	37
		59	30
		54	35
		90	57
	No **	4	25
		7	27
		10	22
		1	11
Enough dates at Yale	Yes **	47	30
		54	31
		55	27
		61	41
	No **	14	45
		17	46
		18	46
		17	35
Ease of making friends at Yale	Very easy	40	12
		36	23
		28	17
		45	33
Wanted more time for social activity at Yale	Yes **	16	32
		12	23
		22	39
		29	50
Thing liked least about Yale	Academic matters	70	38
		57	43
		72	32
		*	*

* Question not asked this year.
** This is a summary term to denote the fact that although different response categories were used in the different studies, the quality of the response was the same in all studies.

As indicated above, each of the individual items contributing to the total satisfaction score was highly related to that score. In addition, the MS students are observed to prefer Harvard or Princeton as their second choice for a college to attend. The contention that the satisfaction score is measuring satisfaction is supported by the findings that the MS students say they are more satisfied with their college experience than do the LS students and that in general they are satisfied, not dissatisfied, people. The contention that satisfaction is a feeling tone associated with the successful handling of internal needs and external pressures is supported by the findings that the MS students are more successful getting what they want out of college; they receive what they expect from college, if not more than they expect; they indicate fewer shortcomings in their experience (hence presumably fewer needs thwarted or unfulfilled); they are better adjusted to life at Yale; they have less difficulty adjusting to that life; and that they are more likely always to have felt adjusted to life at Yale. In addition, they feel they have fulfilled their parents' expectations of them at Yale better than do the LS students.

They come to Yale having attended private secondary school from a family of high income. In athletics and extracurricular activities at secondary school their performance was not adversely affected by personal problems. They have a somewhat clearer idea of what Yale is like at the time they matriculate. While at Yale they have more spending money than the LS students and do not engage in student employment. They participate in extracurricular activities as much as the LS students but are more successful in their participation in the sense of achieving positions of higher prestige. Their performance in academic, social, and extracurricular activities at Yale is less likely to be affected adversely by personal problems. They are also less likely to be bothered by insomnia and by feelings of loneliness and nervousness. They relate well to their peers of both sexes, make friends easily at Yale and manage to have enough friends and dates during their stay on campus. They feel they have had sufficient time for social activity and when asked what they like least about their experience mention something in the academic area such as specific faculty members or courses or regulations such as those requiring them to take certain courses. On an adjective check

TABLE 6. ADJECTIVES RELATED TO SATISFACTION WITH THE
COLLEGE EXPERIENCE *

		1954		1955		1956	
Variable	Response	MS	LS	MS	LS	MS	LS
Cheerful	Yes **	27	8	86	66	98	79
Confident	Yes	24	3	67	51	88	60
Conforming	Yes	77	69	83	57	67	47
Consistent	Yes	90	87	84	68	78	60
Contented	Yes	21	6	60	23	70	38
Cordial	Yes	23	15	85	67	96	85
Enthusiastic	Yes	35	23	92	82	90	74
Genial	Yes	27	13	84	68	95	85
Gregarious	Yes	85	74	73	57	64	46
Happy	Yes	—	—	90	51	96	71
Integrated	Yes	11	3	64	44	77	53
Masculine	Yes	12	5	86	68	96	86
Natural	Yes	22	20	83	68	90	76
Optimistic	Yes	—	—	69	53	84	67
Poised	Yes	18	8	67	45	83	64
Relaxed	Yes	12	6	58	41	65	47
Satisfied	Yes	87	75	80	56	63	40
Sociable	Yes	23	18	85	61	95	76
Well-balanced	Yes	24	13	80	58	88	73
Aloof	No	91	79	91	74	73	62
Anxious	No	83	72	53	42	44	33
Cynical	No	89	78	79	51	72	40
Dissatisfied	No	61	23	71	47	79	51
Easily dominated	No	—	—	90	75	90	76
Immature	No	55	38	72	58	83	66
Indifferent	No	58	41	91	80	89	70
Insecure	No	—	—	78	46	78	52
Lonely	No	—	—	74	46	70	52
Moody	No	45	16	56	37	64	40
Restless	No	18	6	40	21	46	27
Shy	No	39	30	76	47	74	59
Unrealistic	No	42	33	85	65	85	72
Withdrawn	No	50	33	78	65	84	74

* In the 1954 study students were instructed to cross out those adjectives which were definitely not true of them, to check those adjectives which were somewhat more true of them than the majority of their classmates, and to leave blank those adjectives which were about as true of them as of their classmates. In the 1955 study they were asked to cross out those which were more untrue than true of themselves, to check those words which were more true than untrue, and to circle those

list they describe themselves as cheerful, confident, conforming, consistent, contented, cordial, enthusiastic, genial, gregarious, happy, integrated, masculine, natural, optimistic, poised, relaxed, satisfied, sociable, and well balanced. They deny being aloof, anxious, cynical, dissatisfied, easily dominated, immature, indifferent, insecure, lonely, moody, restless, shy, unrealistic, or withdrawn.

5. DISCUSSION

In the preceding sections we have sketched in broad outline an approach to the problem of satisfaction with college. The approach includes not only a way of viewing the problem but also a method of studying it at any college. We have also indicated the kind of results obtained when satisfaction is studied in this manner at one particular college—Yale. The results obtained at Yale, of course, may be true only of Yale. Further research will serve to isolate those variables which are characteristic of satisfied students in general as they interact with their college environment and those variables which may pertain only to a certain college or type of college. Nevertheless, the results obtained at any one college are useful in several ways. They afford an over-all view of the general level of satisfaction on campus and indicate some of the high and low spots in the college experience for the student body as a whole. Within the student body they indicate the type (s) of persons (s) who is/are most satisfied with the college experience. Even when in the form of first-order differences in which the Yale results have been presented, they are useful, for they call attention to aspects of the local scene which may not be readily apparent to the casual observer. Indeed, they may even escape completely the attention of those who by preference or circumstance have little sustained contact with student life as it is lived by the students. In brief, such findings serve as firm anchor points for further exploration.

------

where they could not decide. In the 1956 study they were asked to check those words which were more true than untrue of themselves and to cross out those words which were more untrue than true of themselves.

** Yes: subjects tend to accept word as being descriptive of themselves. No: subjects tend to reject word as not being descriptive of themselves.

Such further exploration may take several forms. First, and most desirably, one should seek interrelationships among those variables already known to be related to satisfaction with the college life. One may ask such questions as: What happens to the in-college variables when one controls the precollege variables? At Yale, for example, graduates of private preparatory schools tend to come from wealthier families, to enter knowing more of their classmates, to have no student employment, to have more spending money and time for social activities, to have more friends and dates, and to participate more fully in student life than do the public school graduates. When one eliminates the effect of a wealthy family and attendance at a private school, one finds that achieving high campus prestige, having enough friends and dates, and making friends easily are variables still related to satisfaction. Thus the high school graduate from a less wealthy family who achieves high prestige, relates well, and has sufficient contacts with his peers is also satisfied, but it is more difficult for him to achieve this because of pressures of limited time and finances.

One may continue his exploration by looking more closely at the interaction process and examining types of students such as those who are very successful in achieving their academic goals but not their social ones, and vice versa; or those who have little difficulty adjusting to the demands of the official culture but a great deal to the demands of the peer culture, and vice versa; or those who are more successful in achieving their goals than in adjusting to environmental demands, or vice versa. In brief, by formulating such broad but directive questions as "What students with what needs are how successful in satisfying their needs in this environment?" and "What pressures are exerted on what students with what effects by this environment?" one may begin to unravel and to understand better the complexities of student life in terms of the individual and environmental factors which together operate to influence the "satisfactoriness" of the college experience.

CHAPTER 3

Personality and Academic Achievement:
A Questionnaire Approach

BY RALPH M. RUST

Academic achievement represents a measure of intellectual attainment, a central aim of the college. Here, by statistical analysis, the author demonstrates a relationship between academic achievement and student behavior in several areas. It is suggested that this behavior is related to the internal acceptance of values conducive to academic work, and evidence supporting this idea is presented. This report is an extension of a paper by the author and F. J. Ryan which was read at the American Psychological Association meetings in San Francisco, September 1955.

THIS IS A REPORT of a continuation of a series of studies on personality or nonintellectual factors and academic achievement initiated by the author and F. J. Ryan. Previous papers have reported results of the application of the Rorschach (7) and Strong Vocational Interest Blank (8) to groups of college under-, normal-, and overachievers. This report presents the results of an extensive questionnaire used in two further studies of academic achievement and discusses findings common to both. The questionnaire was designed to elicit information about various aspects of the students' background, precollege and in-college behavior, moral and cultural values, and relationship with parents.

BACKGROUND OF THE STUDY

The investigation of nonintellectual factors associated with academic achievement holds considerable interest for the clinician who is called upon to evaluate the reasons for the failure of the individual student to attain an expected scholastic performance. Such an investigation is also of interest to the admissions committee which, because of the increasing applications for admission to college, is forced to select a smaller and smaller proportion of those applying.

The present status of the prediction of college achievement on the basis of "intellectual" factors has been summarized by Travers (11) and Harris (6). In general, multiple correlations of .6 or .7 are obtained at most universities between freshman grades and a predictive battery comprised of secondary school grades, achievement tests, and tests of intelligence or scholastic aptitude. After a review of the relevant literature, Travers concludes that "At the present time, the evidence indicates that the best single measure for the selection of the college student is his average grade in high school." Secondary school grades are better predictors of success in college than aptitude or achievement tests, probably not only because they represent a longer work sample but because they represent indirect measures of personality variables essential to academic achievement.

At present the best available approximation of an entering student's grades at Yale is his "general predicted score" (2, 3). This measure is based on a weighted combination of secondary school grade average, score on the Verbal Section of the Scholastic Aptitude Test and the sum of three College Entrance Examination Board Achievement Test scores. Of these, the secondary school grade average carries the most weight, particularly when the college records of previous graduates of that school are known. Differences between predicted score and academic achievement would seem to be not merely a function of the unreliability of college grade averages or of the predicted score, but perhaps primarily a reflection of variables not adequately measured by the predictive battery—personality or nonintellectual variables.

Included among the summaries of the literature dealing with the relationship between academic achievement and nonintellectual factors are those of Harris (5, 6), Stagner (10), and Travers (11). Orientation in this field is particularly difficult because the literature presents a vast multiplicity of experimental variables, deals with all academic levels, and is characterized by a wide variation in the adequacy of experimental design. Most of the published work seems to be reports of single studies. They are seldom replicated by the author and even less often by others. Most studies are essentially empirical and have little if any tie to psychological theory. Perhaps in a relatively new and complicated field like this, such empirical exploration is a necessary first step.

Many studies in this field are concerned with the deviation of academic performance from a measure of intelligence. Although such investigations are of considerable theoretical and practical importance, a more urgent subject for investigation for the college official would be those variables which operate to produce deviations over and above secondary school record. If we can assume that the chief reason for the superior predictive value of secondary school record is that there are vital nonintellectual factors already reflected, then the college admissions officer has a measure of their operation even if their identification is difficult.

THEORETICAL FORMULATION

The present series of studies was designed to investigate factors related to deviation from the best available prediction of college achievement—the general predicted score. Since the secondary school grade average receives the most weight in this prediction, the selection of subjects reflects primarily a change in achievement from secondary school to college.

It is hypothesized that the change in academic achievement from secondary school to college is associated with a change in behavior favorable to good grades. Those students who achieve relatively higher grades at college might be expected to spend more time in study, to be less distractible when studying, to get reports and papers in on time, to take better notes, etc. Relative performance on these variables is investigated as a part of this study.

How might such a differential performance be accounted for? Certainly it is not to be expected that there are great differences in well-established personality or motivational patterns in the short space of time elapsing between secondary school and college.

It is hypothesized that possible changes in study-habit patterns are a function not of personality changes in the subjects, but of changes in the environment which differentially effect established personality patterns already existing in college students.

Why might a previously well-established habit pattern break down when a student leaves secondary school and goes to college? The academic task in college is quite similar to that of secondary school. There are still tests to take, papers to be written, and studying to do.

The most obvious difference would seem to be a difference in the amount and kind of supervision present in the two situations. At secondary school, be it private or public, the student is called upon to recite more frequently, and he expects to be called upon. He has more frequent quizzes and examinations, and he is marked more often. This is supervision that is built into the system. Other kinds of supervision are less universal but are more direct. The high school student studies under the watchful eye of the parent and the preparatory school student is similarly encouraged by the master. If the student falls behind or becomes deficient in his work, his privileges may be quickly removed—and quickly restored if he responds.

At college, supervision is still present but is not omnipresent. Generally speaking, on any given night the college student can do just about as he pleases. He can go to the movies or to the fraternity house, get into a bull session with the boys, stay in his room, or go to the library and study.

The differences in supervision from secondary school to college are assumed to be real differences. No attempt to evaluate the nature and extent of such supervision was attempted in this study.

Why might this tendency to study persist differentially? The achievement of good grades may, in general, be considered a desideratum of parents and of society, particularly so for the parents of college-bound students.

It is hypothesized that the tendency for habits and attitudes favorable to good grades to persist is related to the degree to which such values have been adopted by the student as his own. In a sense he becomes self-propelled rather than externally motivated. The incorporation of these and other such values held by parents has been variously labeled "superego," "conscience," "sense of responsibility," "goodness," etc.

The incorporation of such values is seen as the result of a relationship between an individual and his parents. An attempt is made in the present study to evaluate the nature of this relationship.

The Questionnaire

The questionnaire was a long one; it contained almost 300 items. Questions were designed to elicit information about, and where possible measurement of, the following variables: (a) behavior favorable to good grades at secondary school and at college, (b) moral values and socially approved behavior, (c) the nature of the relationship with the parents, (d) background, (e) vocational orientation, and (f) extracurricular participation in college. Since parts of the F scale (1) and of Eysenck's (4) Liberalism-Conservativism and Toughmindedness-Tendermindedness were included in a scale of moral values, the remaining items in these scales were also included.

Many of the items were derived from an open-ended questionnaire given to similar groups of subjects in an earlier study. Almost all the items were multiple choice, precoded items.

Subjects

Subjects were chosen by means of scattergrams which plotted general predicted score against average grades. Such plots yield correlations of the order of .6 or .7. Approximately the ten per cent most negatively deviant and the ten per cent most positively deviant from predicted scores were selected. A third group of ten per cent who fell on the regression line was also chosen. This selection procedure yielded three groups of subjects equated for prediction and its three components but differing widely in average grades. A three-group design rather than the more frequently used two-group design was selected since it seemed possible that the variables studied might be curvilinear. Subjects were designated as under-, normal, and overachievers.

In each of two studies subjects were chosen from the junior and senior classes in Yale College and in the Yale School of Engineering. Four separate plots were used in each study in selecting subjects but the groups were later combined for analysis, since over-all characteristics were of primary concern.

In the first study subjects were asked to come in at appointed times and fill out the questionnaire, while in the second study the questionnaire was mailed and subjects were asked to return it in a stamped envelope provided. Somewhat less than half of those asked to come in and fill out the questionnaire did so, while almost eighty per cent of the mailed questionnaires were returned. There were 267 subjects in the first study and 388 in the second.

RESULTS

Results of the two studies were analyzed by means of chi-square. Results were considered significant if consistent differences were obtained in both studies between any two experimental groups and if these differences were significant at the .05 level of confidence. Findings are reported in terms of the percentage of each group making a particular response to a questionnaire item or scoring in a certain fashion. Where responses to an item fell along a continuum, the item was split as near the median as possible.

Table 1 shows the proportion of each group (under-, normal,

TABLE *1*. RESPONDENTS

Proportion of Each Group Completing the Questionnaire

	UNDERS	NORMALS	OVERS
Study 1	39	43	47
Study 2	76	82	80

and overachievers) responding to the questionnaire. Although there is a consistent tendency for a higher proportion of overachievers to respond, the obtained differences are not significant.

STUDY HABITS AT SECONDARY SCHOOL AND AT COLLEGE

The three experimental groups do not differ significantly in secondary school study habits (see Table 2). None of the items pertaining to study habits in secondary school yields significant and consistent findings in both studies. Where significant differences are found in one study, they are clearly lacking significance in the other. There were no significant trends in a scale of secondary school study habits composed of these items. It seems clear that such differences as do exist are the result of the unreliability of the items rather than a reflection of any consistent differences in the groups. These students see their secondary school academic experience as essentially similar. The secondary school situation seems to demand a certain uniformity of conduct of the three achievement groups.

TABLE 2. SECONDARY SCHOOL STUDY HABITS

ITEM	Percentage of Each Group Making the Response at Left		
	UNDERS	NORMALS	OVERS
While at secondary school:			
Spent an hour every night or most nights in study	58 67	53 58	59 60
Spent eleven or more hours per week in study outside of class	59 60	59 56	62 59
Never overslept and consequently missed a morning class	88 93	93 88	87 91
Was usually abreast of work from day to day	75 80	83 87	78 84
Reports and papers were always on time	68 78	78 82	81 [a] 81
Never missed class for reasons other than actual illness	47 61	57 47	39 [b] 56 [c]
Secondary school study habits (scoring above the median)	49 60	52 54	56 57

Note: Results of the first of the two studies are the upper figure of each pair; those of the second study the bottom one.
a. The difference between unders and overs is significant at .05.
b. The difference between normals and overs is significant at .05.
c. The difference between unders and normals is significant at .05.

In contrast to this picture of uniformity in secondary school is the difference in the study habits of these students when they come to college. The results of the application of these same items plus some additional items to the college situation are shown in Table 3. On all items reported, overachievers consistently and

Table 3. College Study Habits

Item	Percentage of Each Group Making the Response at Left [a]		
	Unders	Normals	Overs
While at college:			
Spend an hour every night or most nights in study	70 68	70 82	90 91
Spend twenty-one or more hours per week in study outside of class	25 39	30 37	53 74
Never or very seldom miss class except for actual illness	40 32	47 39	55 54
Never oversleep and consequently miss a morning class	15 20	22 25	33 40
Usually abreast of work from day to day	17 18	27 30	39 52
Reports and papers always on time	39 32	48 53	62 55
Work the same times each day	26 27	42 26	41 47
Work when the pressure is on	59 47	39 43	24 21
Frequently find themselves napping while trying to study	21 29	26 14	11 13
Take comprehensive and complete notes	49 48	37 58	66 64
Spend at least twice as much time in study as in secondary school	43 44	54 54	59 71
Keep a schedule and stick to it pretty well	02 02	07 05	09 13
Work efficiently during exams	47 43	44 55	63 62
Never accompany friends to the movies if asked to go while writing a paper due early the next day	64 60	70 72	79 75
College study habits scale (scoring above the median)	35 35	46 49	65 69

significantly report that at college they spend more time in study, seldom miss class, are more likely to work the same times each day, are less distractible, get reports and papers in on time, take better notes, work with greater efficiency during exams, and are less likely to be lured away from studying.

Evidently behavior favorable to good grades as reported by the subject does change differentially from secondary school to college as a function of achievement status.

It seems particularly significant that in the face of pressure from peer groups (as demonstrated by the item on accompanying a friend to the movies) that overachievers are less likely to give in to such pressure. This would seem to demonstrate a certain self-propulsion which operates even when adult supervision is absent or diminished.

MORAL VALUES

In order to measure acceptance of moral values subjects were asked to express degree of agreement with thirty-nine statements of moral and cultural viewpoints. Examples of such items were:

> Observance of Sunday is old-fashioned and should cease to govern our behavior.
> Obedience and respect for authority are the most important virtues children should learn.
> Success is primarily a function of hard work.
> When one has work that should be done, one shouldn't take time off for other things.

Some of the items in this scale were taken from the California F scale (1), which purports to measure authoritarianism, and some from Eysenck's scales of Liberalism-Conservativism and Toughmindedness-Tendermindedness (4). The remaining items in these scales were also included in the questionnaire.

Each subject was also asked to indicate for nineteen of the items designed to measure moral values the way he thought his father, his mother, and his best friend would respond. The purpose

---

Note to Table 3: Results of the first of the two studies are the upper figure of each pair, and those of the second study are the bottom one.

a. Results of both studies are generally consistent and yield significant differences at .05 on all items reported.

of this procedure was to expand the basis for measurement of moral values, permitting a measure of the value system of the subject's significant others. Results of the above scales are presented in Table 4.

TABLE *4*. ATTITUDE SCALES

SCALE	Number of Items in Scale	Corrected Odd-even Reliability	Percentage Above the Median of the Scale [a]		
			UNDERS	NORMALS	OVERS
Moral values, subject (subtotal)	19	.80	52	45	44
			46	50	45
Moral values, subject (total)	39	.83	54	50	48
			45	47	53
F scale (total)	28	.80	61	51	39 [b]
			52	44	54
F scale: conventionality	4	— [c]	68	57	51 [b]
			48	39	45
F scale: authoritarian submission	7	—	62	50	46 [b]
			52	49	61
F scale: anti-intraception	4	—	60	56	46
			53	54	56
F scale: superstition and stereotypy	6	—	53	49	41
			58	54	58
F scale: authoritarian aggression	8	—	62	55	40 [b]
			52	43	54
F scale: power and toughness	6	—	56	52	39 [b]
			50	49	46
F scale: projectivity	5	—	54	51	43
			43	44	48
F scale: sex	3	—	54	43	34 [b]
			44	41	47
Moral values: mother	19	.76	43	52	48
			48	45	54
Moral values: father	19	.79	52	47	51
			53	44	55
Moral values: best friend	19	.84	45	59	42
			54	47	49

TABLE *4* (cont.)

SCALE	Number of Items in Scale	Corrected Odd-even Reliability	Percentage Above the Median of the Scale [a]		
			UNDERS	NORMALS	OVERS
Eysenck's Liberalism-	14	.54	41	41	56 [b]
Conservatism			41	47	38
(high score is liberal)					
Eysenck's Toughmindedness-	14	.53	49	49	59
Tendermindedness			58	54	59
(high score is tenderminded)					

a. Results of the first study are the upper figure of each pair; those of the second study are the bottom one. The median in each case was based on the particular study involved and may differ from study to study.

b. Indicates a significant difference for the particular study.

c. Blanks in this column indicate results not computed.

None of these scales yielded results which were both consistent and significant. Where significant differences were found in one study, not only were the results in the other study almost invariably lacking in significance, but the differences obtained were in the opposite direction. The lack of consistent differences in these scales may be due in part to their relatively poor reliability. The corrected odd-even reliabilities for the F scale (total), and for the moral values scales range from .76 to .84, while similar measures of Eysenck's scales are .53 and .54.

Clearly, these various attitude scales do not differentiate achievement groups. Perhaps the measures used are not pertinent, perhaps the items do not adequately reflect the attitudes these scales were designed to measure, or perhaps moral values are not related to college achievement.

SOCIALLY APPROVED BEHAVIOR

Subjects were asked a number of items concerning certain behavior which might be broadly designated as socially approved or disapproved. These items attempted to get at behavior rather than attitudes. Actually, when these items were included in the questionnaire, it was thought that they would tap the same variable as the moral attitude items. The items asked about smoking, drinking, sexual intercourse, church attendance, cheating on exams, and time of arising. These results are shown in Table 5.

TABLE 5. SOCIAL BEHAVIOR

	Percentage of Each Group Making the Response at Left [a]		
ITEM	UNDERS	NORMALS	OVERS
Don't smoke	27	31	54
	35	40	53
Don't drink	02	07	21
	11	05	23
Never had sexual intercourse	49	50	71
	52	63	68
Attend church once or more a month	45	50	54
	53	50	60
Never cheated on an exam	43	34	46
	44	42	48
Usually arise before 8:00 A.M.	39	56	60
	51	61	66

a. Results of the first study are the upper figure of each pair; those of the second study are the bottom one. Results of both studies are generally consistent and yield significant differences at .05 on all items reported except church attendance and cheating.

In contrast to the attitude items these behavior items consistently differentiated the achievement groups in four of the six items. Overachievers in both studies were less likely to report that they smoke or drink or that they have had sexual intercourse. They are more likely to report that they usually arise before 8:00 A.M. The other two items, church attendance and cheating, showed small consistent differences in the expected direction but were not significant. Overachievers were somewhat more likely to attend church and somewhat less likely to have cheated on exams.

RELATIONSHIP TO PARENTS

Attempts to identify the sort of relationship between the subject and his parents most likely to be associated with overachievement or underachievement were no more successful than were the moral values items. Scales designed to measure what was labeled authoritarianism of the mother and of the father yielded nothing. Some 40-odd items were used to investigate the parent-subject relationship—past and present. Examples of the type of item used were:

> Do you or did you look upon your father as a strict parent?
> What kind of physical punishment did you receive from your father?
> Do you and your father have activities (recreational or otherwise) that you share?
> If you feel your mother is wrong, can you criticize her openly?

These items were designed to measure the degree and extent of supervision or control ("authoritarianism") exercised by the parents over the behavior of the subject—either in childhood or at present—and to assess the degree of accord or harmony between parents and subject. None of the items included showed significant differences in both studies. Perhaps the pertinent items were not included, or perhaps the subjects cannot report such information accurately.

In addition to the above, scores based on the differences in reported attitudes of the subject, his mother, and his father on the moral values items were computed. It was thought that such scores would measure in a somewhat different way the extent of accord or harmony between parents and subject in what was conceived to be an important area.

Differences scores were also computed between mother and father and between the subject and his evaluation of the moral values of his "best friend." It was believed that if there were differences in these scales among the achievement groups, the difference scores obtained for mother–father for overachievers would be lower than for the other two groups, while those for the subject – best friend would be higher. It seemed likely that where the mother's and father's values were essentially in agreement, the value system of the parents would be more easily transmitted and this in turn would result in a better grade record. Conversely, where the subject seemed more like his peers, he would be less like his parents, more subject to their influence, and consequently less interested in academic achievement.

The results of these difference scores and of the "authoritarianism" of the mother and of the father are shown in Table 6.

TABLE 6. RELATIONSHIP TO PARENTS

SCALE	Number of Items in Scale	Corrected Odd-even Reliability	Percentage Above the Median of the Scale [a]		
			UNDERS	NORMALS	OVERS
Father's authoritarianism	17	.51	37	39	39
			55	42	38 [b]
Mother's authoritarianism	11	— [c]	48	47	56
			57	70	63 [b]
Difference score, subject–mother	19	.77	47	56	56
			54	44	44
Difference score, subject–father	19	.72	41	52	51
			56	45	49
Difference score, mother–father	19	.67	42	57	58 [b]
			54	42	49
Difference score, subject – best friend	19	.56	44	52	53
			49	50	48

a. Results of the first study are the upper figure of each pair; those of the second study are the bottom one. The median in each case was based on the particular study involved and may differ from study to study.

b. Indicates a significant difference for the particular study.

c. Not computed.

The corrected odd-even reliabilities of these scales are again rather low, ranging from .51 to .77. Some of the scales yield significant differences in one of the studies but none is significant in both and, as in the moral values scales, the results of the other study show almost identical results for the three groups or are even in the opposite direction. In at least one scale (difference score, mother–father) the significant difference obtained in one study is in the opposite direction to that expected.

It is difficult to conclude that such variables are unimportant for college academic achievement. Perhaps future attempts to explore parent–subject relationships should emphasize behavior which can be more accurately reported. Perhaps items that tap actual present behavior of parents and of subjects would be more likely to yield the sort of differences hypothesized.

ADDITIONAL FINDINGS

The remaining findings that show significant and consistent differences in the two studies are difficult to summarize. They are presented in Table 7.

TABLE 7. OTHER RESULTS

ITEM	Percentage of Each Group Making the Response at Left [a]		
	UNDERS	NORMALS	OVERS
Attended high school only	34	37	56
	37	47	68
Attended both prep school and high school	25	23	13
	18	16	09
Taking an intensive rather than a standard departmental major	01	12	20
	08	16	28
Father attended Yale	28	21	11
	22	15	11
Belong to a fraternity	28	38	17
	43	37	19
Believe there is a positive relationship between grades and postcollege success	71	88	95
	73	88	85
Have selected an occupation	89	90	98
	87	95	96
Expect their family, relatives, or close family friends will have little or nothing to do with obtaining their first permanent job	55	54	70
	61	59	80

a. Results of the first study are the upper figure of each pair; those of the second study are the bottom one. Results of both studies are generally consistent and yield significant differences at .05.

Each of the items presented is perhaps worthy of individual comment. Some seem to be reflections of the variables mentioned earlier, some do not. Overachievers are more likely to take an intensive rather than a standard major. This would seem to indicate that overachievers place a higher value on academic work than do the other two groups. Similarly, the attitude of the three groups toward academic achievement is reflected in the relative importance each group places on grades for post-college success. It is possible that both of these items, but particularly the latter, are a reflection of present status rather than a determining factor in achievement. Having achieved high grades the overachievers may feel (or hope) that this will lead to greater success after college.

Overachievers are more likely to have selected an occupation, although as juniors and seniors in college relatively few students are without an occupational choice.

The remaining variables reflect a number of things. Perhaps most important is the socio-economic variable. Overachievers are less likely to have a Yale father, are more likely to have attended high school only and are less likely to expect help from their family, relatives or from close family friends in getting their first permanent job. Yet these are not really quite so simply explained. One might expect that where a subject's father had attended Yale that this, possibly reflecting an identification with the father, would tend to be associated with overachievement rather than with underachievement. Perhaps the difficulty is that it is not always a reflection of such an identification but merely an acquiescence to a parental demand.

Those subjects who attended both prep school and high school were found more likely to be underachievers than overachievers. Possibly this reflects an added external pressure on the part of the parents, pressure designed to enable the subject to gain entrance to college. If so, it might be expected that when this pressure is removed, the student's "natural" tendencies would emerge. On the other hand, the differences obtained in various secondary school groups may be a reflection of an error in prediction for these groups.

One more difference should be mentioned. In the present study, as in previous studies (7, 8, 9), a three-group design was used rather than the more customary two-group design. Again, overachievers seem to be a rather distinct group. Differences seem to be greater between overachievers and normal achievers than between normal achievers and underachievers. Although some of the significant findings yield differences between underachievers and normal achievers, these two groups are generally quite close together.

Summary and Conclusions

Achievement as defined in this study is based on the differential between general predicted score and grade average at college. Groups of under-, normal, and overachievers were selected from Yale College and the Yale School of Engineering from the junior and senior classes in two separate studies.

It was suggested that achievement in college reflects, primarily, a change in environment which acts differentially on previously determined differences in personality and value systems in the subjects studied. These differences are perceived as a result of the extent to which the generally accepted values of parents and of society have been incorporated in the individual. Overachievers are perceived as essentially self-propelled, while the behavior of other achievement groups is more dependent on external demands.

The three achievement groups reported essentially similar study habits in secondary school but quite different study habits in college. On this level the thesis of the study seems upheld.

Attempts to measure moral values yielded no consistent differences among the three achievement groups. So far as could be determined with the measure used in this study, there were also no consistent differences between the achievement groups in the extent to which subjects held or did not hold moral values similar to their parents. Attempts to measure the sort of relationship between parent and subject which might be most conducive to the inculcation of these values also were unsuccessful.

Achievement groups did differ, however, in reported social behavior which was considered to be a reflection of such values.

Results of the present study seem sufficiently worth while to attempt a further exploration of the nature of the value systems of college students and their parents and the ways in which such value systems are transmitted. Behavioral items which reflect these value systems will be explored and used in place of attitudinal items wherever possible. Differences among subtypes of achievers will also be explored.

REFERENCES

1. Adorno, T. W.; Frenkel-Brunswik, Else; Levinson, Daniel J.; and Sanford, R. Nevitt, *The Authoritarian Personality,* New York, Harper, 1950.

2. Crawford, A. B., and Burnham, P. S., Entrance examinations and college achievement, *School and Society, 36:*344–52, 378–84. 1932.

3. —— *Forecasting College Achievement,* New Haven, Yale University Press, 1946.

4. Eysenck, H. J., Primary social attitudes: 1. The organization and measurement of social attitudes, *International Journal of Opinion Attitude Research, 1*(3):49–84. 1947.

5. Harris, D., The relation to college grades of some factors other than intelligence, *Archives of Psychology, 131:* 1931.

6. —— Factors affecting college grades: a review of the literature, 1930–37, *Psychological Bulletin, 37:*125–66. 1940.

7. Rust, Ralph M., and Ryan, F. J., The relationship of some Rorschach variables to academic behavior, *Journal of Personality, 21:* 441–56. 1953.

8. —— The Strong Vocational Interest Blank and college achievement, *Journal of Applied Psychology, 38:*341–45. 1954.

9. Ryan, F. J., "Personality differences between under- and over-achievers in college," Ph.D. thesis, Columbia University, 1951. University Microfilms, Ann Arbor, Mich., Publ. No. 2857.

10. Stagner, R., The relation of personality to academic aptitude and achievement, *Journal of Educational Research, 26:*648–60. 1933.

11. Travers, R. M. W., Significant research on the prediction of academic success, in W. T. Donahue, C. H. Coombs, and R. M. W. Travers, eds., *The Measurement of Student Adjustment and Achievement* (Ann Arbor, University of Michigan Press, 1949), pp. 147–90.

CHAPTER 4

Clinical Study of Academic Underachievers

BY BERNARD NEUGEBOREN

The author, a psychiatric social worker, here explores problems of achievement in college by a modified case study method. He demonstrates that patterns of academic performance are related to clinical diagnosis, that is, to aspects of personality structure. His cases also show that such patterns of performance may sometimes be modified by new experience, that of psychotherapy. Thus final achievements depend on growth of the personality.

COLLEGE administrators have been increasingly confronted with students who, although they have intellectual ability to do college work, are unable for various reasons to function in the college setting. Wolfle reports that of the brightest fifth of our young people only one third finish college (8). In our contact with such students at the Division of Student Mental Health, it appears that they are bright enough to score well on the customary aptitude and achievement tests and were previously able to succeed in secondary school, yet in their day-to-day college work their functioning is impaired by such problems as concentration difficulties, a general lack of ability to be self-directed, inability to establish their own goals, and a lack of motivation to achieve goals. In some students these difficulties appear to be long-standing ones. They have had troubles in previous academic settings and it appears that only because of high innate ability are they able to get to college. However, in many situations there are students who had previously done well in secondary school but for various reasons have difficulties when they reach college. It is suggested here that the demands (both internal and external) made upon young people during the college years may be an important factor that must be considered and understood in any attempt to explain why the functioning of these students is impaired. Erikson has written about these important years as the time when the young person must make a transition from adolescence to adulthood and establish an adult sense of identity (4). Pressures on the young person to make decisions in such areas as vocational choice, social relationships, and sexual identity may be a source of conflict and so drain much of their energy, leaving little for investment in the area of academic achievement. For those students with more chronic problems the stresses of this period may further accentuate their difficulties.

The purpose of this project is to study a group of students who achieved below their predicted ability to determine what factors in their personality, attitudes, background, and type of academic functioning can be related to performance in academic work.

The goal of this study may be viewed as twofold. One is to determine what psychological factors in the individual personality make-up and background can be related to success or failure in the academic setting. The second is to attempt to study the patterns of academic functioning in the college setting to determine whether certain types of students function in certain ways and, therefore, whether concrete measures of grades and patterns of grades may be used to predict personality make-up and future academic functioning. The hypothesis here is that a student's grade in a course is some measure of his functioning during the time that the course meets. Therefore, an examination of the forty or so course grades that a student makes during his four years at college may reveal patterns and clues as to how he functions in both an academic and a psychological sense.

It is realized that quantitative measure of achievement cannot be used to evaluate the more qualitative aspects of intellectual growth. Nevertheless, patterns of academic achievement, rather than grade averages alone, may be useful in differentiating between certain types of students.

METHOD

The data in this study were obtained from case records of patients who had been seen at the Division of Student Mental Hygiene and from their academic records, including course grades and information as to whether the student had been in academic difficulty. These cases were selected from the clinic files on the basis of whether their achieved average for any term was below their predicted grade (3). Case files not containing fairly complete background history were excluded. Data were obtained from the cases in accordance with a previously formulated schedule and placed on index cards so that information as to various aspects of present adjustment and past functioning was systematically listed. Individual and group comparisons were attempted only with those variables where there was sufficient data. The variables studied will be listed below.

The study group consists of 48 students who entered Yale as undergraduates between the years 1948 and 1954. As mentioned, all these students achieved below their predicted grade sometime during college. The difference between freshman average and predicted grades was computed. The median difference was 6.5 points below prediction.

Fifty per cent of the group attended high school, 44 per cent went to prep school, and 6 per cent attended both high school and prep school. These percentages differ only slightly from figures for secondary education of the college population as a whole.

The median number of treatment hours at the Division of Student Mental Hygiene for the study group was seven. The median for the clinic as a whole is five hours. The difference is not significant. Twenty-three per cent were self-referred, which differs slightly from the 31 per cent self-referred for the clinic caseload.

Statistics for the group by diagnosis are as follows: adjustment reaction of adolescence, 60 per cent; psychoneurosis, 4 per cent; character disorder, 19 per cent, and borderline psychosis, 17 per cent. Comparable figures for the total caseload are not available, but it appears that there may be a greater percentage of "adjustment reaction of adolescence" students in the study group. The median predicted grade is 79, which is slightly higher than the average predicted grade for their classes of 76. Comparison of median predicted grade between diagnostic groups reveals little difference except that the neurotic group tends to be slightly higher.

In the study group 47 per cent did not graduate with their class because they either resigned, were dropped, or took a leave of absence sometime during their stay at college. This is much higher than the percentage for the college as a whole, which is approximately 25 per cent.

Definition of Variables Used in the Study

Data on nine variables were obtained (see Table 1 below, page 69). A median score for each quantifiable variable was calculated and each student was given a high or low score according to whether he was above or below the median. Below is a listing of these variables and their explanation.

1. *Diagnostic category*. Diagnoses were obtained from the case records. Of the 29 instances of adolescent adjustment reaction, 12 displayed passive-resistive behavior and 13 dependency traits, while 4 cases showed chronic adolescent disturbance. There were 2 cases of neurotic reaction, 9 of character disorder, and 8 instances of borderline psychosis, making a total of 48 cases.

2. *Grade pattern—upward or downward*. This is a measure of the over-all pattern of the direction of the student's grades during his college career. It was obtained by subtracting the average of the term averages during the second half of college from the average during the first half. Above and below the median (plus 2.58) were considered better criteria of the direction-of-grade pattern than plus or minus (whether the grade went up or down) because of the general tendency for all students' grades to increase during college.

3. *Grade variability*. Variables 3a, b, and c deal with statistical measures of variability of course grades and term averages. The hypothesis here is that different types of students might have different grade variability patterns. Variability measures were not available on some students because they were not in school long enough (for example, freshman, drop-outs after one year) so that variability data were available for only 43 subjects. (a) *Between-term variability:* this is a measure of grade fluctuation from semester to semester. It is the variance of term averages around the total average. Thus a student with high between-term variability might be one who had sharp differences from one term to another. (b) *Within-term variability:* this is a measure of fluctuation within terms of course grades in contrast to the fluctuation from term to

term (variable 3a). This may be viewed as a measure of fluctuation of individual course grades, so that a student who has high within-term variability might be considered to be more motivated by interest or lack of interest in specific courses rather than by the goal of achievement of high grades in general. This variable was obtained by computing the variance of individual course grades around the term averages. *(c) Total variability:* this was obtained by calculating the variance of the individual course grades around the over-all college average. This might be considered a composite of variables 3a and 3b.

4. *Student attitude toward problems.* The students were placed in one of two categories: (a) admit problems, (b) deny problems. These data were obtained from the observations made in the initial interviews.

5. *Pressure from parents for achievement.* Students were placed in one of four categories by the author according to information in the case record: (a) pressure from mother, (b) pressure from father, (c) pressure from both parents, (d) insufficient information.

6. *Graduate or left school.* Two categories: (a) graduates, (b) left before finishing. There was one student who was still in school, therefore the N for this variable was one less than the total N.

7. *Source of referral to clinic.* Two categories: (a) self-referred, (b) not self-referred.

8. *Length of treatment.* Again, students were placed in two categories: (a) above median number of treatment hours, (b) below median. The median number of hours of therapy was seven.

9. *Change in grades before and after treatment.* The average of all grades after treatment was subtracted from the average of all grades before treatment. Grades during treatment were not used in deriving this measure. This variable is an attempt to obtain a measure of grade change in relationship to the time when treatment occurred.

FINDINGS

The following presentation will be an analysis according to clinical groups. Illustrative cases will be presented accompanied by a graph of their academic records including term averages, predicted grade, notation when treatment occurred, the number of hours of therapy, and whether the student interrupted his schooling. A summary will be included in each section of any trends noted in other variables when these were compared with the clinical group.

Table 1 summarizes the relationship occurring between the different diagnostic groups and other variables. These findings should be viewed as possible trends rather than statistically significant findings. Comments on inter-group comparisons will be made at the end of this section.

Adjustment Reaction of Adolescence

1. Passive-resistive traits (12 cases). These students seemed to be engaged in a struggle with their parents and authority figures in general in an effort to assert their independence and establish their own identity. The academic setting becomes the arena for the struggle, and rather than openly rebel they express their resentment indirectly through academic failure. In several cases where the parents were pressuring for a specific vocational goal, academic difficulty centered around the subjects which were necessary in preparation for this vocation. When the student can overtly assert himself and change his major, his grades may rise dramatically, often going from failure to honors. In other situations where no solution can be worked out in the academic area, the student may leave school or be dropped, later to return with considerable improvement in his academic functioning. In these instances it appears that the few years they spent away from school, either in service or working, provided some opportunity to work out their struggle and establish their own identity.

The primary complaints of this group when seen at the clinic centered around the areas of vocational indecision and concern regarding the relationship to their parents. Their attitude toward themselves was somewhat self-critical, while their attitude toward treatment was for the most part either positive or ambivalent.

An examination of Table 1 reveals the following patterns. These students tend to have a grade pattern that rises somewhat more than the other sub-groups in the "adjustment reaction of adolescence" group. The passive-resistives have a low total and within-term variability. There is some fluctuation in grades which is present mainly in their between-term averages. The dependent group, in contrast, have less fluctuation in grades but also less of an increase in their grades during college. Scrutiny of the grade records of the passive-resistives indicated that the increase in term averages could be associated chiefly with one of two factors: treat-

TABLE *1*. RELATIONSHIP BETWEEN DIAGNOSIS AND OTHER VARIABLES

1. Diagnosis	Adjustment Reaction of Adolescence				CHARACTER DISORDER	BORDERLINE PSYCHOSIS
	PASSIVE-RESISTIVE	DEPENDENT	CHRONIC	TOTAL		
N	12	13	4	29	9	8
2. Grade pattern	H *	—	—	H	L *	—
3. Grade variability						
Between-term	H	L	—	—	L	—
Within-term	L	L	—	L	—	H
Total	L	L	—	L	—	H
4. Attitude toward problem						
Admit–deny	A	D	D	—	D	—
5. Pressure from parents						
Mother	L	H	H	H	—	L
Father	H	L	—	—	—	—
Both	L	—	—	L	H	—
No information	L	—	—	L	—	H
6. Graduate – not graduate	G	—	G	G	N.G.	—
7. Self-referred — not self-referred	S	N.S.	—	—	N.S.	—
8. Duration of treatment	—	—	—	—	—	L
9. Change in grades and therapy	H	—	—	H	L	L

* H = high; L = low.

ment at the clinic and change in major. The dependent group, in contrast, had relatively few students whose change in grades could be associated with a change in major. It may be speculated that when the passive-resistive students rebelled, it mainly affected their major subject, which in turn caused their term averages to drop. However, through treatment or changing their major some resolution did occur, so that they were able to function better.

The passive-resistives tend to admit to their difficulties much more readily than the dependent group. They also tend to have a greater change in grades from before to after treatment, which may relate to the finding that they were self-referred. This group tends to assume more responsibility for their academic difficulties and therefore respond better to help offered them. It is not surprising that a greater proportion of this group tend to graduate. Of the three students in the study who left school and later returned to finish successfully, two were in this passive-resistive group.

The family constellation was characterized by pressure for achievement from the father, while the relationship to the mother was generally positive. This was in sharp contrast to the family constellation of the dependent students, where just the opposite was the case. It may be postulated that in the passive-resistive group the students had the emotional support of their mothers and were therefore able to assert themselves in their relationships to their fathers and eventually move toward an establishment of their own identities.

The variable that did not appear to relate to this group was duration of treatment. However, upon further examination of those students whose grades went up at the time when treatment occurred, it was found that these students generally had longer-than-average periods of treatment.

CASE 1. This student is an illustration of a situation where conflict with parental figures is focused on vocational goals and rebellion is expressed through failure in the major needed to prepare for the vocation.

The student was referred by the medical department because of concern about whether he should continue with his premedical program, since he was doing very poorly in his zoology course. His presenting complaint centered around his conflict as to whether he should continue in medicine. His attitude toward his poor grades in zoology was one of stating openly that he was not interested in the subject and that he couldn't get himself to put the work into mastering the material. Previously he always had a good deal of confidence in his intellectual ability, and the present experience of failure raised questions in his mind as to his ability. He was quite upset at the possibility of having to give up premed and saw switching to another major as a failure on his part to live up to the expectations of others. He stated that he had never had to make a decision like this before but he felt very strongly that he must make the decision by himself. He seemed interested in examining his motives and had a generally positive attitude about treatment.

The student's father was president of a bank and the paternal grandfather was a very successful surgeon. The father originally intended to go into medicine but changed to law, which led to banking. The student stated that the father would feel he was quitting if he gave up medicine and that his switching to another field might be an indication of lack of backbone.

As far as his immediate interests and long-term goals were concerned, he stated that he found himself becoming more interested in economics, since he worked in the stock exchange over the summer and enjoyed this experience very much. However, he had always considered medicine as the field he would go into. Since he was a child, whenever anyone asked him what he was going to be, he would say that he was going to be a doctor. The doctors in his home town had always encouraged him to go into this field.

This boy was seen for three hours of therapy and discussed his feelings of switching from medicine to economics. He talked of his somewhat glorified picture of medicine, of his attraction to the field because of the prestige factor rather than any real interest in medicine. He also discussed the whole question of his relationship with his father, his resentment toward the father's domination of him, and how his desire to be a doctor was one way of excelling the father because the father had failed in his efforts to be a doctor. He described situations where previously he had been fearful of competing with the father in such activities as golf, but how in recent years he was less fearful of such competitive situations. During this discussion the patient came to the decision to switch from premed to economics and seemed fairly comfortable in making this decision.

The diagnosis made was adjustment reaction of adolescence with passive-resistive traits. Dynamically it appeared that the student was striving to establish his own identity and was in a competitive struggle with the father, medicine representing a way of excelling where the father had previously failed. The father was pressuring him to stay in medicine, and the student seemed to have rebelled by failure in the specific course needed to prepare for this field.

The academic record indicated a very high predicted grade: 89. His average during freshman year was around 76 but dropped to a 71, primarily because of a very low grade in zoology in the third term. He switched to a major in economics in the fourth term; his grades immediately jumped to Dean's List level and remained at a high level until he graduated.

In summary, it may be said that this student, who had very high abilities, was unable to use them because of conflict around his own goals and goals being imposed on him by his parents. He came to the clinic at a time when he was almost ready to assert himself in his relationship to the family and seemed to use the three therapy hours as a means of clarifying his own thinking, gaining support in establishing his own goals.

Figure 1 is a graph of this student's academic record. This graph

FIGURE I

ADJUSTMENT REACTION OF ADOLESCENCE, PASSIVE-RESISTIVE TRAITS

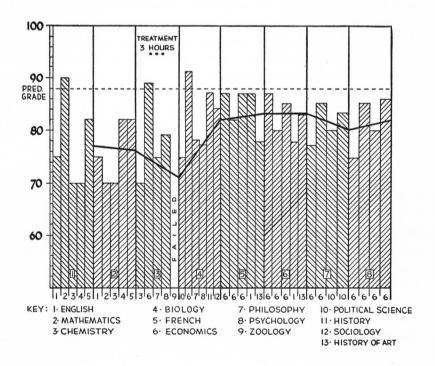

KEY: 1· ENGLISH   4· BIOLOGY   7· PHILOSOPHY   10· POLITICAL SCIENCE
       2· MATHEMATICS   5· FRENCH   8· PSYCHOLOGY   11· HISTORY
       3· CHEMISTRY   6· ECONOMICS   9· ZOOLOGY   12· SOCIOLOGY
                                                                     13· HISTORY OF ART

and the ones that follow illustrate individual course grades by a bar graph and term averages by a line graph. A key to courses taken is listed below the graph. A broken line indicates the predicted grade for the student. Treatment is noted on the graph at the time during the academic career when it occurred.

2. *Dependency traits* (13 cases). These students were characterized by strong dependency ties to their families and persistent attempts to conform to the wishes of others and in particular follow goals set up for them by their parents. They often were immature socially and had difficulty orienting themselves to the college environment. They expressed guilt and self-blame over their failures, particularly at their feeling that they had let their parents down. The background history of some of these students revealed a pattern of being overindulged by their parents and therefore never having developed much inner discipline.

Their presenting complaints to the clinic centered around dissatisfaction with social life at college, preoccupation with fear that they would be rejected by girl friends back home, or concentration difficulties.

This group tended to refuse to accept the responsibility for their problem but rather projected the blame onto others and engaged in self-pity. They saw their present difficulties as caused by poor social life or lack of discipline in their previous training.

Their attitude toward themselves was self-critical, with feelings of inadequacy which had existed for some time. They also felt strongly their lack of self-discipline. They were somewhat ambivalent toward treatment, more so than the passive-resistive group.

Table 1 (page 69) indicates that this group tends to have low grade variability both within and between terms.

Examination of the academic records revealed that there was a tendency for students in this group to have a gradual increase in grades from freshman to senior years. It may be hypothesized that for these students time is an important factor in obtaining a good adjustment. Perhaps their difficulties are mainly developmental and with the opportunity for further experiences in college they are able to gain greater clarity in their goals and therefore improve their functioning. Munroe (6) in her discussion of the academic performance of the "rigid or conscientious student" points to patterns that are similar to those observed in these dependent ones. However, her explanation is somewhat different. She feels that these students learn what will please the teacher and thus their grades improve. This pattern of conformity and compliance toward adults was also observed in these dependent students.

Table 1, above, reveals further that the dependent students tend to deny their difficulties, which may relate to the finding that they tended not to be self-referred.

The family constellation in these students was one in which the pressure for achievement came mainly from the mother. Often the father was seen as weak and ineffectual, the mother being the dominant parent. It may be postulated that the dependent group had difficulty establishing their own identity because of strong dependency-hostility ties to the mother and lack of a masculine father-figure for identification. Instead of rebelling openly like the passive-resistives, via poor work in their major subjects, these students tend to be more conforming and therefore maintain a fairly even level of functioning, so that there is relatively little fluctuation in their grades. Their grades are passing and they eventually graduate, although a relatively higher proportion interrupt their schooling.

Other variables that did not appear to relate to this group were grade pattern, graduate or not graduate, duration of treatment, and change in grades and therapy. However, as in the passive-resistive group, the students whose grades improved during the time of treatment had longer-than-average periods of treatment.

CASE 2. This student is an example of a dependent young man who seemed to benefit considerably from treatment. The grade pattern was one of gradually increasing grades. This increase seemed related to the therapy he received as well as to spontaneous growth toward independent self-responsibility.

This student was referred to the clinic by his freshman counselor because of stammering difficulties. Although he stressed the stammering as his main complaint, when seen in the intake and later in therapy, the stammering was hardly noticeable. The actual precipitating factor that brought him in was concern over his responsibility toward his girl friend. So far as the stammering was concerned, he stated that it hadn't been a problem till age thirteen and he hadn't been aware of it until his mother became concerned and stressed the difficulty. He had difficulty speaking freely when he felt nervous and had particular difficulty when talking on the telephone or when reciting in class. He had received some speech therapy at age sixteen but felt that this didn't help much. An additional complaint was a feeling of homesickness.

He blamed his academic difficulties on his stuttering and said that when he was younger, he had avoided classes because of the speech problem. He expressed some guilt about not doing things that he ought to do, not living up to the expectations of others, and thought the "selfish side" of himself had been coming out more since he came to Yale.

The patient complained that other students did not have similar interests, and in general he felt homesick for friends back home, particularly his girl friend. When first seen, he thought that he would quit Yale and enter the service. He compared Yale with his home, saying that they were quite different—being at Yale was like being in a "world by itself."

He felt, in general, that his parents were ideal and denied feeling that they had ever done anything to hurt him. He said his father tried to cover up for his son and seemed to cling to him. The father compared himself with the son and apparently had had similar problems when he was the student's age. He described his mother as being much concerned about his speech difficulty. The mother also appeared to be somewhat fearful for her son, afraid that he would be hurt when he participated in athletics. In general he was afraid of the mother, as she was the disciplinarian in the family. The mother attempted to control him by telling him that he would make father ill if he did something wrong. He described the mother as having a sharp tongue and sympathized with the father when the mother berated him. The student complained about the fact that there were always many women around the house, aunts and grandmothers, and in general the family seems to have been run by the women.

A diagnosis of adjustment reaction of adolescence was made, with symptomatic habit reaction of stuttering.

This student received a total of twenty-six hours of therapy. Treatment extended from the second half of his freshman year through the sophomore year. Therapy focused on his relation-

ship with his family and his difficulty in taking independent steps.
The speech difficulty was related to his concern of what people
would think of him. His feelings of inadequacy as a male were
discussed and his fears about not being masculine enough were
aired. One of the results of the therapy was a change in his relationship to the family. He obtained more distance from the
family and became more assertive in his relationships with other
people as well.

FIGURE 2
ADJUSTMENT REACTION OF ADOLESCENCE, DEPENDENT TRAITS

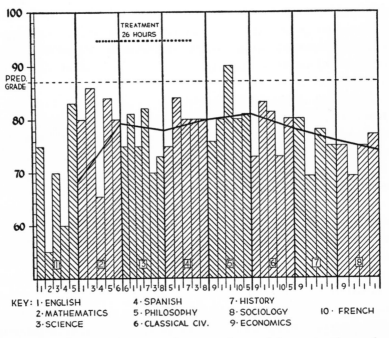

KEY: 1·ENGLISH   4·SPANISH   7·HISTORY
     2·MATHEMATICS   5·PHILOSOPHY   8·SOCIOLOGY   10 · FRENCH
     3·SCIENCE   6·CLASSICAL CIV.   9·ECONOMICS

In general, this appears to be a student with strong dependent
needs who had not been able to establish his identity as a man because of an inadequate father-figure and a domineering mother.

This student's grades increased eleven points from the first
term to the second term. He maintained fairly good grades, although he never attained his 87 prediction. His grades varied
little and he was below the median in both within- and between-
term variability.

In summary, it appears that this student with the help of treatment was able to gain some understanding of his relationship in the family, with the result that he was able to establish his own goals and to gain some success in achieving these goals. Figure 2 is a graph of this student's academic record.

3. Chronic adolescent disturbance (4 cases). The students in this category were those remaining in the adjustment reaction of adolescence group who could not be placed in either the passive-resistive or dependency subgroups.

These students appeared to have more serious and long-standing difficulties than those in the other subgroups. Two of these students were referred by their therapist for more intensive treatment after graduation.

Since the group cannot be described in dynamic terms, no attempt is made to discuss any general patterns. A case illustration is presented for the purpose of showing how one student's achievement problems related to his underlying psychological conflict.

Case 3. This case illustrates how an underlying conflict may be symbolized by failure in the student's chosen major. With the aid of treatment and a change in major, the student was able to regain his previous level of functioning.

For a full description of presenting complaints, family background, and treatment, see Case 1, Chapter 14.

Academically this student's failure was primarily in architecture courses (his major), which he started taking junior year. He wanted to change his major to American Studies, stated he felt more "comfortable" taking these courses. His initial interest in architecture started in high school and he related it directly to the fact that his parents lived in a fairly crowded apartment and he always felt somewhat uncomfortable in the home. It was later revealed that there was an open display of nudity in the home, even to the extent that family members shared the bathroom at the same time for different functions.

The grade record indicated that this boy had fairly high grades until the term he started taking architecture, when the average of his grades dropped about 35 points. However, after he switched to American Studies, he again was able to achieve high grades and continued to do so until he graduated. The increase in grades coincided with the change in major as well as with the time of treatment.

Dynamically it appeared that architecture symbolized public display of the concealed exhibitionistic pleasure he had in the home, and since he could not admit to this pleasure he defended himself by showing a lack of interest in these courses. With the active intervention of the therapist, he was able to change his major to a field which he felt was closer to his real interests and which was more detached from the family situation. These conflicts did not appear to affect his further academic work as he was eventually able to graduate after obtaining high grades for three semesters. Figure 3 is a graph of this student's academic record.

FIGURE 3
ADJUSTMENT REACTION OF ADOLESCENCE, CHRONIC

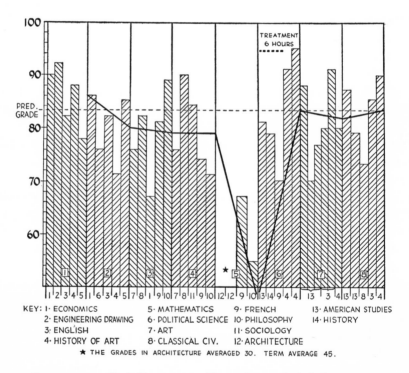

KEY: 1· ECONOMICS   5· MATHEMATICS   9· FRENCH   13· AMERICAN STUDIES
       2· ENGINEERING DRAWING   6· POLITICAL SCIENCE   10· PHILOSOPHY   14· HISTORY
       3· ENGLISH   7· ART   11· SOCIOLOGY
       4· HISTORY OF ART   8· CLASSICAL CIV.   12· ARCHITECTURE
           ★ THE GRADES IN ARCHITECTURE AVERAGED 30. TERM AVERAGE 45.

Summary of Adjustment Reaction of Adolescence
(29 Cases)

The following is a discussion of trends that appear to be present in this diagnostic group as a whole (see Table 1, page 69).

The grades of the students classified as adjustment reaction of adolescence tend to rise during college. An examination of the grade records suggests that the increase in grades is related to treatment or to change in major. The treatment records indicate that this accompanies the achievement of greater independence from the family. Variable 9 (Table 1) also indicates that this group has a high change in grade before and after treatment. As would be anticipated, members of this group graduate.

The variability of grades tends to be low, particularly within terms. This suggests that students with a lesser degree of psychopathology tend to be more consistent in their achievement from course to course than students with a greater degree of pathology.

As far as family constellation in this group is concerned, it appears that there is a tendency for many of these students to come from families where the mother is the dominant parent and exerts the pressure for achievement. This constellation evidently makes for difficulties in attaining firm, active, masculine-identity components.

The variables that do not appear to relate to this diagnostic group are between-term variability, attitude toward problem, attitude toward father, source of referral, and duration of treatment. Further examination of the length of therapy for those students whose increase in grades can be associated in time with occurrence of treatment indicates that most of them had a greater than average length of treatment.

In summary, it appears that the adjustment reaction of adolescence group tends to function adequately enough to graduate. This is in contrast to the character disorder group (see below), who in general do not graduate. On the other hand, the borderline psychotic group (see below) also are able to graduate but to a lesser extent than the adjustment reaction group. It appears, furthermore, that when these students do have difficulties, they are able to resolve them by taking some definite action, such as seeking treatment or changing their major.

Psychoneurosis (2 Cases)

Only two students were diagnosed as psychoneurotic in the study. Although it is difficult to draw any generalizations because of the few cases, certain trends seem worth mentioning here.

The grade pattern of both cases tended to be downward, although both students graduated. The variability of course grades appeared somewhat higher than the study group as a whole. This was particularly evident in the between-term fluctuation. This variability may be due to periods of acute, interfering anxiety from which neurotics may suffer.

In both cases the dominant parent was the mother, with the pressure to achieve coming from the mother.

CASE 4. This is the case of a neurotic young man who twice had to leave school because of his illness but following treatment away from school was able to return and complete his work.

This was a senior who came to the clinic on his own with the main complaint of guilt regarding masturbation. His excessive concern with masturbation prevented him from doing his school work. His attitude about his problems was to see the conflict mainly in terms of morals and he felt terribly guilty because he could not control his masturbation.

In his social relationships he felt quite upset and guilty about his relationship with girls, seemed to engage in somewhat compulsive petting, and had a particularly close relationship with one girl, to whom he wrote daily.

He had spent some time in the service, having enlisted in the Air Force, and felt that he had functioned quite well. There was no concern about masturbation at that time. He was discharged because they discovered that he had a physical defect, one leg being shorter than the other.

He felt that his academic difficulties were related to the amount of sexual activity in which he was engaged and the anxiety he had about it. During his junior year he seemed to feel so guilty about his sexual impulses that he wanted to transfer from engineering to the ministry but was discouraged by his father; it was at this point that his grades dropped to their lowest.

His parents' attitude about sex, he felt, was always one of condemnation, that it was bad to engage in any sexual activity. He stated that the father never discussed sex with him and gave him a YMCA booklet which stressed the need for sexual control. He thought his father had very high ideals and morals and compared himself unfavorably with the father in this regard. The mother was described as very intelligent. He said she required a good deal of affection, which he gave her. He was always closer to the mother than to the father, although she tended to be hypercritical.

His brother, several years older, was successful academically and had graduated from college.

The diagnosis was obsessive-compulsive reaction, with compulsive masturbation and obsessional thoughts about sexuality. It was felt that he had a lifelong sensitivity regarding the congenital defect of the leg. His examination anxiety was felt to relate to anxiety about exposing his defect. He was seen for two hours but because of excessive anxiety and inability to take his exams, he

FIGURE 4
PSYCHONEUROTIC

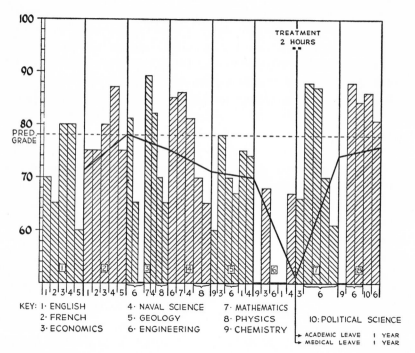

KEY: 1· ENGLISH   4· NAVAL SCIENCE   7· MATHEMATICS
2· FRENCH   5· GEOLOGY   8· PHYSICS   10: POLITICAL SCIENCE
3· ECONOMICS   6· ENGINEERING   9· CHEMISTRY
ACADEMIC LEAVE   1 YEAR
MEDICAL LEAVE   1 YEAR

was given a medical leave and advised to seek private treatment. He returned a year later after having some therapy, appeared to have improved in his ability to handle his problems, and was readmitted.

The academic record indicated that this student had a prediction of 76 and during the first five terms was able to achieve this. In the sixth term his grades dropped 20 points and he took an academic leave. He returned after one year, again had difficulties, and it was at this point that he contacted the clinic. He was again given a leave, returned a year later after therapy, was able to achieve a 75 average during his senior year, and graduated. The variability of his grades was high; he was above the median of the study group for both within- and between-term grade variability.

In general, it appears that this young man's neurosis created so much anxiety that he could not function without taking a leave of absence and receiving treatment. However, with treatment, he was able eventually to return and get a degree. A letter received at the clinic from this student six months after his graduation indicated that he was performing successfully on an engineering job. Figure 4 is a graph of this student's academic record.

Character Disorder (9 Cases)

The presenting complaint of this group when coming to the clinic centered around their complete lack of interest in their school work and lack of motivation to invest time and energy in this work. Other complaints, such as excessive drinking and anti-social activities, suggested that they were acting out their problems. They were differentiated from adjustment reaction of adolescence by the lack of internal turmoil and the fixing of the behavior pattern.

Their attitude toward their problems was to deny them. They did not accept responsibility for their academic difficulties but placed blame on inadequate social life and conflict with parents, particularly with the father. Even if admitting to their difficulties, they did not take responsibility for doing anything about them but expected some sort of mechanical and magical solution from the therapist.

Their attitude toward treatment was either openly negative or ambivalent. Ambivalence was frequently expressed by the statement that their parents were opposed to treatment and they did not want to antagonize the parents.

Table 1 indicates the following patterns. This group tends to have a downward grade pattern with a large proportion (eight out of nine) leaving school without graduating. This is in sharp contrast to other diagnostic groups who have a much lower percentage of drop-outs. This finding is similar to that found by Harrison (5) that students diagnosed as character disorder were more likely to fail again as compared to other diagnostic groups. Further examination of the grade records of the character disorder group indicated that half of this group had low grades with little change occurring, while in the other half the grades went down. A relatively large proportion of those who left were dropped by school authorities for poor grades. Of those who left school, a relatively large proportion did not return.

The between-term variability of grades for this group was low. This is explained by the pattern of having low and unchanging grades.

As mentioned above, this group tended to deny difficulties, which seems to relate to the finding that they generally were not self-referred to the clinic. The low change in grade in relationship to therapy may also relate to the implied lack of motivation for therapy.

It appears that in these patients a good deal of pressure was exerted by the parents and there was little support from either parent. In several cases the relationship with the father was extremely stormy, with open hostility expressed by both father and son. Several of the patients' families had unusually rigid and strict moral standards so that the sons were severely restricted in their peer relationships. These restrictions were carried over to college, so that social adjustment to the relatively more free college culture was difficult for them.

In general, these students were much too involved in pathological relationships in their own families to be able to find the energy and motivation to work for a college education. Their consistently poor performance seems to indicate that they could find no academic area which they "could call their own" and the college experience was frustrating and ungratifying. School was completely identified with conflicts at home and perhaps the only purpose of college was as a weapon to be used in their struggle with their parents.

CASE 5. This exemplifies a young man with a long-term character problem and passive-aggressive traits. He seemed to act out his aggression both in the area of academic achievement as well as by refusing to comply with college rules and regulations. The acting out also appeared in his therapy, in that he broke appointments.

This student was referred as a freshman after the father had called the dean because of concern for his son's physical difficulties, which his father understood as being the cause of the academic difficulties. The dean referred him to the medical clinic and after a thorough physical examination, he was referred to the mental hygiene clinic. His main complaints were of a loss of interest in his work, being generally discouraged and unable to concentrate or remember what he read. He was preoccupied with negative thoughts of his father which distracted him from his work.

He blamed his negative feelings toward the father for the academic problem. He was quite negative about referral to the clinic and terribly afraid his parents would discover his contact and would object to his coming.

He appeared to be somewhat isolated in his relationship to peers and complained about the lack of opportunity to date. At prep school he had done very well but he attributed the deterioration in his work to his increasing awareness of negative feelings for the father. At college he selected the most difficult courses in the curriculum and was somewhat unrealistic in estimating his ability to take on these courses.

This student seemed completely preoccupied with feelings of anger toward the father's lack of understanding of him and blamed all his failure on the father. He listed his complaints against the family systematically and had actually presented these complaints to them. These included his resentment that they wanted to know in detail every move he made, were somewhat Victorian in their social mores, and were rigidly strict in their religious beliefs. His parents felt in general that too much freedom was not good for a college student, and they had no confidence in the way he used his time. They were very critical of his poor grades and punished him by restricting his social life.

This student was seen for two hours during his freshman year, seemed to react to the therapist in the same way in which he re-acted to the family, and discontinued because he said the parents opposed his coming. He returned to the clinic during sophomore year on his own and received thirteen hours of treatment, but again acted out his negative feelings, did not keep appointments, and, in general, did not take responsibility for working on his problem. He assumed a somewhat passive role in the interview situation. He wanted to terminate treatment after his marks went up at midyear, but following this he overcut his classes and was put back on General Warning.

The academic record indicated that he had a prediction of 87 but was never able to obtain grades close to this. His grades during the first half of the year usually were higher than grades the second half. After his grades fell off at the end of his sophomore year, he was dropped by the college. The variability of this stu-

FIGURE 5
CHARACTER DISORDER

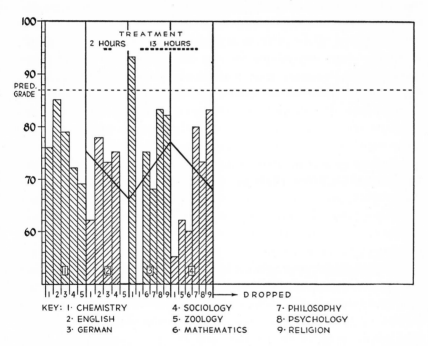

KEY: 1· CHEMISTRY   4· SOCIOLOGY   7· PHILOSOPHY
2· ENGLISH   5· ZOOLOGY   8· PSYCHOLOGY
3· GERMAN   6· MATHEMATICS   9· RELIGION

dent's term averages was low, which was rather typical of students diagnosed as character disorder.

It is interesting to note that the father's reaction to his son's expulsion was to blame the problems on physical factors and to refer him to the Mayo Clinic for a physical examination. Later the student applied to a university near his home town.

In general, this appears to be a student who acted out his negative relationship with his father in the school situation, since he could not successfully oppose his parents in any other way than by failing in school. The parents' denial of his difficulties seemed to fit into the student's own need to deny them and not assume responsibility for doing anything about them. Figure 5 is a graph of this student's academic record.

Borderline Psychosis (8 Cases)

The presenting complaints of these students when seen at the clinic stressed their concern with inner feelings of unreality, tendencies toward excessive daydreaming, and bizarre fantasy life. They also verbalized chronic states of depression and anxiety.

Their attitude toward their difficulties did not reflect a consistent pattern. Some of these students flatly denied they had any problems, while others admitted to difficulties even to the point of saying that perhaps they had "unconscious" desires to flunk out.

They tended to be ambivalent toward treatment and to see acceptance of treatment as admission of weakness. They expressed suspiciousness about confidentiality and were afraid of being rejected after admitting their difficulties. Some expressed a passive expectation that the therapist would solve their problems for them.

Table 1 (page 69) reveals the following patterns. The variability of grades for the borderline psychotic group tends to be higher than the other groups. Fluctuation in grades occurs particularly within terms. Examination of grades in individual courses revealed no consistent explanation for change in functioning. It is striking how these students can achieve very high and very low grades in courses taken in the same department in the same term. Astronomy seems to be more popular with this group than with other groups. Usually their grades in this course are fairly high. Perhaps this interest is related to the fantasy life of these students, which often dwells on thoughts of the universe.

Many of the students in the group graduated, which is striking in view of their severe pathology. The finding that psychotic students can function successfully in academic setting corroborates a similar finding by Arnstein (1) and Harrison (5).

Information on family relationships in this group is significantly lacking. This is understandable in view of the fact that these patients are so involved in their own inner fantasy world that they do not produce meaningful data on their relationships to others.

The average duration of treatment for these students is lower than in other groups. This may be related to the finding that the change in grade in relationship to therapy is also low. However, examination of the therapy experience for these students indicated that some of them were in treatment for unusually long periods. Often therapy appeared to be a necessary support to enable the student to continue functioning.

In summary, it may be said that this group of students, although having serious psychological problems, are able to function adequately enough to obtain their degrees. It appears that they can isolate personal problems from the academic area sufficiently to be able to find some courses which they can associate with their own goals and interests. Their very great fluctuation in performance may be explained by a temporary association of individual classes, courses, or instructors with their own inner difficulties.

Case 6. This case illustrates the borderline individual who shows great variability in course grades. This is particularly striking in the grades the student received in physics. He was able to graduate in spite of fairly long-standing problems.

This student was first referred when he was a freshman. He was sent to the clinic by a faculty member because of a general feeling of doubt about himself and a feeling that people doubted him and were laughing behind his back. Another complaint was a tendency to daydream, which detracted from his studying. In therapy he showed very little psychological curiosity, was somewhat passive, and wanted to be told what to do.

The student stated that as a child he tended to stay by himself. He preferred to daydream rather than play with other boys of his age. His social relationships at college appeared to be those of a somewhat isolated individual.

His parents were divorced when he was two years of age and he had had very little contact with his father. His mother overprotected him and was fearful that he would injure himself in sports, so that he was never encouraged to play with other boys.

A diagnosis of schizoid personality in an extremely immature, narcissistic young man was made. He was seen for two hours during his freshman year, which was terminated somewhat abruptly, but he returned again at the end of his sophomore year and was seen for thirteen hours. The main problem in the therapy was to arouse some psychological curiosity in this student, and to some extent this was successful. His passive-aggressive relationship to his parents was discussed and the attempt to punish his parents by

FIGURE 6
BORDERLINE PSYCHOTIC

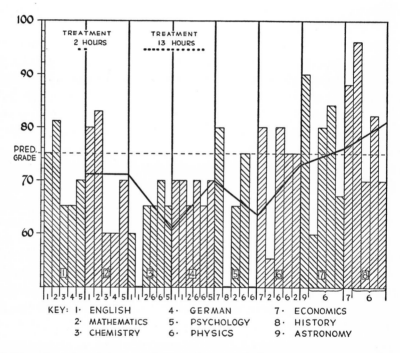

failing in school was understood more fully by the patient. The therapist felt that treatment helped the student to gain greater insight, to become more outgoing in relationships with people and to function better in his academic work.

The academic record indicated that his term averages fluctuated greatly and that in response to treatment his grades seemed to go up temporarily but then dropped the next term. However, starting with the sixth term his grades continued to rise, so that he overachieved in his seventh and eighth terms. In the seventh term, in particular, it is interesting to note the great variation in his physics grades.

In general, this borderline young man seemed to have gained some benefit from therapy as seen by his improved functioning the latter part of his college career. Although his underlying psychological problem appeared to remain unchanged, he was able to graduate from college. Figure 6 is a graph of this student's academic record.

Summary of Neurotic, Character Disorder, and Borderline Psychotic Cases (19 Cases)

The following is a discussion of those subjects diagnosed as neurotic, character disorder, or borderline psychotic (see Table 1, page 69).

The grade pattern of these cases was generally downward with a high proportion interrupting their schooling and less than the expected number graduating. Also, they tended to have a low change in grade before and after therapy, which seems related to the finding that the length of treatment tended to be short.

The fluctuation of grades in these cases tended to be high. This was particularly true for the within-term variability. This finding seems related particularly to the neurotic and borderline psychotic groups.

In the family it appeared that a larger than expected number of students were pressured by both parents. Also, a large number did not reveal any information regarding parental attitudes toward achievement.

In general, it appeared that the students with structural psychological difficulties tended to do poorly academically. They came from families where a lack of emotional support was coupled with parents' critical attitudes. The high fluctuation in grades seemed to indicate a lack of consistent goals or perhaps constantly shifting academic goals. Their identifications seemed somewhat fluid because of lack of acceptance in their homes, so that they were not free to choose the direction they wished to take and gain satisfaction out of achievement.

The variables that did not appear to relate to this group were between-term variability, attitude toward problem, and source of referral.

Summary of Group Differences

For grade pattern it appeared that the adjustment reaction of adolescence students tended to have an upward grade pattern, in contrast to the neurotic, character disorder, and borderline psychotic students who had a downward grade pattern. This finding seems related to the one that the former group tended to graduate, while the opposite was true for the latter students.

The adjustment reaction of adolescence group tended to have less variability in grades than the neurotic, character disorder, and borderline psychotic students. The dependent adolescent group tended to have the least fluctuation in grades, while the borderline psychotics had the greatest. Within the "adjustment reaction of adolescence" group the passive-resistive and dependency sub-groups had opposite trends in between-term grade variability. The former had high and the latter had low variability. The variation in grades of the borderline psychotic group was primarily in the within-term variability. The character disorder group, on the other hand, tended to have low between-term variability.

There appeared to be a difference between the "adjustment reaction of adolescence" group and the other diagnostic groups in respect to the change in grade before and after therapy. The neurotic, character disorder, and borderline psychotic students tended to have less of a change in grade than the adjustment reaction of adolescence students. This seems related to the finding that the former groups tended to have relatively shorter periods of treatment.

As far as referral source the only differences appeared between the passive-resistive group, who tended to be self-referred, and the dependency and character disorder groups, who tended not to be self-referred.

In respect to family constellation it appeared that in the adjustment reaction of adolescence group there was a marked contrast between the dependency and passive-resistive groups. In the former group the mother exerted the pressure for academic achievement and the father assumed a somewhat passive role in the family. In the passive-resistive group the father was the dominant parent and exerted the pressure for achievement. For the adjustment reaction of adolescence group as a whole there was a tendency for the students to come from families where the mother was the dominant parent. This was in contrast to the borderline psychotic group, where there were few instances of sons being pressured by the mothers. For this group there was a large number of students who did not reveal information regarding family relationships. In the character disorder group the main finding was that there were a large number of students who were pressured by both parents. This group seemed to have a greater degree of conflict in family relationships than any other group.

As far as attitude toward the problem is concerned, the passive-resistive group was the only one which tended to admit to their difficulties. The dependent and chronic students in the adjustment reaction of adolescence group and the character disorder group tended to deny their problems.

SUMMARY AND CONCLUSIONS

This study is an attempt to determine what factors in college students' personality, background, and type of academic functioning relate to performance in academic work. Forty-eight undergraduate students who achieved below their predicted ability were selected from the patient caseload and the material in clinical files and academic records were studied. Variables of personality, background, grade patterns, and fluctuations were analyzed according to diagnostic and dynamic groups. It has been observed that there are many possible explanations for academic underachievement in the college student. In general, it is felt that a formulation taking into account the psychopathological, educational, and social factors can be used to explain why students do not function up to ability in college. It has been found that there are similarities in patterns of academic functioning for students given the same diagnosis. Also revealed is the fact that the severity of emotional disturbances cannot be used as the sole criteria to predict success in college.

Some of the findings suggest the following hypotheses regarding the relationship between personality dynamics and patterns of learning. It was observed that in the adjustment reaction of adolescence group the passive-resistives made the greatest increase in grades while in college and also had the largest fluctuation in term grades. In contrast, the dependent students had less of an over-all increase in grades but also had relatively little fluctuation in grades. Although it is certainly not assumed that high grades are in themselves evidence of intellectual growth, it may be speculated that the greater quantitative improvement made by the passive-resistives may have also been accompanied by a greater qualitative gain. Brown, in his study of female college students (2), discusses a group of students who, in spite of their underachievement in grades, showed evidence of a good deal of intellectual growth during college and especially in subsequent years following graduation. He states that this type of girl "is too busy with problems of growing up, establishing herself as a person independent of parental ties, to take interest in academics in college." Unfortunately there was little data available in this study of the more qualitative aspects of intellectual growth of the students. However, the hypothesis suggested is that the desirable learning curve may be a variable one, with the fluctuation viewed as a result of active exploration and experimentation.

Robinson and Shor (7), in a study of academic failure of engineering students, point out that those students who were able to regain good academic standing tended to be extrapunitive. This finding seems similar to the one obtained in the study in that the passive-resistives made most gain. It raises the theoretical question that healthy learning, which includes re-examination of past values and active experimentation to establish standards appropriate to the individual, might also necessarily involve some rebellion in order to gain liberation from parental and familial ties. It is further speculated that in contrast to this variable type of learning curve the pattern for the dependent student, which is not variable, might be an effort to conform and meet the demands of persons in authority with the sacrifice of inner intellectual growth for quantitative achievement.

The developmental aspects of achievement for college students, referred to in the introduction of this paper, must also be considered for understanding of these patterns of academic functioning. The material available is inadequate to explain whether the gradual rise in grades of the dependent students was an illustration of conformity or more a matter of gradually developing maturity. At any rate, the fact that several students in the study were able to interrupt their schooling and return later and graduate suggests further that time and life experience may be a needed ingredient for them to function successfully in college.

It appears that causes for underachievement are multiple and complex and our understanding of this area is still quite limited. Further study of individual students is needed to clarify whether other educational patterns can be isolated. This would require investigation of a larger number of cases than was possible in this study. It then would also be possible to test whether statistically significant differences do occur between diagnostic and dynamic groups.

Yet another area that might warrant further investigation is the use of grades as a tool in evaluating psychotherapy. In most clinical situations there is a paucity of data on follow-up of patients. It is believed that clinical work in the academic setting offers a unique opportunity to follow up the group of patients who suffer with academic difficulties as a symptom of inner problems. An assumption implied in this study, which may not be fully warranted for certain students, is that successful resolution of inner difficulties should result in improved academic performance. There are probably a number of students whose needs, at the time they are in college, cannot be met by the kind of program offered at the particular college. Perhaps successful therapy for these students may result in a temporary withdrawal from school or transfer to a college with a different type of program. As mentioned above, there were several students in this study whose academic functioning improved considerably after a leave of absence from school. In further research in the area of academic follow-up of psychotherapy, it would be important to single out this group.

An additional factor that would have to be controlled in further study of the use of grades for follow-up purpose is the question of successful vs. unsuccessful therapy. In this study it was difficult to obtain a measure of result of treatment from the clinical material in the records. In future work in this area it would be necessary to come to some evaluation of the success or lack of success in

therapy. As mentioned above, only students whose academic underachievement is seen as a symptom of inner problems would be
expected to improve their grades after therapy. This assumption
was arrived at after a previous attempt at a comparison of change
in grades between a patient and nonpatient control group who
were not selected because of their being underachievers. The findings of this study revealed that there were no significant differences between the two groups. Another study using a control group
of nonpatient underachievers as a base for comparison with the
underachiever patient group is planned.

REFERENCES

1. Below, Chapter 10: Arnstein, "The Borderline Patient in the College Setting."

2. Brown, Donald, Personality and higher education (Nevitt Sanford, ed.), *Journal of Social Issues, 12:*3–71. 1956.

3. Crawford, A. B., and Burnham, P. S., *Forecasting College Achievement,* New Haven, Yale University Press, 1946.

4. Erikson, Eric H., The problem of ego identity, *Journal of the
American Psychoanalytic Association, 4*(1):56–121. 1956.

5. Below, Chapter 5: "Leaving College because of Emotional Problems."

6. Munroe, Ruth L., *Teaching the Individual* (New York, Columbia
University Press, 1942), Chapter 8.

7. Robinson, H. A., and Shor, Joel, "The Study of Academic Failure,"
Unpublished manuscript, 1947.

8. Wolfle, D. C., *America's Resources of Specialized Talent: a Current Appraisal and a Look Ahead,* New York, Harper, 1954.

Leaving College because of Emotional Problems

BY ROBERT W. HARRISON

1. FACTORS INFLUENCING RETURN AND GRADUATION

Students who drop out of college are of serious concern to every educator. Such drop-outs, especially in a student population carefully selected in terms of intellectual ability and past performance are frequently the result of emotional failure, at least a failure of the student and the college to "make connections." The author's unique study follows up such cases by statistical and descriptive methods. The over-all tendency, even in this considerably disturbed group, is for eventual achievement of a satisfactory life adjustment with or without further education. Surprisingly few of the group admitted to college become so fundamentally ill as to be permanently disabled.

EVERY YEAR many students, perhaps thousands, leave college because of emotional problems. In such instances university officials are faced with important decisions that affect the welfare not only of the individual student but also of the university. Initially, of course, there arises the question of whether leaving school is the best course of action. For those students who do leave, an appropriate and useful program of activities must be recommended. Eventually candidates for readmission must be evaluated.

In view of the vital nature of the decisions which must be made in this area, it is astonishing that there have been so few systematic studies. Even the skilled and experienced clinician would welcome the guidance afforded by research findings. But perhaps the greatest general contribution of the research data would be the human savings brought about by a re-examination of the assumptions upon which decisions concerning the "emotional drop-out" are based. There are already findings which challenge universally held assumptions. For example, Darling has shown that in some cases even students formerly diagnosed as psychotic may successfully resume their academic careers.*

A group of 179 students who for emotional reasons left Yale sometime during the period between September 1947 and June 1952 were studied. The study attempted to investigate (a) the characteristics of this "drop-out group," (b) the subsequent course of events for these students, particularly with reference to their academic careers, (c) the factors that characterize those students who returned and those who did not, and (d) variables associated with successful completion of the academic career among members who returned.

All but 6 of the 179 students had been seen in the Division of Student Mental Hygiene at some time prior to their leaving school. It was only at the time they were seeking readmission to the University that these 6 students were seen in the clinic. A medical leave of absence was granted by the clinic to 145 of the 173 students who were seen before they left school. The other 28 students either resigned or were asked to leave by the University.

The two sources of data for this study were administrative records and case records in the Division of Student Mental Hygiene. The students' case records yielded the following information: class at the time of leaving, source of referral, date of leaving, diagnosis, number of clinical contacts prior to leaving and following return to college, type of treatment recommended by the clinic psychiatrist, and whether the student had treatment after leaving school. The administrative records provided information about the student's scholastic performance and his eventual status in the University.

The three experimental groups were: those students who did not return, those students who returned and graduated, and those students who returned and left again. Comparisons were made among these three groups with respect to class, academic status, psychiatric diagnosis, and psychiatric treatment. Tests of statistical significance were made by means of the chi-square technique.

* "Case Reports of the Cornell University Infirmary and Clinic," *Student Medicine*, 3:102–9, 1955.

Characteristics of the Total Group

Class and source of referral. The largest group of students, 76, came to the clinic referred by administrative personnel (deans, masters, counselors, and others). The next two largest groups were those referred by the Department of University Health medical staff and those who were self-referred. It is noteworthy that a smaller proportion of cases in this study were self-referred than is true of the total patient group.

Over three-fourths of the total group of 179 students were in Yale College. There was an almost even distribution of the students throughout the four undergraduate years. The largest group of students among the graduates, 11, was from the Law School.

Age and sex. In the total group of students there were only 5 women, all of them from the graduate group, since Yale College has only male students. The age range of the group ran from 16 to 36 at the time of leaving, with the median age being 21 years.

Treatment prior to leaving. All but 6 of the students were seen at the clinic prior to leaving. The remaining 173 cannot necessarily be considered as having been in treatment in the clinic. Some students' contact with the department turned out to be only for the evaluation which led to the recommendation that they leave school. There were some students who were not in treatment at the time of leaving, their psychotherapy having been at some earlier time. Of the 179 students, 112, or 63 per cent, were not considered as having been in treatment when they left. Thirty-seven per cent, or 67, were considered as having been in treatment.

Psychiatric diagnoses. The diagnoses of the 179 cases were based on the records of the Division, including hospital reports. Where the diagnosis made in the clinic was incomplete, the records were reviewed by a psychiatrist, who classified them according to the Standard Psychiatric Nomenclature. Table 1 classifies the 179 students according to psychiatric diagnosis.

The largest diagnostic group is that of the character disorders. Classified as character disorders are those cases in which neurotic or psychotic symptom formation is minimal and in which the major disorder is found in maladaptive patterns of behavior, e.g. passive-aggressive reaction. This diagnosis is used only when such patterns are relatively fixed and longstanding, as distinguished from adolescent adjustment reactions. It corresponds to the various categories of personality disorder listed in the Standard Psychiatric Nomenclature.

TABLE *1*. TOTAL GROUP OF STUDENTS CLASSIFIED BY PSYCHIATRIC DIAGNOSIS

Diagnosis	No.	%
Character disorder	67	37
Psychoneurosis	57	32
Psychosis	52	29
Transient personality reaction	3	2
TOTAL	179	100

The next two largest groups were the neurotics and psychotics, representing approximately the same number of students. The three students with a diagnosis of transient personality reaction constituted only 2 per cent of the total group.

TABLE 2. RELATIONSHIP BETWEEN DIAGNOSIS AND CLASS IN TOTAL GROUP OF STUDENTS

Diagnosis	Total		FRESH.		SOPH.		JUNIOR		SENIOR		GRAD.	
	No.	%	No.	%	No.	%	No.	%	No.	%	No.	%
Character disorder	67	37	19	50	13	39	15	41	11	33	9	23
Neurosis	57	32	12	33	13	39	12	32	9	27	11	28
Psychosis	52	29	4	11	6	18	9	24	13	39	20	50
Transient personality reaction	3	2	1	3	1	3	1	3	—	—	—	—
TOTAL	179	100	36	100	33	100	37	100	33	100	40	100

An examination of the relation between the diagnosis and the class of the student (Table 2) shows that one of the most striking factors is the linear increase in the diagnosis of psychosis from the freshman class to the graduate school group. The increase here is from 11 per cent for the freshmen to 50 per cent for the graduates. This table also shows that the diagnosis of neurosis exists in almost equal proportions from class to class. More freshmen were given the diagnosis of character disorder than were any other group.

The relatively high incidence of character diagnoses among the freshmen would appear to represent the effects of the impingement of the college environment on the personalities of incoming students. Those whose character problems render them unable to make an adequate adjustment to college life tend to come into conflict with the environment early in their academic careers. In the advanced classes these individuals have either left school as a direct or indirect result of their conflicts or have made some kind of adjustment to the academic scene.

Each student's academic standing was rated on the basis of information obtained from the Deans' Offices. For purposes of this study an undergraduate was considered to be in academic difficulty if at the time of the last marking period he was (a) on the General Warning list—midterm or end of the term—(b) incomplete in a course, or (c) flunking a course. Graduate students were assigned to this category if their last grades contained a failure or an incomplete.

Fewer students diagnosed as psychotic were found to be in academic difficulty than were those in the other diagnostic groups, a finding significant at the .01 level of confidence. With more than half of the character disorder group in academic difficulty, this diagnostic group was the largest in this category. The greater incidence of academic difficulty among students with character disorder diagnosis was significant at the .01 level. The relationship between diagnosis and academic standing is shown in Table 3.

TABLE 3. TOTAL GROUP OF STUDENTS' DIAGNOSES AND ACADEMIC STANDINGS

Diagnosis			*Academic Standing*			
			NOT IN DIFFICULTY		IN DIFFICULTY	
	No.	*%*	*No.*	*%*	*No.*	*%*
Character disorder	67	100	29	43	38	57
Psychoneurosis	57	100	32	56	25	44
Psychosis	52	100	41	79	11	21
Transient personality reaction	3	100	3	100	—	—
TOTAL	179	100	105	59	74	41

Psychiatrists' recommendations. Recommendations were given by the psychiatrist in all but 29 of the cases. Of the 150 cases where a recommendation was given, in 137 of them it was to obtain treatment—hospitalization and/or psychotherapy. In a little over one-fifth of the cases hospitalization was recommended and it was carried out except in one instance. On the other hand, where psychotherapy was recommended, in approximately two-thirds of the cases, it was obtained by only half of the group. Table 4 shows the extent to which the psychiatrists' recommendations were followed.

TABLE *4*. PSYCHIATRISTS' RECOMMENDATIONS COMPARED TO HOW THE STUDENTS ACTED ON THEM

HOW STUDENTS ACTED	*Nature of Recommendation* *							
	HOSPITAL-IZATION		PSYCHO-THERAPY		WORK		MISC.	
	No.	*%*	*No.*	*%*	*No.*	*%*	*No.*	*%*
Followed through	33	97	53	51	22	81	5	72
Did not follow through	1	3	42	41	4	15	1	14
Unknown	—	—	8	8	1	4	1	14
TOTAL	34	100	103	100	27	100	7	100

* The total group of students who were given advice concerning treatment is represented, but the recommendations total more than 150, since more than one recommendation was made for some students.

What Happened to the 179 Students

Of the 179 students who left school 52 per cent had not returned to Yale as of August 1955; 48 per cent had returned. To obtain an over-all picture of the academic fate of these students and to set up experimental groups for further study, the 179 students were divided as follows: (a) the nonreturnees, (b) the returned and graduated and (c) the returned and left. Table 5 designates the number of students in each category.

Of the 86 students who did return, 31 per cent left again. Over half of the nonreturning group had been out of school six years or longer as of August 1955.

The returnees. Most of those students given a medical leave of absence by the Division of Student Mental Hygiene were required to appear for psychiatric evaluation before readmission to the University. Those students who had been in treatment while out of school were asked to have their psychiatrist submit a report of their progress.

Eighty-six students were readmitted to Yale; 52 of these within a year, 34 after more than a year. Of the 86 returning students, 64 per cent were screened by the clinic. Of these 55 students, 41 were seen in readmission interviews, while 14 were screened through correspondence with the student and with his interim therapist, if he had been in treatment while out of school.

TABLE 5. TOTAL GROUP OF STUDENTS CLASSIFIED ACCORDING TO OUTCOME

STATUS AS OF AUGUST 1955	No.	%
Not returned	93	52
Returned and graduated	59	33
Returned and left	27	15
TOTAL	179	100

Of the 55 students they readmitted, the psychiatrists felt the prognosis for the student's adjusting successfully was good for 42, guarded for 10, and poor for 3. Twelve students seen in readmission interviews were advised not to return, while 11 other students seeking to return were refused admission by their respective deans.

Factors Influencing Return

Comparisons were made between returnees and the nonreturnees on the basis of (a) class at the time of leaving, (b) academic standing at the time of leaving, (c) treatment before and after leaving, and (d) psychiatric diagnosis.

Only academic standing before leaving was significantly (p < .01) related to a student's chances of returning; those students in academic difficulty at the time of leaving were much less likely to return than those who were not. There was some tendency for graduate students to be less likely to return and for students who

had had treatment in the clinic before leaving to be more likely
to return. Treatment after leaving did not significantly affect a
student's chances of returning, nor did the type of psychiatric
diagnosis, as shown in Table 6.

TABLE 6. TOTAL GROUP OF STUDENTS' DIAGNOSES COMPARED TO
EVENTUAL STATUSES

			Eventual Status			
DIAGNOSIS	TOTAL		NONRETURNEE		RETURNEE	
	No.	%	No.	%	No.	%
Character disorder	67	100	36	54	31	46
Psychoneurosis	57	100	31	54	26	46
Psychosis	52	100	25	48	27	52
Transient personality reaction	3	100	1	33	2	67
TOTAL	179	100	93	52	86	48

Factors Influencing Success upon Return

The two groups of students comprising the returnees—the returned and graduated and the returned and left—were compared
in regard to (a) class at the time of leaving, (b) academic status
before leaving, (c) psychiatric diagnosis, (d) psychiatric treatment
before and after leaving, (e) length of time out of school, and (f)
treatment after returning to school.

The three factors of class, academic status, and psychiatric diagnosis were found to be significantly related to a student's chances
of successfully completing his academic career upon return to Yale.
Graduate students did better ($p < .02$) than any other group of
returnees. Students in trouble academically at the time of leaving
were much more likely to have to leave again ($p < .01$). Those students given a diagnosis of character disorder were just as likely to
fail again as to succeed, while those students having left because
of a neurotic or psychotic disturbance had better than a three-to-
one chance of succeeding once they returned ($p < .02$). The figures
in regard to diagnosis and success upon return are shown in Table
7.

TABLE 7. THE RETURNEES' DIAGNOSES COMPARED TO INCIDENCE OF
ACADEMIC SUCCESS

			Incidence of Success			
			RETURNED AND GRADUATED		RETURNED AND LEFT	
DIAGNOSIS	TOTAL					
	No.	%	No.	%	No.	%
Character disorder	31	100	16	52	15	48
Psychoneurosis	26	100	20	77	6	23
Psychosis	27	100	21	77	6	23
Transient personality reaction	2	100	2	100	—	—
TOTAL	86	100	59	69	27	31

The three factors which had a significant bearing on a student's chances of academic success after he returned—academic standing before leaving, diagnosis, and class—were also found to be significantly related to each other.* A student with a diagnosis of character disorder was much more likely to be in academic difficulty, and the incidence of this diagnosis decreased as the educational level went up. Since the type of personality patterns indicated by the diagnosis of character disorder are shown to be inimical to academic success, one would expect to find a lower incidence of this diagnosis as the educational level goes up. This reasoning is borne out by the finding that 19 per cent of the freshmen in this study were given the diagnosis of character disorder. Fourteen per cent of sophomores, 16 per cent of juniors, 10 per cent of seniors, and 9 per cent of graduate students were similarly diagnosed.

Psychiatric treatment, whether obtained before leaving, after leaving, or upon return to school, had no significant effect on whether or not a student remained to graduate once he returned. This was also true in regard to the amount of time a student had been out of school.

* By means of the chi-square technique the relationship between diagnosis and class was significant at the <.05 level and the relationship betwen diagnosis and academic standing at the <.01 level.

Discussion and comment. The meaning of the diagnosis of psychosis in this age group is shown to be less serious prognostically than might be expected from experience with psychosis in the general population. Fifty-two per cent of patients with this diagnosis returned to Yale, and of these, 78 per cent continued to graduation. This is comparable to the record of students with diagnoses of neuroses. It tends to support the view that the occurrence of psychosis at this transitional period of psychological development may represent a developmental crisis and, at least in some instances, serves a constructive function toward integration of the personality.

Students who were diagnosed as suffering from some form of character disorder always presented a history of long-standing and firmly established attitudes which interfered with their ability to adapt to the academic scene at Yale. That these attitudes tend to remain relatively fixed is demonstrated by the evidence that although students in this group were as likely to return as those in other diagnostic groups, a significantly smaller percentage remained to graduate. The existence of a character disorder in this special age group, however, does not necessarily imply an unalterable condition, as evidenced by the finding that 16 out of the 67 students on whom this diagnosis was made returned and graduated at a later date. Still others, as will be shown in a follow-up study of those who did not return, are able to find life situations in which they can adapt successfully, including attendance at other educational institutions.

Transient personality reactions led only three students to leave college, although students with this type of disturbance constitute the largest diagnostic group seen in the Division of Student Mental Hygiene. In general, these reactions, usually adolescent adjustment reactions, can be resolved through treatment and tolerant understanding by the University administration.

Perhaps the outstanding impression derived from this part of the study is that there are no absolute psychiatric criteria on which the academic prognosis of students can be based. The trends indicated may be considered as suggestive of the chance of success of students in various psychiatric categories, but they cannot be applied to individual cases with certainty. It is especially valuable to support the impression of Darling that students who suffer from psychotic episodes may, in many instances, resume a successful academic career. In all psychiatric categories there are instances of satisfactory resolutions of problems which interfered with students' education. We believe that each case of student psychiatric illness must be evaluated individually and separately in relation to the advisability of the student's leaving or returning to school. There is no evidence to justify, on medical grounds, categorical refusal to give academic opportunity to a student with a given psychiatric condition.

Summary

1. A study of 179 students leaving Yale sometime between September 1947 and June 1952 because of emotional difficulties showed that they fell into four diagnostic categories: character and behavior disorder, 67; psychoneurosis, 57; psychosis, 52; and transient personality reaction, 3. The incidence of character disorder was highest among the freshmen, while there was a linear increase in the diagnosis of psychosis from the freshman to the graduate school group. More than half of the students with a diagnosis of character disorder were found to be in academic difficulty, as opposed to 44 per cent of those diagnosed as neurotic and only 21 per cent of those diagnosed as psychotic.

2. Eighty-six of the 179 students had returned to Yale as of August 1955. Sixty-nine per cent of these returning students remained to graduate.

3. Only the factor of academic standing before leaving was significantly related to a student's chances of returning to Yale; those students in academic difficulty before leaving were much less likely to return.

4. Three factors had a significant effect on a student's chances of successfully completing his career upon return to Yale: (a) graduate students did better than any other group, (b) students in academic difficulty at the time of leaving were much more likely to have to leave again, and (c) those students given a diagnosis of character disorder were just as likely to fail again as to succeed, while students who left because of a neurotic or psychotic disturbance had a better than three-to-one chance of succeeding once they returned.

5. The three factors which had a significant bearing on a student's chances of academic success once he returned—academic standing before leaving, class, and diagnosis—were also found to be significantly related to each other. The position taken is that the personality patterns which lead to the diagnosis of character disorder interfere with academic success; as a consequence of this relationship it would be expected that class and prior academic standing would relate to success.

2. Follow-up of Students Who Left without Graduating

Those students who never returned to Yale and those students who returned and left again have been further studied to learn more about the outcome of their difficulties. More specifically, it was the hope that this study would yield information as to a student's later educational status, occupational adjustment, marital status, and current emotional adjustment. Very little systematic data have been available on the eventual careers of students who for emotional reasons were unable to complete their education at the institution they initially entered. This is not only an effort to gain some systematic view of this group of students but also, since they left for psychiatric reasons, an attempt to shed some light upon the natural history of psychiatric disturbances among individuals in this age group who go to college.

There were 120 students in the group studied, 93 of whom were nonreturnees and 27 of whom were students who had returned to Yale and left again. At the time the study was initiated in August 1955, seven of the students were deceased; one additional death occurred in the course of the study. To the present, information has been obtained either from or about 63, or 53 per cent, of the total group of students. This number includes the eight deceased students.

The only means of contact available with these students was through correspondence, since they were so widespread geographically. The original contact was with the nonreturning students, who were sent a letter in which they were asked to give an account of their experiences in relation to work, marriage, military service, and problems of a health nature, both physical and emotional. In all, there have been three contacts with this group, the first two by letter and the third in the form of a questionnaire. Responses were received from or about 45, or 52 per cent, of the 86 living students in this group.

Those students who had returned to Yale and left again were contacted only once. The questionnaire sent to this group was returned by 10, or 38 per cent, of the 26 living students.

Comparisons were made between respondents and nonrespondents with respect to (a) treatment before leaving Yale, (b) psychiatric diagnosis, (c) academic standing at the time of leaving, (d) length of time out of school, and (e) class at the time of leaving. The major differences between the two groups were in terms of treatment before leaving, diagnosis, and academic standing. Thirteen per cent more of those students having treatment before leaving responded than those who had not had treatment. Nine per cent less of the students diagnosed as neurotic responded than students diagnosed as psychotic or as suffering from some form of character disorder; 13 per cent more of those students responded who were not in academic difficulty at the time of leaving than those who were.

The majority of the students had been out of school five years or more. The actual distribution of the students as to length of time out of school is as follows: 5.5 per cent out three years or less, 9.2 per cent out four years, 12.9 per cent out five years, 20.3 per cent out six years, 24.5 per cent out seven years, and 14.8 per cent out nine years.

Mortality. At the time the follow-up study was initiated in August 1955 seven students were deceased. One additional death occurred in the course of the study. These eight deaths occurred as follows: war casualty (Korea), 1; auto accident, 1; suicide, 4; and unknown, 2.

One of these students had returned to Yale and left again. The other seven were all nonreturnees. Four students of this group had been diagnosed as psychotic at the time of leaving Yale, two as neurotic and two as suffering from some form of character disorder. There were two freshmen, two sophomores, three juniors, and one senior in the group. One student was 19 years of age, four were 21, one was 23, one was 24, and one was 28. In four instances death occurred one year after the student had left Yale.

The deaths of two students occurred two years after they left school. One student died after being out of school six years and one after being out eight years.

Two of the four students who committed suicide were freshmen at the time they left Yale. Of the other two, one was a junior and one a senior. Their respective ages at the time of death were 19, 24, 28, and 23. Three of these students had suffered psychotic breakdowns, while the fourth had been diagnosed as psychoneurotic. Two of the suicides occurred one year after the students left school. Of the other two, one occurred six years after the student left and one eight years after the student left.

The data to follow will deal only with the 55 living students. It will give a picture of what has happened to these students since leaving Yale, without any attempt to draw conclusions of a statistically significant nature.

Life circumstances at follow-up. Of the 55 students six, or 11 per cent, were unable to work because of psychiatric illness. Four of this group were in mental hospitals at the time of follow-up and two had been recently discharged from mental hospitals. Seventy-seven per cent of the remaining 49 students were considered to have a satisfactory work adjustment.

The occupations of the 49 students who were employed were as follows: 18 were working as lesser executives, professionals, and proprietors; 12 were engaged in studies at other institutions; 6 were employed in small independent business activities; 4 were classified as higher executives, professionals, and proprietors; 3 were doing clerical work; 2 were skilled laborers; 2 were in military service; and the employment of 2 was undetermined. It was observed that on the whole this group was employed at a level commensurate with the different degrees of educational attainment that had been achieved. Sixty-three per cent of the group had continued their education after leaving Yale and over half of this number had secured their undergraduate degrees at the time of follow-up.

Thirty-seven per cent of the students were still single at follow-up. All but one was of an age (22 or older) where on the basis of this factor alone one would have expected marriage to have taken place in a majority of instances.

In summary, those students who left without graduating have

achieved a satisfactory occupational and educational status in the majority of instances. Though 37 per cent of the group were still single at an age when one would expect marriage, there are obviously too many other unknown factors to judge the meaning of their marital status.

Psychiatric experience at follow-up. Only 21 per cent of the students appeared to be more than slightly disabled and only 9 per cent more than moderately disabled. The rating of disability was based primarily on the man's work adjustment. The mere presence or absence of psychiatric symptoms or defective attitudes was not in itself considered evidence of disability.

TABLE 8. PSYCHIATRIC DISABILITY AT FOLLOW-UP

Disability	No.	%
Essentially none	40	72.7
Slight disability	2	3.6
Moderate disability	7	12.7
Severe disability without hospitalization	1	1.8
Total disability with or without hospitalization	4	7.2
Unknown	1	1.8
TOTAL	55	100.0

Sixty-five per cent of the students said they had had emotional difficulties since leaving Yale, and the majority of this group felt these problems were not yet resolved. In the opinion of the writer 75 per cent of the students appeared to have improved, 21 per cent to have remained the same, and 4 per cent to have become worse. In comparing diagnosis and change in a student's condition, it was found that the character disorder group of students were by far the most improved at follow-up, some 92 per cent of them being rated as "improved." Less than 50 per cent of the psychotic students were so rated, and this was the only group having students considered as "worse." Sixty-nine per cent of the neurotic students appeared to have improved.

At the time of follow-up psychiatric treatment had been ob-

TABLE *9*. NATURE OF TREATMENT OBTAINED BY STUDENTS

Nature of Treatment	*No.*	*%*
Brief psychotherapy (up to 7 months)	9	31.0
Prolonged psychotherapy (7 months or more)	6	20.6
Hospitalization	6	20.6
Hospitalization and psychotherapy	5	17.2
Psychoanalysis	3	10.3
TOTAL	29	100.0

tained by 53 per cent of the students. Table 9 shows a breakdown of the students according to the nature of treatment they obtained. The attitude of 24 per cent of the students who had had treatment is unknown. Another 24 per cent felt their treatment had not helped; 52 per cent felt it had. Only one of the seven students who felt treatment had not been of help had had more than a brief psychotherapeutic experience. This student had been in

TABLE *10*. PSYCHIATRIC DISABILITY AT FOLLOW-UP AND DIAGNOSIS AT THE TIME OF LEAVING SCHOOL

	Psychiatric Diagnosis							
PSYCHIATRIC DISABILITY	CHARACTER DISORDER		NEUROSIS		PSYCHOSIS		TRANSIENT PERSONALITY REACTION	
	No.	*%*	*No.*	*%*	*No.*	*%*	*No.*	*%*
Essentially none	23	88.4	9	69.2	7	50.0	1	100.0
Slight	2	7.6	—	—	—	—	—	—
Moderate	1	4.0	2	15.3	4	28.5	—	—
Severe	—	—	2	15.3	3	21.4	—	—
TOTAL	26	100.0	13	100.0	14 *	100.0	1	100.0

* No disability rating on one student.

analysis for four years. Ten of the 26 students (38 per cent) whose diagnosis at the time of leaving was that of character disorder had had treatment since leaving Yale, while at least 60 per cent of the students diagnosed as neurotic or psychotic had had treatment.

The majority of students with a diagnosis of either character disorder or neurosis were considered to have essentially no disability. Students diagnosed as psychotic were equally divided between being without disability and having a moderate or greater degree of disability as shown in Table 10.

The low number of students from the character disorder group who sought treatment, coupled with the low rate of disability at follow-up, tends to confirm the hypothesis that their failure to adjust to the Yale scene can be explained in terms of their being "square pegs in round holes." Among the entire group of students an overwhelming majority of those who were considered to have essentially no disability at follow-up had improved, while students rated as severely disabled either remained the same or had gotten worse.

Discussion and comment. A judgment as to the meaning of the different psychiatric diagnoses among this group of college students can be viewed in terms of two major phases of adjustment: (a) whether or not a student returned to Yale and his success if he did, and (b) adjustment at follow-up among the students who left without graduating.

Fifty-two per cent of the students diagnosed as psychotic returned to Yale, and of these 78 per cent continued to graduation. This is comparable to the record of students with diagnoses of neuroses. Students diagnosed as suffering from some form of character disorder were as likely to return but a significantly smaller percentage remained to graduate.

At the time of follow-up of the students who did not return, over half from each of the three major diagnostic categories continued their education after leaving Yale, the neurotic group having the highest percentage of students who did continue and the psychotic group the lowest.

The majority of students with a diagnosis of either character disorder or neurosis were considered to have essentially no disability. Students diagnosed as psychotic at the time of leaving Yale were equally divided between being without disability and having a moderate or greater degree of disability.

The character disorder group of students were by far the most improved, while less than 50 per cent of the psychotic students had shown improvement. Sixty-nine per cent of the neurotic students appeared to have improved at follow-up.

At least 60 per cent of the students diagnosed as neurotic or psychotic had had treatment, while only 38 per cent of the character disorder group had sought help of this nature. Half of these students felt their treatment had been helpful, while the majority of the students from the other two diagnostic groupings felt treatment had been of help to them.

Summary

The over-all study shows that the great majority of students who left Yale for emotional reasons tend to improve and to make a satisfactory adjustment either in terms of eventually completing their education at Yale or in terms of successful adjustment at other educational institutions and in employment, as seen in a follow-up study. Implicit in this data is the impression that there are no absolute psychiatric criteria on which the academic prognosis or the prognosis for future life adjustment can be based. In this context the study presents a challenge to the universally held assumption that psychosis in this age group usually leads to unalterable disruption in the academic career. Though the material showed that students diagnosed as suffering from some form of character disorder are less likely to graduate if they return to Yale, it also made clear in the follow-up phase of the study that the great majority of these students do improve and adapt successfully to other life situations, usually without the assistance of psychiatric treatment.

Clearly, dropping out of college is not necessarily damaging to a student's development or to his possibilities of eventual academic success. In fact, constructive changes frequently take place following the experience of dropping out. This includes striking changes in attitude, the resolution of conflicts—often with the help of treatment—and maturation through the experiences of meeting realistic problems. Perhaps the most outstanding impression derived from this study is that leaving college may often be a constructive event in the development of the individual student whether or not he returns to college.

CHAPTER 6

An Investigation of Personality Differences Associated with Competitive Ability

BY FRANCIS J. RYAN

The author is both a psychologist and a coach of field events. He is thus in an unusual position to study the role of athletic experience in personality development. Chapters 6 and 7 represent an exploration of the relation of behavioral and personality variables to athletic performance. The first of these validates observations of characteristics of athletes in relation to competitive performance. Chapter 7 applies case observation methods to formulate a description of the athlete who is inhibited in performance, and offers explanatory hypotheses for the phenomenon.

ATHLETICS provides an enormous area of interaction in which personality is vividly expressed and very possibly shaped. Particularly, athletics occupies an extraordinary place in the American college scene. This activity plays a central role in the lives of many undergraduates, with probably few completely unaffected by it. Thus the study of the male college student must include his athletic behavior.

Extraordinary opportunities for the examination of certain behavior patterns are provided by the various athletic events. Performance under varying conditions if often measured with great precision. Unlike many laboratory and other experimental situations, behavior in the athletic framework is observable and recordable over long periods of time. Further, this behavior occurs in a meaningful life situation.

One pattern of great interest is the differential reaction to the competitive situation. Each individual athlete tends to show a consistent and characteristic way of reacting to formal competition in his event. In competition the "good" competitor tends to achieve above his practice or "base" rate; the "poor" competitor usually fails to approach his base rate.

In the track and field events, for example, a base practice level can be readily established for most athletes. Almost completely reliable indices of capacity are available. To give a simple illustration of the pattern, two shot-putters may both make practice puts almost daily of 45 feet. In formal competition one may achieve 48 feet and the other 42 feet. In practice sessions their performances may again converge, only to separate once more in competition— and in the same direction as before. As another example, there are high jumpers who have frequently bettered 6 feet in practice and never in competition; others may have cleared 6 feet only in competition, never in practice.

Preliminary Case Studies

This division's interest in the behavior and personality development of the college student led to a series of seminars (3, 4) designed to make a preliminary exploration of the field of athletic participation. Chief reliance was placed upon nontechnical descriptions of behavior by athletic coaches. These descriptions along with the tentative interpretations offered by seminar members from the fields of psychiatry, psychology, and sociology permitted a preliminary structuring of the area (5). Among the various topics and patternings that emerged from the sessions were those involving the differential abilities of athletes to compete effectively. Great interest in this phenomenon was evidenced not only by the frequency with which it was described but also by the number of synonyms used to designate it. Yet, for the most part, coaches tended to regard competitive ability as an isolated facet of the personality. There had been practically no efforts to theorize or to associate this ability with other personality traits.

With the description of succeeding cases, it became increasingly clear to the group that the good and poor competitors seemed to exhibit differential expressive behavior in a number of areas. Distinctive portraits, at first largely empirical, began to emerge. Validation of these early findings was indicated.

Procedure

A questionnaire was formulated to be sent to track coaches throughout the nation. This sport was selected for two reasons.

First, performance is measured with almost perfect reliability to a tenth of a second and a fraction of an inch. Second, the observational opportunities offered by track are exceptional in that the coaching method is largely tutorial and the competitive season is longer than that of other sports.

Though various theoretical views were held by conference participants, the questionnaire was not primarily designed to test these formulations. Instead, it was constructed to test, in the most direct way, the empirical observations that had previously been made. Not all these observations could be further explored by the method used. It was necessary to restrict questions to behavior that a coach could be expected to observe in the normal course of four years of coaching contact with the athlete.

Each participating coach received two questionnaires—one to apply to a good competitor and the other to a poor competitor. Directions were as follows:

Good Competitor

By checking the appropriate box, please answer the below questions about the best or one of the best competitors you have ever coached. The man you consider for these questions need not be a present member of the squad. He can be anyone who generally seems or seemed to rise above his practice performance in competition. We won't need his name. If the responses listed for a question are not adequate, please write in the appropriate answer. Use the reverse side if necessary.

Poor Competitor

By checking the appropriate box, please answer the below questions about the worst or one of the worst competitors you have ever coached. The man you consider for these questions need not be a present member of the squad. He can be anyone who generally seems or seemed to blow up or go to pieces in competition, i.e. not be able to approach his practice performance. We won't need his name. If the responses listed for a question are not adequate, please write in the appropriate answer. Use the reverse side if necessary.

The questionnaire consisted of thirteen behavioral and personality items. Sixty-five sets of questionnaires were mailed. All but three were returned. In all, there were fifty-seven usable question-naires on the good competitor and sixty on the poor. About half of the respondents wrote personal letters expressing their views.

SUBJECTS

Subject selection was, of course, determined by the coaches, who were each given the option of selecting a single good com-petitor and a single poor competitor.* It might be argued that this nomination technique could have been improved by a more objective approach. The pattern under consideration represents a disparity between a base performance level (which reflects practice performance and other indications of capacity) and com-petitive performance. Measures of the latter are matters of record, but the base levels are less amenable to direct measurement. The very use of predetermined measurements, even in the absence of formal competition, would tend to create a test atmosphere. Thus such measurements would likely reflect competitive ability. The poor competitor might be sensitive to even the most informal type of measurement. Case data indicate that his good practice per-formance can cease abruptly if there is much attention focused on it by either teammates or his coach. Also, an unexpectedly good practice performance by a poor competitor seems able to throw him into a slump.

In short, the base level of performance for an athlete is usually well known by his coach, who has observed him over a four-year period and in some cases for a thousand or more practice trials. A base level could probably be established independently of coaches' evaluations, but there is little assurance that the neces-sary laborious and subtle procedure would improve subject selec-tion.

RESULTS

The comparative ratings received by good and poor com-petitors for the various items are given in Table 1. Differences among the distributions of responses assigned to the groups were tested for significance by means of the chi-square technique.

* Though coaches were not asked to name the subjects, most of them did so. Thus it is known that our good competitors include most American world record holders and Olympic champions.

Item 1 did not produce a significant difference. All other items separated the experimental groups at better than the .01 level of confidence. However, the results of Item 4 were not in the predicted direction.

Item 1 is the only behavioral one that failed to produce a statistically significant difference. Our preliminary findings had indicated that the poor competitor has a tendency to practice at odd hours and to avoid the regular workout routine. Too, we

TABLE *1*. COACHES' RATINGS OF GOOD AND POOR COMPETITORS

Item	*Responses*	*"Good"*	*"Poor"*
1. What time of the day does he (did he) usually come to practice?	Earlier in the day than most men	11	12
	About the same time as most	43	38
	Later than most	3	6
	Other	0	4
2. Does he work hard in practice?	Lazy—needs to be pushed	1	5
	About average	4	19
	Hard worker	50	32
	Other	2	2
3. When he talks about future performance, is he shooting for	The next meet?	40	23
	Late season?	2	3
	Some eventual performance?	10	28
	Other	5	6
4. After a poor competitive showing, does he blame	Conditions, officials, etc.?	2	10
	Himself?	44	38
	Both?	1	10
	Other?	10	2
5. Is he considered	A lone wolf?	1	18
	Very friendly?	42	12
	About average?	13	28
	Other	1	2
6. Does he seem to be happy?	Usually in good spirits, has plenty of belly laughs	31	16
	Smiles easily, but seldom laughs heartily	24	29
	Seldom smiles or laughs	1	15
	Other	1	0
7. Does he tend to be	The life of the party?	15	9
	About average?	35	25
	Very quiet?	7	21
	Other?	0	5

TABLE *I* (cont.)

Item	Responses	"Good"	"Poor"
8. Does he make sense in his conversation?	Always rational and coherent	46	15
	About average	10	32
	Conversation sometimes seems strange and hard to follow	1	12
	Other	1	1
9. Does he follow coaching instruction well?	Usually follows instructions well without comment	43	19
	Follows instructions well but often with comment	14	16
	Usually makes out a case for doing something different	0	21
	Other	0	4
10. Does he learn easily?	Learns well	47	13
	An average learner	8	31
	Has great difficulty in learning some things	2	14
	Other	0	2
11. Does he talk easily?	Communication good	48	23
	About average	9	23
	Difficult to talk to	0	13
	Other	0	1
12. Is he popular with his teammates?	Well liked	48	14
	About average	7	30
	Unpopular	1	15
	Other	1	1
13. What is his reaction following a good competitive performance?	Likely to make another good performance the following week	51	0
	Likely to make an average performance the following week	4	21
	Likely to fall off badly in the next meet	1	29
	Other	1	10

Note: Distributions of responses on each item for good and poor competitors were compared by means of the chi-square technique. With the exception of Item 1, differences were significant at less than the .01 level of confidence.

seemed to find that the athlete could operate in such a subtle fashion that often a coach is not immediately aware of the pattern. There is only a slight tendency for the "poors" to show less conformity in their workout patterns. However, a single question is probably not adequate for the exploration of this behavior. It is interesting to note that four coaches were unable to categorize the workout behavior of their "poor" competitors.

Item 2 was given to establish that the "poor" competitors are committed to the activity in some way—i.e. that their poor performances are not a result of indifference. The good competitors were considered harder workers, but only six subjects, one good and five poor, were labeled lazy. A "halo" effect may be reflected, yet, obviously, such an effect was not completely rampant.

Item 3 supports the preliminary finding that the poor competitor shows more interest in some ultimate performance than in a present one. It was interesting to note that some of the "poor" competitors reported in the preliminary case studies seemed to have informal timetables calling for good performances sometime after they would actually be finished with competition. The poor competitor can take achievement when it does not seem too imminent.

Item 4, the only one to reverse preliminary findings, reports the poor as being somewhat more extrapunitive than the good competitor. This reversal is somewhat surprising in view of the very strong tendency among early cases for the poor competitor to accept (or almost proclaim) the blame for his poor performance.

Items 5 through 8 represent, as do the other items, an attempt to validate an empirical pattern. Yet these items do seem to have the flavor of an "adjustment inventory." Certainly, the poor competitor would appear to be unhappier, more constricted, and, in general, more poorly adjusted. The poor competitor seems to have difficulty expressing his aggression generally, and his inability to compete in athletics may be a specific instance of such an over-all difficulty.

Since there is an expectation that the inadequate competitor has an ambivalence of motivation, there is a theoretical expectation that he would show greater personal conflict.

The differential reaction to coaching instruction, shown in Item 9, may represent the operation of a number of factors. There is theoretical reason to expect a negative reaction to authority and adults on the part of the poor competitors. In addition, our preliminary findings had suggested that the poor competitor prefers to structure his workouts in such a way as to preclude real achievement. In other words, a fear may exist that the instructions given by the coach may bring about success. A similar, and equally tentative, view may be taken toward the results of Item 10, which indicate that the poor competitor has greater difficulty in learning.

The differential ability to communicate, reported in Item 11, may represent both a difference in attitude toward adults and a more general ability to express aggression.

The results of Item 13 seem to have implications for our views on learning and achievement, principally the "law of effect." The prevalent coaching approach to the poor competitor is indicated by such expressions as: "He'll be all right after he gets a performance under his belt"; "As soon as he 'tastes a little blood,' he'll have a desire to win"; "Nothing breeds success like success," etc. Apparently, a taste of success does anything but reassure a "poor" competitor. Whatever anxieties or other interferences with good performance may exist, apparently these are stronger following some success.

At the very least the data strongly support the position that competitive ability, as it has been defined, is not an isolated aspect of the personality. Further, the results tend to validate the partial portraits emerging from earlier findings with a smaller number of cases. The good competitor is not, as the stereotype would have it, a tight-lipped, uncommunicative lone wolf. He tends to be more conflict-free, less constricted, and better adjusted; in general, the "good" competitor seems freer to express his aggression.

The competitive situation does produce anxiety and it is stressful. Yet, at the moment, it is felt that the experimental literature concerned with the topics of *anxiety* and *stress* may not be directly relevant to the pattern under study.

Observation suggests that our experimental groups will not be easily distinguished on the basis of manifest anxiety. Both groups display great anxiety prior to competition. If differences do exist, the preliminary data suggest they exist in the direction of the good competitor showing the greater anxiety.

Under the stress of competition nearly all athletes will regress to a somewhat earlier level of technical proficiency. This observation can be supported in several ways, e.g. slow-motion movies. However, the regression phenomenon can be seen more dramatically in cases where there have been radical shifts in form. Under stress, in such instances, the athlete often discards his recently acquired techniques and reverts to a form used months or even years before. But the important point is that the tendency to regress form-wise under stress cannot in itself act as a permanent bar to performance. The athlete who piles up great frequency in his activity over a period of years can afford considerable regression and still retain sufficient technical proficiency for a good effort.

The competitive situation, though it is also stressful and anxiety-provoking, primarily represents the formally specified conditions under which achievement is to take place. To be meaningful, achievement in this activity must occur under predetermined conditions, including both the presence of opponents and usually measurement of some kind. Only in this way is the achievement recognized and recorded.

Thus it is felt that *achievement* is the key word in the competitive situation, and the behavioral pattern under consideration is viewed as a differential freedom to accept achievement. At least for the present the good and poor competitors are seen as separated by their differential ability to accept achievement.

There would appear to be little literature directly concerned with the negative effects of achievement in a meaningful situation. Freud (1), when he speaks of "those who are wrecked by success," may be dealing with a similar pattern. Ernest Jones (2) has discussed the "curious case of Paul Morphy." Morphy, perhaps the greatest chess player of all time, was able to stand his great success only under certain conditions. With the violation of these conditions Morphy gave up the game and eventually developed a psychosis.

Both Freud and Jones relate the inability to stand success to the resolution of the oedipal situation.

For obvious reasons great caution must be observed in generalizing to areas other than athletic performance. Yet it would be odd indeed if such a constellation of expressive behavior had implications only for the athletic area. The present results permit speculation concerning personality factors associated with high-level achievement in other activities. Perhaps further work might be concomitantly concerned with (a) additional and more intensive explorations of the personality patterns related to athletic achievement, (b) efforts to examine the systematic implications of the material with a view toward more theoretically oriented research, and (c) the applicability of the findings to other areas.

SUMMARY

Preliminary work with a limited number of cases had indicated that certain personality characteristics are associated with the ability to perform well in athletic competition. This investigation was designed to check early findings by obtaining the reports of a large group of skilled observers. Questionnaires concerned with expressive and other behavior were sent to track coaches with instructions to rate one specific good and one specific poor competitor.

Of thirteen items, eleven produced highly significant differences between competitive groups and in the predicted direction. Thus the preliminary findings are supported.

The view is tentatively taken that differences in competitive ability represent relative differences in freedom to achieve or to express aggression.

REFERENCES

1. Freud, Sigmund, *Collected Papers* (London, Hogarth Press, 1925), Vol. *4*.

2. Jones, Ernest, *Essays in Applied Psychoanalysis,* London, Hogarth Press, 1951.

3. Proceedings of the seminar on psychological aspects of athletics and coaching held by the Department of University Health, Division of Psychiatry and Mental Hygiene, Yale University; unpublished manuscript, 1953.

4. Ibid., 1954.

5. Ryan, F. J., Some aspects of athletic behavior, *Clinic Notes, 26th Annual Meeting, National Collegiate Track Coaches Association* (1955), pp. 1–9.

CHAPTER 7

Further Observations on Competitive Ability in Athletics

BY FRANCIS J. RYAN

PERSONALITY variables associated with competitive ability in athletics were investigated by means of the questionnaire method. The statistical results of this study were presented and discussed in the previous chapter. It now seems useful to go a bit behind the quantitative scene and present some observations yielded by the early case material on which the questionnaire was based. In this procedure, of course, precision is sacrificed, but perhaps there is a compensatory gain in drawing further attention to a pattern that may have systematic interest.

The description of the behavior seen as characteristic of the "poor" competitor is pursued under several headings. The first of such headings is concerned with the athletic settings of competition, precompetition and postcompetition. The other headings merely are convenient devices for presenting observations. The sequence of the divisions was chosen with an eye to orderly presentation. Yet the sequence does not arise from compelling reasons. Rather, the effort is to present a portrait, and the relationship among the parts is more a gestalt than a linear arrangement.

THE PATTERN

The pattern can be both described and labeled, the latter process involving some interpretation. In brief terms, the pattern refers to the ability to perform well under conditions of actual competition. The poor competitor consistently fails to approach an achievement level that appears warranted by his practice performances. The good competitor does well in competition, often exceeding all of his practice trials. For example, high jumpers

A and *B* may both be able to clear a height of six feet in practice and with about the same relative effort. In actual competition *A* may perform at the 5′ 9″ level, whereas *B* may consistently better 6′ 4″. The pattern appears to be stable.

The position taken here is that the pattern represents differential emotional ability to accept high-level athletic achievement. Other topics suggest themselves, e.g. reaction to stress, anxiety, etc. Nevertheless, it is felt that, at the present time, it will be more fruitful to consider competitive ability within the framework of achievement. The rationale for this position has been developed in the previous chapter. In substance, the view taken is that, despite its stressful and anxiety-provoking characteristics, the essence of the competitive situation is that it represents the standardized conditions under which achievement occurs.

It is hard to know whether to view the phenomenon under consideration as one that is normally distributed in the population or as a discrete, almost all-or-none pattern. It may well be that the achievements of all people are limited to some extent by emotional factors and our subjects are simply those in which such limitations are more extreme. Thus it is possible that good and poor competitors differ from each other only in a quantitative way, perhaps in the way that tall men differ from short ones. On the other hand, the pattern may represent a functional disorder and thus be no more continuously distributed than any other disease entity.

As succeeding cases of poor competitors were described, the material increasingly suggested that this inability was associated with a constellation of other expressive factors. Some "common threads" were extracted. To extend our observations, and to do so in a systematic way, questionnaires were constructed which embodied as much of our material as seemed amenable to the method. These questionnaires, sent to track coaches throughout the nation, yielded results that lent striking support to our early findings.

SUBJECTS

The descriptions and inferences that follow can best be evaluated and unwarranted generalizations avoided if certain aspects of our subject selection are kept in mind.

1. All subjects are selected from athletic activities that are both individual and quantitative. The conditions for achievement may be different in team sports.

2. Our subjects are "committed" to the activity as measured by time and effort invested. Thus students who are disinterested and those who for other reasons avoid the athletic setting are excluded.

3. All have considerable athletic talent. In most instances the great disparity between talent and performance has forced these subjects to our attention. The mediocre talent with a similar problem would be less conspicuous.

THE COMPETITIVE EFFORT

All of the athletes who at times compete poorly cannot be considered poor competitors in the sense in which we are using the term. On occasion many men with no chronic inability to compete will do badly in competition. Especially is this true of them during the early parts of their careers. Yet, even when the poor and normal competitors make performances that are quantitatively similar, there are instructive differences in behavior.

An anxiety to do well can interfere with the proper timing and execution of technique. Gross errors of anticipation can be brought about by a full and violent effort to reach the goal. Good performance depends upon the proper execution of a series of integrated steps. Anxiety to achieve, or reach the end goal, can disrupt this series with a consequent poor performance. Thus the normal competitor who competes badly is usually the temporary victim of his overanxiety.

The competitive behavior of the poor competitor is remarkably different. There appears to be no interference by an impetuous pull toward the goal. Instead he exhibits a feebleness of effort, almost a kind of paralysis.

As examples, the ordinary high jumper may do poorly in competition by rushing headlong into the perpendicular plane of the crossbar. The poor competitor simply makes a feeble jumping effort; there seems to be very little error of anticipation. The ordinary pole vaulter who is having a poor competitive day will often further destroy the efficiency of the vault by increasing the violence of his effort. The poor competitor reduces the power or drive with which he leaves the take-off. This distinction is seen even more clearly in the throwing events. When the relatively unblocked athlete makes a poor competitive throw, it is usually an anxious, inefficient effort with many errors of anticipation but is made in a full and sometimes vicious manner. The poor competitor simply appears to be making a feeble and almost gentle effort.

This qualitative aspect of competitive behavior has diagnostic and predictive value. Let us assume that both *A* and *B* have in a given competition performed below expectation to the same degree. *A* has performed in a semiparalyzed, feeble way; *B* has made many gross errors but has made a violent try. The prognoses for these two cases will be different. Subject *A* will probably remain a chronically poor competitor, whereas *B* may become an adequate competitor. This paper cannot include a full discussion of the pattern indicated by case *B*. His path to achievement may be a bit thorny in that he may, because of certain anxieties, be plagued from time to time by errors of anticipation. Yet the outlook is generally good in that he apparently is not seeking to avoid athletic achievement.

Another aspect of the competitive pattern of the poor competitor should be mentioned. He will sometimes negate an otherwise adequate performance by an apparently unnecessary action. The thrower will foul a good effort by falling or stepping out of the circle when from the standpoint of body mechanics it appears that he can easily remain in the circle for a fair throw. The broad jumper may, after a good trial, destroy his achievement by falling or placing a hand backward into the pit. The vaulter or high jumper who has apparently cleared the bar with a good effort will often, unnecessarily it seems, brush off the bar with his hand. This pattern of behavior is in dramatic contrast to that of the good competitor who will, in the face of a foul, fight for body balance, or who will squirm to keep every inch of his body clear of the crossbar.

Attitude toward Opponents

The good competitors seem for the most part to enjoy reasonably warm friendships with many of their opponents—but not during the actual competition. The situation is fairly well illustrated by the familiar behavior of professional boxers. They are usually cordial to each other during prefight ceremonies. During the actual boxing they attack each other viciously. At the final bell they embrace like long-lost brothers. Thus for the good competitor the opponent becomes a temporary enemy. Perhaps most important, this state of affairs is frankly faced.

Both the ethics of competition and the mores of sportsmanship preclude most overt shows of hostility, yet the good competitor reports violently hostile thoughts. In the field events, where trials are taken in turn, each athlete has a chance to concentrate on the efforts of his opponents. The "evil eye" is a common practice. For example, a high jumper will often report concentration on his opponent's foot slipping or the wind blowing off the crossbar. The discus thrower may concentrate on a possible foul for his opponent.

The recent death of Al Simmons, a great competitive baseball player, recalls his savage hatred of opposing pitchers. When asked about this hatred, he replied that "they are trying to take the bread out of my mouth." Apparently, he functioned best when visualizing the pitchers as enemies who were trying to starve him to death.

The good competitor may look forward to a number of "grudge matches." In such instances there may not be even a token show of friendliness. The athlete frankly states his dislike for his opponent and openly announces his intention of trouncing him. There appears to be little fear of counteraggression. One outstanding competitor took particular delight in defeating an opponent because "this fellow gets so upset." The existence of grudge opponents is in itself an interesting phenomenon. Among a wide circle of opponents some personality clashes are probably inevitable, yet some of the good competitors may need "grudge" opponents.

The poor competitor prefers an atmosphere of friendliness. The coach is sometimes startled and enraged to see one of his men offering not only encouragement but actual coaching aid to an opponent. When the good competitor offers "help," it probably represents a form of gamesmanship, but the poor competitor's efforts seem to represent a genuine attempt to establish a friendly relationship. By becoming friendly with an opposing good competitor, the poor competitor probably gains a relative advantage.

The poor competitor does not speak with anger or bitterness of his opposition; he does not have grudge matches. Even a practice duel in mock anger can impair his performance. Teammates and coaches who try to motivate him by savage criticisms of the opposition probably interfere greatly with his achievement.

PRACTICE PATTERNS

Time. Many poor competitors tend to arrive at practice either very early or very late. An individual sport, such as track or swimming, does afford considerable flexibility in the time selected for practice and to adjust for a late laboratory or class a squad member will occasionally practice at an odd hour. Yet the "poor" competitor may habitually select a fringe hour and without any known external reason.

This pattern may meet several needs of the poor competitor. If he arrives either before the coach or as the coach is leaving, he avoids a supervised workout. As will be indicated, he prefers to work alone. In fact, some poor competitors have been known to seek other facilities on the same campus.

There is strong evidence that the performances made in the private practices of these athletes are vastly superior to their public performances. Corroboration comes from distant observations of the coach, reports of groundskeepers, marks left by implements, and the positions of jumping standards. One athlete who barely made his college team had private performances of Olympic caliber.

Method. Despite great aptitude for his event, the poor competitor seems far more comfortable when working in the manner of the beginner. Even after five or six years of experience, he prefers to work on the material usually assigned to the first-year man. He may report that he plans to go on to more advanced material but he must first "polish a few fundamentals."

Related to this workout pattern is one in which the athlete works hard but in such a manner as to preclude achievement. It is a startling thing to watch an athlete assiduously reinforcing a habit that is definitely known to interfere with good perform-ance.

Both of these patterns apparently permit the athlete to resolve a conflict. He can satisfy his need to work hard for achievement and still relieve his anxieties about actually achieving.

Search for Excalibur. In lieu of attention to principles and techniques which have a demonstrated relation to successful per-formance, the poor competitor makes vague references to some secret and almost magical aspect of form. He seems to feel that high-level performance will rapidly follow the acquisition of such a gimmick. Such a search therefore dominates a large portion of the practice sessions. Naturally the coach takes a dim view of such a procedure and usually interferes. Gentle persuasion by the coach may bring some sort of incoherent description of the nature of the athlete's search. The stronger methods are upsetting to the athlete and may result in his avoiding the coach or leaving the sport.

Off-season performance. In the out-of-season practice sessions with competition not imminent, the good competitor usually has great difficulty approaching anything like his best performances. For example, the discus thrower who has reached 160 feet the previous June may in his workouts the following October find himself struggling for 140 feet. But for the poor competitor the situation tends to be reversed. He is often at his very best in the off-season with diminishing performance as the competitive sea-son nears. There are instances of poor competitors actually ap-proaching world records during the off-season only to become mediocre performers with the arrival of the competitive season. The enthusiastic coach who extrapolates performance for the poor competitor is usually due for a bitter disappointment.

An eye to the future. It seems that nearly all, and perhaps all, athletes who do eventually reach high-level achievement have previously harbored fantasies about such achievement; they do not simply stumble into championships. Yet even with such long-range goals or fantasies, they are able to concentrate on the sub-goals, the imminent competition. Each successive competitive trial seems viewed as an opportunity to confirm the feasibility of at-taining the fantasied goal.

The poor competitors from time to time make vague references to rather grandiose goals. They, too, have fantasies of great achievement but it is a far distant achievement. They seem to have difficulty in focusing on the subgoals. The next scheduled competition receives relatively little attention. Orientation is toward the distant goal. Even when they are completing their athletic careers, their athletic goals remain in the distant future.

Verbal behavior. Many of the poor competitors routinely berate themselves after each practice effort. Almost before completion of the trial they hang their heads in a guilty fashion and bitterly reprimand themselves. One gets the impression that they are trying to forestall criticism, particularly from the coach. In a sense they are almost trying to "beat him to the punch." In several cases I have made persistent efforts to eliminate this pattern directly. I tended, particularly some years ago, to view such behavior as an inefficient use of the athlete's time and energy. From a common sense point of view it seemed they might best concentrate on something constructive. I never found these direct coaching efforts to be even slightly successful.

In addition to the verbal pattern of self-condemnation, the poor competitor has curious methods of presenting an "argument." He may, at times, begin a defense of some technique or procedure he has embraced and the coach has opposed. The arguments are at first presented almost boldly, then tentatively. Finally, and even with the most sympathetic listening on the part of the coach, the argument is withdrawn. He reaches the conclusion that his point of view is "really rather silly after all."

Negative approach. The *modus operandi* of most successful athletes is to concentrate on one or perhaps two positive points at any given time. They seem willing to accept the notion that one can work on a particular aspect of technique without great concern about errors in points not under consideration. Not so with the "poor" competitor who is constantly fearful of error. It seems that his exaggerated concern for the possibility of error cropping up in the gamut of points of technique paralyzes his ability to take positive action on one or two constructive points. Reassurance that such errors are expected in the normal course of learning does not alter the pattern.

In general, there is a strong suggestion that for the poor competitor the negative approach is not simply an inefficient learning approach; rather, it is a symptom of an emotional inability to accept achievement.

BEHAVIOR FOLLOWING COMPETITION

Failure. By definition the poor competitors compete poorly most of the time. Hence, their typical reaction following competition is that to failure, at least failure in the objective sense. The young coach is startled to note that these athletes are more relaxed, in better spirits, and generally more talkative following competitive failure. In contrast, the good competitor who has had a poor day is difficult to live with. He becomes temporarily a bitter, morose, and sometimes almost vicious person.

Success. The poor competitors whom we are considering are athletes of high potential and thus on occasion a good performance will come about. The results of our quantitative study show that for them success leads to failure. Of some sixty poor competitors, none was reported to follow a good competitive performance with another such performance. Further, they tend to fall off badly, performing below even their own competitive norms.

By comparison the good competitors are apt to follow one good competitive performance with another. For them, success breeds success.

The quantitative study reports reaction to success along one dimension—level of the next performance. Case studies go further in that they show the great upset and distress that success can bring to the poor competitor. The following two instances illustrate some of the extreme behavior that can follow success:

A poor competitor of great natural athletic talent was entered in two field events. The first effort of his first event went extremely well. Almost before he could prevent it, he had achieved by far the best performance of his career. He appeared pained and anxious. His remaining trials were incredibly poor but, of course, the first mark stood as his performance. When the time arrived for his second event, he was not to be found. Later, it was found that he had left the athletic area in a panic. He could offer no explanation for his absence.

A pole vaulter routinely cleared 12' 6" in competition. Just as routinely, he failed to clear the next height of 13 feet. His teammates noted that he usually had more than six inches of clearance at 12′ 6″ and therefore reasoned that his inability to make 13 feet was "only mental." Thus they conspired to "help him." When his back was toward the take-off, they raised the bar from 12′ 6″ to 13 feet. Unaware of the bar's true height, the vaulter made a successful attempt.

A vaulter's first clearance of 13 feet is something of a milestone and traditionally calls for a minor celebration. Thus, as the athlete landed in the pit and the bar remained aloft, his teammates rushed toward him with cries of congratulations. When he realized his accomplishment, he was stunned. He left the area and never again vaulted.

Both of these instances illustrate rather severe reactions to success on the part of the poor competitor. More typically, perhaps, there is a general loss in competitive effectiveness that may persist for several weeks or longer. Gradually, something like the normal competitive level is resumed. In any event, though the severity of the reaction may vary, high-level achievement is a disturbing factor for the poor competitor. It seems that whatever anxieties prevent routine good competitive efforts are doubly aroused by chance achievement.

OTHER EXPRESSIVE BEHAVIOR

Descriptions thus far indicate that the poor competitor is considerably constricted in the expression of his aggression. The quantitative findings show that such constriction extends to several facets of expression. Individual cases present striking examples of "bottled up" personalities.

The poor competitor tends to speak very little, seldom initiating a conversation. I have had the singular experience of coaching one man for a period of four years without once having had a conversation with him. Nor, as far as I know, did he converse with a teammate. He responded to coaching instruction with nods or one word spoken in a soft voice. On train trips he would sit alone and occupy himself with his books.

Our subjects do not yell messages or call out to teammates. In general, they speak in modulated tones. One athlete spoke in such a barely audible voice that he could seldom be heard at a distance of greater than five feet. Any background noise would completely obliterate his voice.

The conversations that do exist between the coach and "poor" competitor are seldom satisfactory in the sense that any "meeting of minds" is attained. The athlete does not seem to present any view in a coherent, logical manner. There is always the feeling that he has not expressed himself or revealed much of his own feelings and personality. Even after four years of acquaintance and observation, the coach may have only the haziest impressions concerning the athlete's background. There is very little or no comment about the family. His mother and siblings probably won't be mentioned. There is, however, an indirect suggestion at times of a strong father who "stands for no nonsense" from the subject.

The ability to laugh separates the good and poor competitors. The latter is apparently unable to laugh in a spontaneous or uproarious manner. He is, however, able to smile.

The account of the expressive behavior of the poor competitor must be made more accurate by emphasizing one aspect of his introverted behavior. He does not strike one as shy and bashful. Nor does he blush or become easily embarrassed. Even when incoherent in his conversation, he does not appear flustered. He appears to be poised even in competition. In short, he can perhaps be said to be introverted without being particularly self-conscious.

MOTIVATION

If, as it appears, athletic achievement brings about such discomfort and anxiety for the poor competitor, the common-sense question occurs: Why does he do it? Of course, for some generations there has been increasingly less surprise at the persistence of behavior that is not "rewarding." The specific needs that bring our subjects to the athletic setting must remain matters of speculation—at least for a time. However, a few comments on surface aspects of the motivation may be useful.

Most certainly there is nothing to justify a generalization that persons with a fear of achievement in athletics will nevertheless be drawn toward participation in that area. On the contrary, most people with such a pattern will probably eschew the area entirely. Possibly nine out of ten will avoid the area—perhaps 99 in 100.

The subjects with whom we are dealing are perhaps the result of a curious sieve. If factor X accompanies factor Y in only one case in ten, we might by selection and consideration of such special cases create the spurious impression that X and Y invariably are associated.

The topic of motivation for athletic participation is so complex as to be hardly within the scope of this chapter. Competitive running, jumping, and throwing are apparently as old as civilization itself. Motivations must vary with the setting, nature of the activity, age of the participant, and culture of the group.

Testimony by athletes is probably not directly valuable in revealing true motivation, but it does seem illuminating in other respects. Included in a questionnaire administered to an entire athletic team was the item "Why did you go out for track?" Among the group were several fine competitors along with two extremely poor ones. The statements of the good competitors tended to be terse and ran from such matter-of-fact formulations as "always liked it" etc. to frank achievement remarks such as "thought my best abilities lay here and I could do well."

One of the poor competitors simply responded, "to help the team win the big ones." The other said, "spiritual stimulation of physical achievement and of being a needed member of a dynamic group at Yale . . . I also feel physical conditioning to be almost a duty of every man; this is why I chose a sport rather than a nonathletic activity."

Unlike most athletes, the poor competitors avoid the expression of personal achievement needs. They apparently cannot easily confront their own aggression. Instead, they cite "higher" or more noble motives. In this connection there is a striking similarity to Jones' (2) analysis of the case of Paul Morphy, as mentioned above. At the peak of his career Morphy, perhaps the greatest chess player of all time, gave up the game. Eventually he developed a psychosis. Jones believes that a factor contributing to Morphy's downfall was the impugning of his "noble" motives by an opponent.

ATTEMPTS TO MODIFY THE PATTERN

The poor competitor creates the impression that he is almost literally afraid to "stick his neck out," and his defenses keep him from so doing. The defenses seem deep-rooted and strong. Thus far there is no certain documentation of a poor competitor becoming a good one. Any attempts at modification of the poor competitor's behavior show the tenacity with which the defenses are held.

Strong direct efforts. From time to time a situation can be created that makes the prospect of failure more uncomfortable for the poor competitor than the usual discomfort over the prospect of success. In search of a badly needed point, the poor competitor's teammates may line the track and almost force him to perform well. Or, in the midst of a routinely ineffective field event performance, he may be collared by teammates. He may be told in the strongest terms that he *must* do well. There is the implicit threat that things will be very uncomfortable for him should he fail. Under such circumstances a good performance can almost be "wrung out." However, following such an effort, his falling off is more severe than usual and may be accompanied by physical symptoms. The forced performance may be the season's last good one.

The coach's pep-talk is now out of fashion. When things go poorly, the modern coach concentrates on the technical errors underlying poor performance. Yet, he does find a sustained disparity between capacity and performance to be a source of great frustration. One coach reports being plagued over a long period of time by a jumper who had done 6′ 5″ in practice and had yet to clear six feet in competition. Prior to a critical competition the exasperated coach indulged himself in a strong pep-talk, telling the jumper that he had been letting down the team. He concluded by offering the athlete the alternative of clearing six feet in the meet or turning in his uniform. The jumper did clear six feet in his competition and the coach believed he had found a permanent solution not only for the particular case but for all similar cases. Yet the athlete has not made six feet again. Further, he now often misses the 5′ 10″ that was once habitual for him.

Modification of the workout pattern. As previously reported, the poor competitor's workout pattern seems to differ from that of the normal competitor in several respects. Among these are his tendency to report later or earlier than other athletes and his tendency to style his practice session so as to preclude achievement. I recall the case of one poor competitor who was so highly gifted athletically that it took almost a display of ingenuity for him to avoid achievement. Finally, I decided to abandon the usual permissive procedure and literally directed every phase of his practice sessions. Though I sensed that he was growing uncomfortable, his progress was truly remarkable. The only difficulty was that his name appeared on the next General Warning list and he was ineligible for further competition.

Several years after this experiment, or perhaps experience, coaching colleagues in another sport reported a poor competitor who was otherwise stamped with athletic greatness. For some two years this student had appeared for practice at odd hours and each time he seemed to present a plausible excuse. The late hour of his attendance usually required some sort of makeshift workout schedule. His coaches reached the opinion that his failure to achieve was based on his peculiar schedule. Investigation turned up the fact that he could attend practice sessions at the regular time; his excuses were without foundation. Armed with this information, they confronted the athlete and demanded that he now report for practice on time and undergo the regular routine. In view of my own experience, I was curious about the outcome of this case. I discovered that the athlete, a junior with no record of previous scholastic difficulty, made the next General Warning list.

Psychotherapy. Inability to perform well in athletic competition is, of course, not in itself sufficient reason for therapeutic referral. Yet, the poor competitor may be referred for other reasons. Of three cases in recent years who were referred for psychosomatic complaints none completed more than a single psychiatric hour.

These three cases illustrate, I think, the poor competitor's lack of flair for psychotherapy or his unwillingness to have his defenses tampered with. Most certainly it is in line with my own experience. No matter what the approach, no matter how glaring the evidence confronting him, the poor competitor will not outwardly entertain any notion that his competitive difficulties involve an emotional problem. In general, he prefers little or no conversation with the coach; in particular, he is made especially uneasy by references to his competitive showing. If the subject is forced upon him, he speaks of a future performance. At that time, he will have acquired the gimmick that is necessary for success.

After a poor performance a good competitor may ask something to the effect of, "What happened to me?" or "Why didn't I do better?" The poor competitor does not ask such a question.

When pressed for achievement by his coach, some of the verbal behavior of the poor competitor may seem bizarre and even take on a schizoid ring. He may, for example, refer to his "poisoned blood." Yet, no case of such an athlete having been given a diagnosis of psychosis has come to my attention. On the other hand, I do know of two fairly good competitors who were both diagnosed as schizophrenics. Both were given leaves of absence from college, one of them being hospitalized for a time.

The interesting aspect of these two cases is that they were achievers with personality patterns suggestive of the noncompetitor. For example, though both exhibited considerable verbal behavior in the athletic setting, their speech seemed to represent something of a strain. One in particular appeared to be playing some sort of artificial role. One of the two never laughed at all; the other showed a mirthless, artificial laugh.

Upon returning to school, neither resumed athletic activity. One hastily informed me that his crowded schedule would prevent further participation. He appeared much relieved when I quickly accepted his decision.

SPECULATION AND QUESTIONS

The pattern under consideration is essentially one in which the subjects are drawn toward athletic participation and yet are blocked in their achievement. A consistent personality portrait emerges. In general, the poor competitor is badly constricted in other modes of expression. At least this is true in the athletic setting.

For some reason athletic success is anxiety-provoking and such success is warded off by a system of defenses that is held with great tenacity. The two cases of psychosis suggest that in a sense the poor competitor is "correct" in maintaining his defenses in the face of the intense pressures exerted upon him to do well in athletic competition. Should he relinquish his defensive system, he might be overwhelmed by his anxieties.

There seems to be no literature concerned directly with the

problem of inability to achieve in athletics. As indicated in the previous chapter, Freud (1) when he wrote of those "who are wrecked by success" and Jones (2) in his discussion of the "curious case of Paul Morphy" may be dealing with a similar pattern. Both relate the fear of achievement to the oedipal situation, particularly to the wish to displace the father. There may, of course, be other determinants such as the nature of the inherited nervous system and biographical factors other than oedipal ones.

Perhaps the most pertinent question of all is concerned with the implications of such a pattern for other areas of interaction. Does the poor competitor suffer from a disability that will affect his life after college? It would be startling indeed if such a powerful system of defenses had meaning only for athletic events.

A clue may be supplied by the apparent ability of our subjects to achieve in the academic area. Some of the poor competitors have been outstanding students. Since there are individuals who can achieve academically and not athletically, some comparison of the two areas is indicated. One major difference suggests itself. Athletics are traditionally masculine activities, whereas the academic area represents a rather neutral pursuit. Perhaps the constricted behavior of the poor competitor derives from his general fear of "sticking his neck out" in a truly masculine endeavor. He may be relatively free to express himself in a more neutral or possibly even traditionally feminine activity. Hence, we might hypothesize that the degree of vocational disability suffered by the poor competitor will depend upon the nature of his occupation. The more patently masculine the vocation, the greater the disability.

This chapter might appropriately include some speculation concerning appropriate behavior for the coach with respect to the poor competitor.

Obviously enough, the needs of the coach and the poor competitor are in direct conflict. In most settings the mission of the coach is to win and the boy who could be great except for "that queer mental quirk" is a painful source of frustration. Great hostility can be directed toward the athlete. Physical disability is easily understood and tolerated, but an emotional disability becomes cowardice.

It need hardly be said that the coach who becomes hostile

toward the athlete is guilty of unprofessional conduct. He is likely as little suited for his job as the psychiatrist who shows hatred of his patients. Nevertheless, the responsibility of the mature coach to the poor competitor is a complex matter, involving both value judgments and considerably more knowledge than is now available. Several questions become pertinent. How specific to the athletic setting is the pattern? Is the pattern amenable to modification? Should it be modified? How?

Upon graduation the average student can look forward to about a half century of life. By comparison, three years of sports competition does not loom large. Therefore, if the pattern under consideration has meaning only for athletics, the coach's responsibility to the athlete is relatively minor. However, if the poor competitor is to function ineffectively and painfully in many areas of his life, then the coach's responsibility may be great—providing there is something he can do.

Though only research can bring light to these questions and various other aspects of the phenomenon, observations thus far do suggest partial and tentative answers. It does seem likely that the behavior of the poor competitor will be adversely affected in some areas of his life—but probably not all. The pattern appears to be so deeply rooted as to make modification difficult. The defenses are held so tenaciously and resourcefully that a powerful need for them must be inferred. Even if it can be accomplished, there would remain a serious question concerning the desirability of changing the defenses without an accompanying change in character structure. Since no instance has come to attention of a poor competitor becoming a good one or even a normal competitor, we have no material, anecdotal or otherwise, to suggest how such a change might be effected.

REFERENCES

1. Freud, Sigmund, *Collected Papers* (London, Hogarth Press, 1925), Vol. *4*.

2. Jones, Ernest, *Essays in Applied Psychoanalysis*, London, Hogarth Press, 1951

CHAPTER 8

Who Uses a College Mental Hygiene Clinic

BY JAMES S. DAVIE

Here the author focuses on the segment of the student community which makes use of freely available psychiatric services. He uses methods of statistical comparison to show that these students come from all walks of campus life. Their emotional difficulties are related to dissatisfaction with the college experience.

WHEN a clinic exists to serve a community, it is pertinent to inquire whether the facilities of the clinic are differentially utilized by various segments of the community. Such inquiry is simultaneously of administrative and theoretical import. A comparison of users and nonusers of a clinic helps to clarify not only the role of the clinic in the community but also the nature of the problems in which the clinic specializes.

The present paper summarizes the major results of a study of the use of the clinical facilities of the Division of Mental Hygiene of the Department of University Health at Yale University. As part of a large ongoing study of the undergraduate community, patient and nonpatient populations within the graduating classes of 1953, 1954, and 1955 were compared to determine in what ways, if any, those who used the clinic differed from those who did not.[*] Within each class the patient population was defined as all those who had been seen at the Division of Mental Hygiene at any time during their undergraduate years at Yale. The nonpatient population was defined as all members of the same class who had never been seen at the clinic. Because of the size of the latter group (approximately 85 per cent of a class) random samples of the nonpatient population were taken: a 20 per cent sample in 1953, 40 per cent in 1954, and 25 per cent in 1955.

[*] Although the Division functions as a psychiatric clinic for all students at Yale, the present study is concerned only with the undergraduate body.

For each of the three years the patient group was compared with the nonpatient sample by the chi-square method on all variables in the study. These variables were of two types (objective and subjective) and came from two sources (the student and university records). The majority of the data came from a mailed questionnaire which focused on the students' future plans and retrospective reactions to and evaluations of selected aspects of their undergraduate experience. It also asked for certain items of information not available or not readily available from other sources in the university. The questionnaire data were supplemented with data on the students' academic, medical, and extracurricular records, which were obtained from appropriate sources in the university.

Since the content of the questionnaire varied somewhat from year to year, and since the direction and significance of association of any single variable with patient/nonpatient status also varied, the present summary is restricted to variables which were included in at least two of the three studies *and* which either did or did not consistently separate the patient and nonpatient groups. Accordingly, the following criteria of relationship are employed. A variable is said to be related to patient/nonpatient status (a) if it appears in all three studies, and the direction of association is the same in all three studies, and the chi-square is significant at the $p < .05$ level or better in at least two of the studies; and (b) if it appears in only two studies, and the direction of association is the same in both studies, and the chi-square is significant at the $p < .05$ level or better in both studies. A variable is said to be unrelated to patient/nonpatient status (a) if it appears in all three studies, and the chi-square is not significant at the $p < .05$ level in any of the studies, or if the chi-square is significant at the $p < .05$ level in one study but the direction of association is reversed in either or both of the other studies; and (b) if it appears in only two studies, and the chi-square is not significant at the $p < .05$ level in either study. Excluding differences noted on an adjective check list which will be discussed below, a total of ninety-two variables appeared in at least two of the three studies. Of these, nineteen were related and fifty were not related to patient/nonpatient status. The remaining twenty-three are excluded from the present paper for failure to meet the above criteria of the presence or absence of relationship.

Results

Satisfaction with College

We shall focus first on those variables related to patient/non-patient status. These are presented in Table 1 and may be summarized as follows. Compared with the nonpatients, the patients reported they had other than a very good time at secondary school, other than a very or fairly good time at Yale, and were in other than very or fairly good spirits most of the time at Yale. They were more likely to describe themselves as agnostic or atheistic or as having no religious preference. They had more visits to the medical division of the health department and were in the infirmary more often. They were bothered more often by feelings of nervousness and loneliness while at Yale, felt out of place frequently or most of the time, had considered leaving Yale for another college, and felt that their college experience would have been more enjoyable in a smaller college and in a co-educational college. They participated less in athletics and, when describing what they liked most about their experience at Yale, failed to mention the social-interpersonal-extracurricular side of college. They were more likely to write in criticisms of their experience at Yale. They felt they had not lived up to what their fathers expected of them and, in general, reported having quite a bit of trouble adjusting to both the academic and the nonacademic phases of college life at Yale. In brief, the patients appear to have had more trouble with their adjustment to college and to have felt their college experience unsatisfactory. Taken together, most of the differences suggest a general syndrome of neurotic complaints.

Self-descriptive Traits

In addition to the differences presented in Table 1, an adjective list included in the 1954 and 1955 studies yielded differences in self-description between patients and nonpatients. Unfortunately, the different sets of instructions accompanying the check list complicate the comparison of the results of the two studies, but the general direction and tone of the results are similar enough in both samples to warrant reporting them here. Thirty-five of the 160 adjectives in the 1954 study and sixty-six of the 160 adjectives in the 1955 study were related to patient/nonpatient status at the p < .05 level of probability.

TABLE *1*. NONPATIENT/PATIENT DIFFERENCES

(The first line gives the percentage of nonpatients and of patients giving the response to the variable under consideration in the 1953 study. The second line gives the same for the 1954 study and the third line the same for the 1955 study.)

Variable	*Response*	*% Nonpatients*	*% Patients*
Percentage answering ques-tionnaire		82	74
		74	78
		78	88
Kind of time at secondary school	Very good	55	38
		58	51
		62	47
Kind of time at Yale	Very to fairly good	84	71
		92	72
		89	76
Spirits most of time at Yale	Very to fairly good	74	56
		74	44
		86	66
Religious preference	None	9	25
		12	32
		15	26
Number of medical visits	> .9	38	63
		38	79
		25	45
Disabling illnesses	> .1	37	52
		26	44
		27	41
Bothered by nervousness	Yes; often	7	22
		*	*
		6	22
Bothered by loneliness	Often **	*	*
		3	25
	Very to fairly often	22	45

* Question was not asked this year.
** Different response categories were used in 1954 and 1955 for this question.

TABLE *1* (cont.)

Variable	Response	% Nonpatients	% Patients
Felt out of place at Yale	Frequently to most of the time	10	22
		7	22
		10	27
Considered transferring to another college	Never	74	59
		71	50
		71	58
Would prefer smaller college	Yes	28	39
		27	40
		25	41
Would prefer coed college	Yes	34	44
		32	45
		35	46
Any athletics	Yes	63	48
		63	49
		59	55
Any intramural athletics	Yes	55	42
		53	38
		50	40
Thing liked most	Social-extracurricular-interpersonal	49	37
		48	36
		41	38
Fulfill father's expectations	Not so well to poorly	*	*
		13	25
		11	23
Recommend other changes	Yes	53	59
		37	59
		37	53
Academic adjustment difficulty	Quite a bit to a great deal	*	*
		19	36
		18	37
Social adjustment difficulty	Quite a bit to a great deal	*	*
		13	30
		18	35

* Question was not asked this year.

TABLE 2. NONPATIENT/PATIENT DIFFERENCES: ADJECTIVE CHECK LIST *

		1954		1955	
		% Nonpatient	*% Patient*	*% Nonpatient*	*% Patient*
Dependable	yes **	34	19	82	69
Scattered	no	49	34	75	64
Smug	no	63	43	92	82
Worrying	no	22	10	29	54
Anxious	yes	22	43	47	69
Moody	yes	19	38	29	50
Procrastinating	yes	20	38	50	62
Restless	yes	29	43	50	69
Sensitive	yes	43	60	69	84
Consistent	no	10	24	21	39
Efficient	no	10	23	12	32
Relaxed	no	12	27	21	47
Calm	yes	19	8	53	33
	no	14	28	23	43
Prompt	yes	19	8	54	40
	no	12	23	21	39
Self-controlled	yes	21	10	72	58
	no	4	18	9	19
Dissatisfied	yes	12	30	23	40
	no	43	21	58	46
Highstrung	yes	15	30	24	53
	no	44	29	62	34
Idealistic	yes	27	43	51	65
	no	20	10	33	19
Nervous	yes	23	40	32	59
	no	31	8	49	25
Rebellious	yes	10	31	11	26
	no	49	27	69	54
Tense	yes	16	33	23	51
	no	34	16	61	25

* In the 1954 study, students were instructed to cross out those adjectives which were definitely not true of them, to check those adjectives which were somewhat more true of them than the majority of their classmates, and to leave blank those adjectives which were about as true of them as of their classmates. In the 1955 study they were asked to cross out those words which were more untrue than true of themselves, to check those words which were more true than untrue, and to circle those where they could not decide.

** yes: subject checked adjective as true of himself.

no: subject crossed out adjective as untrue of himself.

Of the 138 adjectives appearing in both studies, the twenty-one which were related to patient/nonpatient status in both studies, despite the different instructions, are presented in Table 2. In both samples the nonpatients tended significantly to describe themselves as dependable, calm, prompt, and self-controlled and to deny being scattered, smug, worrying, dissatisfied, highstrung, idealistic, nervous, rebellious, and tense. On the other hand, the patients tended to describe themselves as anxious, moody, procrastinating, restless, sensitive, dissatisfied, highstrung, idealistic, nervous, rebellious, and tense and to deny being consistent, efficient, relaxed, calm, prompt, and self-controlled. Compressing this list by looking at those adjectives which one group significantly denied and the other significantly accepted as true of itself, we note that the nonpatients describe themselves as being calm, prompt, and self-controlled, while the patients deny this. In brief, the self-descriptions of the two groups support the general conclusion from the data in Table 1—that is, that those who came to the clinic had more troubles and self-concerns than those who did not.

Unrelated Variables

Turning to those variables which were not related to patient/nonpatient status, we find that the patients do not differ significantly from the nonpatients with respect to the following precollege characteristics: home state, marital status of parents, parents' religion, father's occupational level, mother's occupational status, father's educational level, mother's educational level, Yale father, family income, size of family, type of secondary school attended, and predicted scholastic average.*

Many in-college variables were found to be unrelated to patient/nonpatient status. In the academic realm, the patients were as likely as the nonpatients to graduate with honors or orations and to belong to scholastic honor societies (Tau Beta Pi, Sigma Xi, and Phi Beta Kappa). Both groups had similar final undergraduate averages. As for future plans, there were no differences

---

* The predicted scholastic average is based on a combination of the student's secondary school record, aptitude tests, and College Board achievement tests. It is the average he is expected to make his freshman year.

with respect to intended occupational field (business versus professions) and certainty of occupational choice.

Both groups were distributed similarly throughout Yale's ten residential colleges. Their financial status was similar. The percentage of each group receiving scholarships, loans, and student employment was similar. One group was as likely to have cars at Yale as the other.

In the realm of extracurricular participation, there were no differences with respect to participation in some extracurricular activity, participation in some nonathletic activities, and participation in some activity in the residential colleges. Both groups showed similar rates of participation in musical groups, political groups, publications, fraternities, and senior societies.

The groups gave similar responses in naming the undergraduate years which they enjoyed most and enjoyed least and the year during which they felt they developed most and developed least. They did not differ in their endorsement of suggested changes which might have made their college experience more valuable to them.* Students' beliefs in the purpose of a college education (to teach one to earn a living versus to teach one to enjoy the living he will earn), the parents' distinction preference for the student (academic versus extracurricular distinction, as judged by the son), and success in fulfilling the mother's expectations of the son were also variables which did not separate the groups.

In brief, the lack of relationship of the above variables to patient/nonpatient status points to the general conclusion that those who used the clinic tended to come from all walks of campus life.

DISCUSSION

One must be cautious in interpreting the results of any user/ nonuser study. Involved in the use of a psychiatric clinic are many separate factors, such as the presence or absence of psychological disturbance, the desire for help in surmounting dif-

* Changes suggested were more: occupational preparation, liberal emphasis, work required, time for social life, time for extracurricular activities, personal direction in studies and course selection, freedom in course selection, time for intellectual pursuits, personal contacts with classmates, personal contacts with other classes, personal contacts with faculty, and discussions instead of lectures.

ficulties, the nature and source of help sought, and the possible effect of help received in coloring the individual's view of himself, his environment, and the interaction of the two. In addition to such general theoretical considerations, one must be aware of limitations in the design of the specific study.

In the present study we were concerned with the similarities and differences of those members of a graduating class who had used the university's psychiatric facilities and those who had not. If we assume that both nonpatient and patient groups were equally honest in their questionnaire responses, we may state that the patient group appears to have more psychological difficulties than the nonpatient group. It appears to be more maladjusted, dissatisfied, and self-deprecatory. Beyond this, one can only speculate as to the meaning of specific findings in the hope that such speculations may guide the course of further research. What, for example, is the meaning of the fact that the clinic sees fewer athletes than expected? Are athletes more problem-free? Or do they have as many problems as the nonathletes but attempt to sublimate them through athletic activity? If the latter, what role does the coach play in this process? Is he functioning, consciously or not, as a therapist? What does it mean that failure to fulfill the father's expectations is related to patient status while failure to fulfill the mother's expectations is not? Does this, coupled with avoidance of athletics, suggest that the patients have trouble in assuming the male role? Is it a reflection of an underlying struggle to develop an adequate self-concept? If so, is the tendency toward agnosticism also a reflection of a struggle to develop an identity? Does it represent a rejection of part of one's background as a step toward a more personally meaningful answer to the questions of "Who am I?" and "In what do I believe?" Is the overuse of the medical facilities a further reflection of this general self-concern?

In the realm of negative findings, how can one square the fact that patients seem to come from all walks of campus life with the fact that most of the variables which are not related to patient/nonpatient status are highly important variables in other studies of adjustment to life at Yale and of the degree of satisfaction derived from the total college experience? It seems contradictory, since the patient group appears more maladjusted and dissatisfied than the nonpatient group. At second glance, however, it may simply mean that these variables are not important indexes of the presence or absence of problems but may be important indexes of the *type* of problem. For an oversimplified example, the ego of an all-A student from an easy high school may be bruised when the student encounters the more rigorous academic standards of Yale. The ego of an upper-class boy from an eastern boarding school may be equally bruised when he does not make the fraternity he expected to on the basis of his social background. Both may come to the clinic but with different types of problems. Accordingly, the variable of secondary school type would be related not to use/nonuse of the clinic but to the type of problem brought to the clinic by those who use it. In any event, the fact that the patient group comes from all walks of campus life would appear to support the basic rationale for having such facilities available for the college community: namely, that young adulthood, with its attendant problems of emancipation from home, peer adjustment, vocational choice, heterosexual relationships, and so on, is a stressful period and that any student, no matter how outstanding or seemingly well-adjusted, may find it helpful to use the clinic's facilities at some point in this period.

The above speculations, reservations, and comments should emphasize the fact that the present study is regarded as one point of departure into the complex area of psychological troubles and their treatment in a college community. Much research is needed in this area from many different viewpoints. For the moment, however, the study of a psychiatric clinic in a college community from a sociological viewpoint indicates that, as might be expected, those members of a typical graduating class at Yale University who have used the facilities of the Division of Mental Hygiene feel more maladjusted and dissatisfied and are more self-deprecatory than those who do not and that, as might not be expected by the non-psychiatrically oriented, they are likely to come from all walks of campus life.

CHAPTER 9

Group Psychotherapy with College Students

BY WALTER W. IGERSHEIMER

The author reports here on a specific clinical experience carried out as an experiment in psychotherapeutic method in the college setting. His description of the group processes illustrates the emotional struggles of the college student in a specific arena, that of peer group interaction. While the demonstration of the possible usefulness of group psychotherapy in resolving psychological difficulties of students is an important contribution, perhaps equally important is the light thrown on the mechanisms of interpersonal processes in personality growth.

IN THE comparatively new field of analytically oriented group psychotherapy, group work with college students has received relatively little attention. Published reports are few: Hinckley and Hermann (4) in their book *Group Treatment in Psychotherapy* describe some of their experiences with group psychotherapy among college students at the mental hygiene clinic of the University of Minnesota. They include many practical and theoretical considerations which should prove very valuable to the psychiatrist, psychologist, and social worker, particularly those who work in a college mental hygiene clinic. Hinckley summarized his experience in a separate paper, "College Mental Hygiene and Group Therapy" (5). At the 29th meeting of the American College Health Association, Wedge (8) summarized his experience during four to thirty-seven weekly group psychotherapy sessions with five college student groups. Explicitly stating that no statistical or controlled methods of analyzing his treatment results were available to him, he nevertheless was able to reach interesting empirical impressions. In the patient population many diverse clinical syndromes were represented, although patients with psychoses and perversions were excluded. He was especially impressed with the manner in which patients who had an adjustment reaction of adolescence often characterized by marked rebelliousness were integrated into the groups and derived much therapeutic benefit in contradistinction to their treatment in individual psychotherapy. Of thirty-six college students so treated no patient seemed worse, nine patients seemed unchanged (three of these had attended only one session, while only two attended all the sessions in their respective groups), seventeen patients seemed "somewhat improved" (at least a partial symptom relief), while ten patients showed "great improvement" (striking change in social relations, academic effectiveness, and complete symptom relief). Only briefly describing the method of selection, composition, and therapy, Wedge suggests that this procedure could be usefully applied to important spheres of campus life such as combined seminar and group psychotherapy situations for educators and administrators, as has already been done in recent years by Leo Berman (2).

Recently Fortin and Abse (3) have described their work with college students at the University of North Carolina. Their students had been diagnosed as having peptic ulcers, both by clinical and by X-ray evidence. A group of nine patients was formed. The large majority had infantile personalities with predominantly passive-aggressive characterology. Treatment was conducted twice per week for one and one-half hours each time over one year and was analytically oriented. In describing this work the writers distinguish rather sharply between five phases during the course of therapy:

Phase One. The frustration of dependency needs leads to covert hostility toward the therapist.

Phase Two. The outbreak of overt hostility between two group members vying for leadership.

Phase Three. Overt hostility toward the therapist and some acting out of destructive tendencies.

Phase Four. Greater group cohesion and interaction with increasingly frank discussions and better reality testing.

Phase Five. Reactions toward the introduction of new members. They conclude that all patients were improved. This improvement was marked by a diminution of autoerotic tendencies and an increase of heterosexual drives. Three of the patients had married. Acting out had diminished and there was an increased ability to sustain emotional stress. Family relationships had generally significantly improved. The ulcer symptomatology lessened in intensity and frequency even though, under stress, it sometimes tended to recur. The authors also present evidence that in these patients the rate of recurrence of ulcer symptomatology was strikingly low compared to generally accepted rates of recurrence. More recently Keeler, Fortin, and Abse, continuing with their studies of group psychotherapy for university students, have been studying and treating students with aprosexia (6).

Axelrod, et al. (1) describe in detail their group therapy with five college women varying in age between twenty-one and thirty-two years in the psychiatric outpatient clinic of the student health service of the University of California. An expressive type of group therapy was conducted two times per week for two hours each time over a period of twenty sessions. This therapy was led by a social worker while another social worker took notes. The patients suffered predominantly from "social anxiety," difficulties with their academic work and their relationships, particularly with men. All patients experienced some alleviation of anxiety and symptoms, although all five could have benefited from a more prolonged course of therapy. Two planned to continue with individual psychotherapy, while one dropped out, apparently unable to withstand her hostility which had been engendered by the sibling rivalry situation.

Sheldon and Landsman (7) have reviewed the literature of non-directive group therapy with students who suffered from difficulties with their academic work. They report an experiment in which one such student group received nondirective group therapy and another group did not. Before and after treatment comparisons of psychological tests and point average revealed no significant difference in the psychological test results in the two groups but a significant difference in point average in favor of the treatment group. A one-year follow-up study showed that 47 per cent of students in the nontreatment group had dropped out of school, while 25 per cent of the treatment group had dropped out of school.

Purposes of This Study

What follows is a clinical and empirical evaluation of group psychotherapy with two college student groups with particular emphasis on the following three main questions:

1. What was the process of group psychotherapy?

2. Was the group psychotherapist able to conduct group psychotherapy with college students in this specific setting?

3. Were these college students suitable for group psychotherapy as conducted by the therapist in this setting?

In order to provide a sound basis for future work, it seemed useful to conduct such an empirical study during the first years of a group psychotherapy program in the Division of Student Mental Hygiene of the Department of University Health at Yale University. It is hoped that a systematic research program can be developed in the future.

1. THE PROCESS OF GROUP PSYCHOTHERAPY

The Selection of Group Participants

The clinic social workers mentioned as part of the intake procedure the various facilities for treatment, one of which was group psychotherapy. They sought to refer applicants to the group psychotherapist if they fell into one of two main groups: (a) patients with psychosomatic illnesses, (b) patients with psychoneurotic conditions. Some patients stating that they did not want to receive group psychotherapy were not referred for screening. The large majority, however, was willing to accept this referral and to schedule an interview with the group psychotherapist. Having read the initial intake interview of the social worker, the group therapist met the prospective patient, introducing himself with a hand shake. He then led him to his office, which was later on used for group psychotherapy. In these initial moments the therapist became very much aware of the fact that he was responding differently to every patient. His general attitude varied widely from a more listening to a more conversational one. While this difference in his attitude may have been partly determined by his own emotional climate on that particular day, it seemed also to be related to attitudes in the patient reflecting degrees of anxiety. In some patients the initial anxiety was so intense that the therapist spontaneously adopted a more conversational tone, while in others the anxiety was relatively mild and he adopted a more listening attitude. Having poor vision, he was particularly sensitive to the grosser body movements: the pitch, timber, and volume of voice; the rate of talking; the spacing of words; the inflection of phrases, particularly at the end of sentences; silences; interruptions; interjections; the strength of the hand shake; motility; the gait; the sitting-down behavior; the choice of a chair and its location in relation to the therapist; postural attitudes while sitting; attire; smoking behavior; etc.

This initial interview was roughly structured into a portion in which the therapist tried to become aware of the above-mentioned clues and his own responses to them, and to evaluate the interaction between the patient and him. He tried to understand the content of the patient's productions and its possible unconscious meaning, the nature of the patient's specific complaints and his motivation for psychotherapy. The remaining portion was devoted to a discussion of group psychotherapy. A general explanation about the procedure and aims of group psychotherapy was given, and misconceptions and superficial resistances were dealt with. Among the more common superficial resistances were the following: "Will group participants discuss other group participants outside the group situation?" or "How can I share some of my more intimate secrets with others in the group?" However, these objections never seemed to be insurmountable. When the therapist felt that he wanted to have a particular patient in the group, he would ask him whether he wanted to participate or whether he wanted to be referred for individual psychotherapy. Most of these students wanted to receive group psychotherapy and said so decisively. If the therapist or a patient felt undecided about this patient's participation, a second and sometimes a third appointment for an initial interview was made. There were few students whom the therapist considered unsuitable for group psychotherapy. Occasionally patients felt so much "improved" after the initial intake interview that they saw no further need for any type of psychotherapy.

A summary of some of the criteria used in the selection of students for group psychotherapy is here presented. However, this is only an approximation and the reader should not infer that all factors either pro or contra selection had to be present to come to a decision as to a particular patient's participation. Often a mixture of pro and contra factors was present, making the selection difficult. It is self-evident that this list of factors is very incomplete.

FACTORS IN THE SELECTION

Pro	*Contra*
Awareness of and some objectivity toward emotional conflicts, accompanied by anxiety.	No awareness of and no degree of objectivity toward emotional conflicts, no anxiety.
Therapist has a feeling of rapport between himself and the patient.	Therapist has no feeling of rapport between himself and the patient.
A clearly expressed wish to participate in group therapy.	No wish to participate in group therapy.
Patients with psychosomatic illnesses, mild to moderate character disorders, borderline psychotics, adjustment reactions of adolescence, and various psychoneurotic conditions.	Patients with frank psychoses, psychopaths, practicing homosexuals and other sexual deviates, and severe character disorders.

Out of a total of twenty-one patients referred to the group psychotherapist, fourteen entered treatment and seven did not. These seven did not become group participants for the following reasons: one was a female, two felt well after initial interview, one failed to appear for the initial interview, one was hampered by a severe language barrier, and two were overtly homosexual and were referred for individual psychotherapy. Over a treatment period of six months, two patients dropped out within the first six group sessions, and three were discharged with group consent in the eighth, twelfth, and seventheenth sessions, because significant reality factors had arisen. The remaining nine students stayed in the groups throughout treatment.

Composition of the Groups

We wished to form two groups. The first group was to be composed predominantly of patients with psychosomatic illnesses. Patients with such illnesses have been found particularly resistive to the intensity of individual psychotherapy in this setting in the past. It seemed worth while to explore the value of group therapy on the theory that the diffusion of the transference in the group, along with the kind of mutual support offered in groups, might permit a more effective resolution of at least the initial resistances. However, we did not want to entirely exclude from this group patients who might fit into the group even though they did not have psychosomatic illnesses. A second group was to consist mainly of patients with various psychoneurotic conditions. Even though the participants were all male college students between the ages of eighteen and twenty-four, it is not to be inferred that these groups were homogeneous. Variables related to personality structure, symptom formation, life experience, social setting, etc., differed widely among group participants. Female students were not accepted because, as mentioned above, there had been only one suitable applicant. However, we hope to have the opportunity to work with mixed sex groups in the future. In composing these two groups the personal and group dynamic aspects of each group participant had to be considered carefully and are summarized below in abbreviated form.

The Psychosomatic Group

D. Duodenal ulcer, obsessive-compulsive symptoms, hypochondriacal, self-destructive tendencies, overly ambitious, ambivalent toward authority, withdrawn, hyperintellectual; cotherapist in group, suppressing and repressing his intense rebellious and negative feelings toward the therapist, as well as his feelings of rivalry toward other group members.

G. Mucous colitis, passive-aggressive character, insecure, ambitious, ingratiating, self-depreciatory, marked pressure of speech, denial of feelings; a yes-man and a me-too man, wishes to follow others, afraid to state own opinion, reverses opinions quickly, provokes irritation.

E. Headaches, obsessive-compulsive symptoms, perfectionistic, meticulous, excessive drive to achieve, narcissistic, hyperintellectual, expects figures of authority to be omnipotent and omniscient; needs to be leader in group, antagonizes if not allowed this role, attempts to control group participants with gifts and with jokes, a monopolist and compulsive talker.

F. Adjustment reaction of adolescence, overt and covert rebellion against convention and authority, withdraws easily; reticent in group; when stimulated to express hostility, he does so in bursts of considerable intensity.

C. Headaches, passive-aggressive character, narcissistic, conflicts with heterosexuality and strongly repressed passive homosexual wishes, compensatory "masculinity," mild depression and denial of feelings; a doer, a catalyst, verbal, articulate, intelligent; will provoke jealousy in others.

B. Headaches, compulsive character, strong projective tendencies, suspicious, mood swings from elation to depression, hypersensitive, projects extensively, socially and scholastically very ambitious, fixed to rigid moral and cultural conventions, marked guilt feelings; verbal, articulate, dramatic, a catalyst; will attempt to control the other group members and the therapist by competing for leadership.

A. Vague somatic complaints resembling neurasthenia, compulsive character, marked need to achieve, social maladjustment, marked inferiority feelings, homosexual fears and repressed homosexual wishes; will attempt to preserve his incognito in the group by being reticent.

The Psychoneurotic Group

L. Question borderline psychosis with speech disturbance, withdrawal reaction, rebellion against authority and convention, intense repressed hostility, anxiety about professional choice; withdrawn in group, skeptical of group therapy, the chronic doubter.

K. Adjustment reaction of adolescence, marked rebellion against authority, repressed hostility, marked feelings of isolation, work inhibition, self-destructive tendencies; articulate and perceptive, will try to be cotherapist and interrogate others, a catalyst.

H. Adjustment reaction of adolescence, compulsive character, anxiety reaction in social situations, obsessive-compulsive symptoms, moralistic, strongly repressed homosexual fears and conflicts, open anxiety toward women, sexual confusion, self-depreciatory, verbal, perceptive; will try to be cotherapist and to interrogate other group participants, a catalyst.

I. A diagnostic problem, either psychopath or borderline psychotic, self-destructive, a social deviate and gambler, marked rebellion against convention, exhibitionistic, poorly repressed homosexual wishes, extensive use of mechanisms of denial and in-

tellectualization; verbal, monopolistic, destructive to group interaction, tends to become the scapegoat, perceptive of unconscious
trends in himself and others, a catalyst.

J. Adjustment reaction of adolescence, passive-dependent character, strong repressed homosexual wishes and feminine identification; baby in the group, stimulates need to be taken care of by
other group members, provokes irritation.

M. Obsessive-compulsive character, intense anxiety about masturbation and conflict about aggressiveness vs. submissiveness in
his relationships, strong unconscious feminine identification,
marked inhibition in social situations, particularly toward women
whom he tends to idealize; reticent in group, will command respect of other group participants because of his superior intelligence and his penetrating, honest, stimulating, and articulate
contributions, a catalyst.

The Method of Group Psychotherapy

The group psychotherapist wished to apply a modified form of
analytically oriented group psychotherapy. In general, he intended
to be relatively nondirective at first, thereby frustrating the
passive-dependent needs of the group. If excessive anxiety developed and could not be alleviated sufficiently well in the group
therapy sessions, he was prepared to give individuals time for
private sessions. He hoped that individual and group resistances
could be sufficiently reduced to allow a maximum development
of cohesion, group-centeredness and orientation toward therapy
to take place. The work with resistances was to be a major task in
the therapy. He planned to encourage free associations and the
reporting of dreams when they seemed to be particularly important to an individual. Since only twenty-seven one and one-
half hour sessions in the psychosomatic group and twenty one and
one-half hour sessions in the psychoneurotic group were planned
for, the development of intense transference neuroses was not
predicted. However, if a particularly intense transference reaction
did develop, the therapist planned to deal with it by allowing
discharge of the affect and then suggesting that it seemed that
here were feelings out of keeping with the actual group reality and
encouraging their analysis. The therapist tried to analyze his own

countertransference feelings to the various group members and to disassociate his own irrational feelings from the ones he could reasonably have at a given time in the group. He avoided giving the impression that six months of group therapy could resolve all the emotional conflicts of the various group participants and stressed the need of a continuing, self-investigative attitude after termination of group therapy.

The Course of Group Psychotherapy

We shall limit our description to the broad developments and special high lights during the progress of therapy in each group. No attempt will be made to do a content analysis of group therapy interviews or to report on the detailed movement of one individual throughout the course of therapy.

The Psychosomatic Group

This was the first group to start. The therapist had arranged seven chairs in a circle with an armchair for himself. At the appointed time he called the group participants into the office, receiving them while sitting himself in the armchair and letting them choose their respective chairs. An expectant and tense silence followed, which was then broken by *A* suggesting that they introduce themselves to one another. The rounds were made and soon their majors in college, the location of their rooms, the goals for their studies emerged as topics of conversation. In brief succession philosophical themes, quotations from poems, definitions of psychological terms, the differences between a psychosis **and a** neurosis, and mental health in general were discussed. After **about** forty-five minutes a lull occurred, and *B* wondered whether they were really here to discuss these superficial matters and felt that they should talk to each other about their symptoms which made them come to the clinic for therapy. *E* resisted this idea strongly and felt that one could not tell others these things in a group. However, he was overruled. Group members began to delineate their symptoms. Having made the rounds *B* wanted to know from the therapist, "how to go at this business of therapy and the analysis of resistances and free associations." With the exception of a few interspersed remarks, this was the first time that the therapist felt called upon to respond at some length. He explained the procedure of free association and introduced the concept of resistance very briefly. He encouraged them not to get stuck in attempting intellectually to understand psychological terms or the therapeutic procedures. The subject of dominance vs. submission was then introduced and broadly discussed. It stimulated much interest and as the first group session came to a close, an intense and interesting interchange was taking place, so that everyone seemed disappointed that the end of the session had arrived. The group atmosphere had been tense, distant, and somewhat hostile for the first three-quarters of the session but became warmer, closer, and less tense in the last quarter.

The next nine group sessions were turbulent. After the third session *A* asked the therapist for an individual interview. He appeared in a state of near-panic, was deeply disturbed, and was diffusely angry. He insisted hotly that he had to leave Yale, that he was failing in all his courses and that he felt very confused. After listening to him the therapist carefully examined with *A* the facts about his scholastic situation, and it became evident that this was not altogether ominous, that in fact *A* could well afford to drop two courses which would allow him to catch up in the others. *A* then said that he had thought of this himself but that he had not felt free to act on it by himself. His acute anxiety diminished. *B* and *E* alternated between feelings of intense hostility toward the group sessions—claiming that they had not been immediately effective—and feelings of great enthusiasm for them. They also were involved with each other in a struggle for dominance in the group. In the fifth session *B* seemed withdrawn and sulky. The therapist saw him for an additional half hour after the session. *B* then unleashed a barrage of angry, frustrated feelings at the therapist and at group psychotherapy in general. He felt that as he was thinking more and more about his "psyche," he thought it looked "grubbier and grubbier" and so did that of the others. He said that during the session he sometimes had feelings of wishing to scream at the others to shut up but quickly added that he didn't really want to hurt anybody. He felt the others and the therapist did not like him and he was ready to leave the group. The therapist replied that he thought *B* was a great asset to the group and that he was certain that the others felt the same way about him. He encouraged him to vent his feelings in the group and said that this was expected as part of therapy. *B* then got up, said with a grin, "Thank you, sir," shook hands with the therapist, and left, returning to the next session feeling much improved.

In the middle of session six a crisis occurred. *E* openly refused to listen to the troubles of the others and stated that he was only interested in talking about his own problems. His attitude was seriously questioned, and he was confronted with a blunt, "Well, if you don't like to listen to us and help us the way you want us to listen to you and help you, why do you come here?" *E* was very quiet for the rest of the session. When the therapist talked individually with *E* after this session, *E* remained adamant in his previous position. The therapist said that he did not think that the group had really and finally rejected him, so long as he showed willingness to participate within the spirit of the group, and invited him to return for the next session. However, *E* never came back. At the end of the seventh session *F* requested an individual interview. He appeared to be in a panic. Pale, somewhat trembling, his teeth chattering, he talked in a tense, suppressed voice about the utter futility of his work and his stay at Yale. He had made up his mind to leave immediately, to join the Coast Guard for four years and be done with it. He mentioned his inability to start on his work assignments, to listen to lectures or concentrate on reading. The therapist felt that *F* should bring this matter into the group and encouraged him not to act upon his feelings immediately and instead to try and think what factors might have contributed in bringing about this situation. He stressed the fact that there did not seem to be any real necessity to leave Yale immediately since there were two months ahead before the end of the term. In the eighth session *F*'s troubles became the focus for group discussion. The various pros and cons of his plans were earnestly debated. As a result of this session it was suggested to *F* that in addition to the regular group sessions he should see the therapist in a few individual interviews so that he would have enough time to think the situation over. *F* took this advice and saw the therapist four times individually, continuing in the group through the end of the tenth session. During this four-week period he came to a reasonable decision which was supported by the group. Instead of leaving Yale immediately, never to return, he now intended to go away on a leave of absence which would allow him to return at a later date if he so wished. Instead of joining the Coast Guard for four years, he now planned to enlist in the Army for two years, which he would have to do anyhow sooner or later. He took his leave with the consent of his parents and the dean of the college instead of without such consent. *F* was discharged from the group after the tenth session. *G* was introduced into this group in the eighth session.

By the end of the tenth session it seemed that the initial anxieties had been effectively dealt with. The group members were settling down and a high degree of group cohesiveness and group atmosphere had developed. It was interesting to note that after the fifth session a marked reduction or total disappearance of their presenting psychosomatic symptoms was reported and maintained for about four weeks. Then came Christmas recess and the students went home. Upon returning, all reported a relapse of their psychosomatic symptoms and related this to the anxieties, hostilities, and discomforts which they had experienced while with their families. The eleventh group session (the first postvacation one) was marked by intense catharses of feelings toward various family members. This session in particular was characterized by a group atmosphere and cohesiveness not attained before. They seemed to be unanimously agreed that they had to do something about these feelings.

Between the eleventh and approximately the twenty-third meetings increasing group centeredness developed. There was a notable shift from the general to the specific, from the impersonal to the personal and from extragroup conflict situations to intragroup conflict situations. There was increasing ability to express hostility toward the therapist and the treatment situation. Group members grappled on the one hand with the wish for the therapist to tell them the answers and on the other hand with the wish to resolve their problems themselves. Several times the frustration engendered by this dependency-independency struggle led to rebellious outbursts and sneering comments. The therapist and the group therapy became occasionally the subject of jokes and mild teasings. Different approaches toward resolving inner problems were discovered by individuals and were reported, compared and accepted by the group. The group work became increasingly oriented toward the resolution of inner problems. The development of objectivity toward themselves and tolerance of emotional conflict increased. Many topics were brought into the group situation for discussion. Only a few will be mentioned here: overt homosexual experiences, homosexual fantasies and dreams, homosexual fears, masturbation, sexual desires, women in general, dating, sexual frustrations, marriage, rejected attempts at establishing relationships with girls, dominance vs. submission, how to get the better of one's fellow men, hostility patterns, achievement patterns, omnipotence vs. inferiority, job situations, future plans, student life at Yale College in all aspects, social aspects of college life, and life in general with its vicissitudes and family relationships. Group participants began to test out new approaches in solving life situations. Acting-out behavior occurred occasionally but never reached a point where it was unmanageable. Toward the end of this period some hostile verbal interchanges occurred between *B* and *C* but also between other group members. During this period of time, covering about four months, the psychosomatic symptoms reappeared in relation to emotional problems but, in general, became less and less pronounced and in some disappeared altogether. There was evidence that changes in behavior toward significant persons in their everyday life were taking place in some of the group members.

The last four group sessions—twenty-four to twenty-seven inclusive—were spontaneously used by the members to discuss plans for their summer vacations and for their future and seemed to relate to the termination of therapy. The group therapist followed the policy of termination in the Division of Student Mental Hygiene, which is to terminate psychotherapy at the end of the academic year. If a student wants further psychotherapy, he has to reapply at the beginning of the next academic year. In general, this way of terminating proceeded smoothly in this group. Actually, *A* had come to the conclusion to leave Yale, where he felt maladjusted, and to enter the Army, hoping to enroll in its division of chemical research and eventually to enter industry. He felt that he had benefited from group psychotherapy but didn't feel that he needed any more of it now. If he felt the need in the future, he planned to obtain it in the Army. *C* said that his headaches had disappeared and he wasn't sure if he needed further therapy. He planned to spend his summer vacation working abroad and was going to try himself out. If he felt the need for further therapy, he would reapply in this department next year. *D* did not think he needed further therapy and was, on the whole, uncertain whether he had gained much from it, even though his psychosomatic symptoms had almost entirely abated and, according to general group consensus, he had emerged from his withdrawal. *G,* whose psychosomatic symptoms had diminished markedly and only appeared in occasional emotional crises, said that he wanted to reapply for further group treatment next year. *B* requested an individual interview in which he expressed his disappointment that he had not progressed more rapidly with obtaining insight into himself. He showed interest in obtaining intensive individual analytically oriented psychotherapy. The therapist promised *B* to help him find a suitable individual therapist if he reapplied for such treatment at the beginning of the next academic year. *B,* who was going to spend his vacation in a difficult family situation, inquired about the possibility of receiving individual supportive psychotherapy while at home. The therapist then referred him to a psychotherapist in that area.

The Psychoneurotic Group

The group members assembled for the first meeting punctually. The therapist was unexpectedly detained for ten minutes and entered his office surprised to find all seven group members already seated and waiting for him. They had arranged the chairs in two rows and were not talking with each other. The therapist smilingly remarked that it looked as if they were expecting a lecture. This remark caused a burst of laughter and tension release and resulted in regrouping to form a circle. The therapist then mentioned that he would leave it up to them to bring their problems to the group meetings and then kept silent. This was followed by introductions and the naming of their colleges. Very quickly an interesting and interactive discussion sprang up, covering a wide scope of topics, such as: security operations, the force of feelings of insecurity, what is anxiety, chronic anxiety because of the threat of ultimate death, stoicism vs. epicureanism, falling in love when the girl doesn't love you, etc. All this had the aspect of a fairly heated debate. They interrupted each other frequently which was gently interpreted by the therapist as a means of blocking rather than facilitating group interaction and communication. At the end of the first session the initial tension had diminished. The group atmosphere was animated and all participants gave the appearance of having had a very interesting time and of being somewhat amazed at the situation.

Between the second and the ninth sessions this group seemed to be in a state of flux and indecision. There was a high rate of absenteeism and unpunctuality. *N* did not appear for the second meeting and dropped out without explanation. During the group sessions there occurred much intellectualization and rationalization and particularly *I* tried to monopolize with entertaining stories and jokes. It required much time and consistent effort to reduce the intensity of this resistance. *L* remained very much on the periphery of the group and after the fifth session came to the therapist wondering whether he should continue with group work, since he felt unable to communicate meaningfully in the group. Reassurance and encouragement seemed at first to be sufficient for him to return. However, *L* excused himself from sessions ten, eleven, and twelve and then telephoned saying that he would like to discontinue. He felt he had gotten out of the group what he had hoped and wanted the permission of the therapist to leave. This permission was given. *K* asked many provocative and intelligent questions about the emotional problems of other group members but did not tell them about his own difficulties. Various group members brought emotionally conflictful personal problems but their detailed discussion was hindered by strong resistances against becoming a cohesive, group-centered, therapy-oriented group. After the seventh session *H* wondered whether he should continue in the group and wondered whether he was getting enough out of it. A twenty-minute postsession discussion with the therapist reassured him and he returned and became an important catalyst in this group. The group therapist repeatedly noticed himself to be unusually verbal in group sessions during this phase of treatment.

Between the tenth and the sixteenth group sessions—a period covering about two months—the group atmosphere became increasingly group-centered and therapy-oriented. Group members were more consistent in their attendance and punctuality and more intent on working on their emotional problems. Concomitantly, the therapist became less verbally active. Some of the previously existing resistances diminished or resolved. The group became interested in bringing their dreams and trying to understand their meanings in the group. Many anxiety-producing inner conflicts were brought to the group and were found to be problems shared by other group members. Of the problems intensively discussed only a few are listed here: homosexual fears, homosexual dreams, dreams of self-mutilation and mutilation of others, women in general and their experiences with specific women, conflicts about masturbation, family relationships, life on the college campus, examination anxiety, anxiety-provoking social situations at Yale, etc. The working through of emotionally charged situations led to occasional acting out and the testing out of new approaches for handling life situations. This period was quite upsetting for all the group members, particularly for *K*, who had tried very hard to deny mounting feelings of hostility and frustration. This finally resulted in an intense outburst of rage which while making him very anxious also broke through the denial. The empathic acceptance of his feelings and their full discussion with the group seemed to relieve his anxiety and was followed by a marked symptomatic improvement. *H* worked through intense dream experiences related in large part to masturbation and castration anxiety. He also related occasional dreams and fantasies in which he seemed to have breasts and began to wonder about his relationship to his mother, stressing her dominance in the family. *M* worked on similar problems. *J*, who had been passive and "babyish" to the point of appearing almost disinterested in the group, gathered his courage one week end and gave his parents a long lecture on how they had been abusing him and his sister. He directly and openly expressed his resentment at being dragged into their marital conflicts and insisted that in the future he wished to be left alone with matters that were not his business. His parents, startled at first, listened attentively and agreed that he had a good point. Subsequently, everyone in the therapy group noticed and commented on how much more decisive and manly *J* seemed to behave in the group. *I*, the nonchalant, apparently anxiety-free playboy (through his dreams) became more aware of his homosexual conflicts and with considerable anxiety related overt homosexual experiences. He became increasingly interested in passing his courses, while before he was proud to be the greatest "goof-off" at Yale. He made a strong conscious effort to study but found that he was incapable of it. He would regularly fall asleep while studying and oversleep in the morning, thus missing his courses. He became somewhat depressed and anxious, and developed headaches. Finally it became obvious that he would either have to leave the University or be dropped. At first he wanted to run away and enlist in the merchant marine, then jump ship and get stranded far away. He did not intend telling the dean or his parents about his plans. Under group pressure he was induced to think it over and eventually left Yale fairly reasonably, having talked it over with his dean and his parents. He was discharged from the group after the sixteenth group session. He had become an increasingly useful group member, especially because he was so capable of intuitive insights into the unconscious mechanisms and motives of other group members and because in tense situations he always had a joke ready for tension release. His leaving was felt as a considerable loss, and this was openly expressed. His leave-taking was a moving experience for everyone.

I's discharge from the group marked the beginning of the termination process for this group. During the next four meetings the remaining group members were frequently unpunctual or canceled meetings. Group interaction was less rapid and sometimes even dragged, and the emotional intensity of the meetings was perceptibly diminished. A discussion of changes that had taken place showed that everyone felt in his own way that he had gained much from the group psychotherapy experience. In the twentieth session, scheduled to be the last one, future planning for psychotherapy was discussed and the department's policy of termination was explained. It turned out that *K* wanted to reapply for group psychotherapy in this department. *J* did not feel that he needed further therapy but would feel free to apply if he did. *M*, who is moving to a different university, will apply for further group psychotherapy there. *H*, who did not appear for this last meeting, said in a letter to the therapist two or three weeks later how much he had gained by, and still was involved in, this group experience, which continued to have meaning for him. He indicated that if he felt the need, he would reapply for further treatment in the fall.

2. Was the Therapist Able to Conduct Group Psychotherapy with These College Students in This Setting?

In empirically evaluating this group psychotherapy experience with college students, it seemed of importance to the writer to appraise some of the factors operating within himself which seemed to have a bearing on the conduct of therapy. Experience with analytically oriented group psychotherapy, and particularly its ego-supportive aspects, led the therapist to believe that emotionally disturbed college students so close to their adolescent crises might benefit from this type of psychotherapy. He felt that with group psychotherapy he could make a significant contribution in the treatment program of the Division of Student Mental Hygiene. His interest was stimulated by the opportunity of working with intelligent, flexible, and relatively young people toward whom he felt, a priori, a general warmth and empathy. Although predominantly interested in the therapeutic aspects of the work, he was also attracted by its possibilities for research and teaching.

The staff of the department consists of psychiatrists, psychologists, social workers, and sociologists in his age group and interested in dynamic psychiatry. They form a comfortable, eager team willing to support a new approach in psychotherapy.

Initial conferences between the group psychotherapist and the three intake social workers, while clarifying the main aspects of his intended work, resulted also in some misunderstandings with respect to the type of patients to be referred to the group psychotherapist. This misunderstanding could be traced to an uncertainty in the group psychotherapist himself with regard to a suitable selection procedure. As soon as this difficulty was handled, referral proceeded smoothly.

The therapist noticed that he had a certain amount of anxiety prior to the beginning of the first group session in each group. Analyzing this he recognized certain attitudes and motivations in himself that had clearly helped to produce this anxiety. Thereafter he no longer felt anxious before the meetings. During the group therapy sessions he felt comfortable and free to direct his attention to the events developing in the group. He noticed the intensely and emotionally charged interaction and the strong demands by the group members for him to do something for them. He perceived and analyzed his own emotional reactions and strove to maintain a benign, tolerant, and interested attitude. This attitude allowed him to localize resistances or excessive emotional reactions in group members and to utilize them therapeutically. He found himself able to maintain this attitude over a prolonged period of time, during which much overt and covert hostility was directed toward him and this method of treatment. Although occasionally he reacted to hostility directed at him with feelings of counterhostility, he had relatively little difficulty in containing his feelings.

In line with the policies of the department he was asked to limit, where possible, the duration of any one group to the academic year (seven months) and to keep therapy to once per week for one and one-half hours each time. Initially he was skeptical about these limitations. His misgivings lessened as therapy progressed and showed results. He did not discover within himself serious resistances against conducting this form of group psychotherapy. He looked forward with pleasure and interest to the group sessions and found real satisfaction in this work. At the end of the year he was already planning to have more groups during the following academic year.

3. Were These College Students Suitable for Group Psychotherapy as Conducted by This Therapist in This Setting?

All of the group participants had applied for psychiatric treatment at the Division of Student Mental Hygiene of the Department of University Health at Yale University. Their ages ranged from eighteen to twenty-four years; their I.Q.'s were in the high normal to superior range.

Out of the fourteen students who were eventually taken into these two groups, six wanted psychotherapy to alleviate their psychosomatic symptoms. They had previously sought medical (organic) aid but no medicinal treatment had been of curative value. Many of the six had been told by their physicians that their medical symptomatology might be connected with a psychological difficulty. Five out of these six were aware of inner states of tension, conflict, or anxiety arising in certain situations or toward certain people, and recognized their feelings as inappropriate. Only one out of these six denied having any emotional problems and applied for therapy solely to relieve the discomfort of his gastric symptomatology. The remaining eight gave evidence of some degree of awareness of manifestations of anxiety in certain situations or toward certain people. A lack of concentration in their work or failure with it, marked hostility toward their teachers and other figures of authority, difficulty with women, feelings of isolation and withdrawal, anxiety over masturbation, anxiety in relation to an uncertain future—these were some of the complaints that brought them to therapy. They demonstrated in the initial interviews with the therapist some of their anxiety and a certain sincerity in wishing to understand their emotional reactions and to attempt to work them out.

The personality structure in many of the students seemed to be still in a state of flux. Among the manifestations of anxiety were: adjustment reaction of adolescence (two), psychosomatic symptoms (six), antisocial behavior (one), hypochondriasis (one), neurasthenia (one), and marked social anxiety (three).

Out of these fourteen participants two dropped out early. All others rapidly learned how to approach therapy in order to make good use of it. After the overcoming of initial resistances they showed an increasing ability to share inner experiences in the group and to investigate their feelings toward each other and the group therapist. The group situation increasingly became a meaningful emotional experience, from which it was possible to extrapolate to general life situations. Four students willingly made certain sacrifices by changing course schedules, and all participants made sacrifices in terms of time and effort so as to be able to continue attending these group meetings.

The rate of attendance was relatively high in each group. In the psychoneurotic group, which ran through five and one-half months with a total of twenty meetings, the total attendance was 89.5 per cent, while the psychosomatic group ran for six months and three weeks with a total of twenty-seven meetings and a total attendance of 95.2 per cent. We would like to interpret these figures as showing the high level of sustained interest among these students in this group work. It also seems implicit that they were getting important therapeutic help from it.

Evaluation of changes

Changes as a result of psychotherapy are difficult to demonstrate conclusively. Many factors tending to obscure the data may enter such an evaluation, both on the therapist's and the patient's side. Therefore, a special effort was made by the therapist to lean more toward the skeptical side in this evaluation. The data were obtained from the patients, either by direct questioning about a certain symptom or by their spontaneous verbalizations, and from the therapist's observations of changes in their verbal and non-verbal behavior during group sessions. Changes in psychosomatic symptoms were evaluated solely on the basis of the patients' statements.

CHANGES IN PSYCHOSOMATIC GROUP

Reported by patients. *Somatic symptoms:* unchanged, 1; improved, 5; worse, 0. *Psychological symptoms:* unchanged, 3; improved, 2; questionably improved, 2; worse, 0.

Reported by therapist. *Psychological symptoms:* unchanged, 2; improved, 1; questionably improved, 4; worse, 0.

CHANGES IN PSYCHONEUROTIC GROUP

Reported by patients. *Psychological symptoms:* unchanged, 1; improved, 4; questionably improved, 1; worse, 0.

Reported by therapist. *Psychological symptoms:* unchanged, 1; improved, 3; questionably improved, 2; worse, 0.

Thus, out of thirteen group participants a major proportion had shown some degree of symptomatic improvement, both in the patients' opinion as well as in that of the psychiatrist, and no patient was worse at the time when group therapy was terminated.

REFERENCES

1. Axelrod, Pearl L.; Baerwald, Ann K.; Finney, Floram; and Coffey, Hubert S., Group treatment of social anxiety in college women, *Journal of Psychiatric Social Work, 19:*107. 1950.

2. Berman, Leo, A group psychotherapeutic technique for training in clinical psychology, *American Journal of Orthopsychiatry, 23:322.* 1953.

3. Fortin, John N., and Abse, D. W., Group therapy of college students with peptic ulcer: a preliminary report (read at the Annual Meeting of American Group Psychotherapy Association, New York, N.Y., Jan. 14, 1956), *International Journal of Group Psychotherapy, 6:383–91.* 1956.

4. Hinckley, Robert G., and Hermann, Lydia, *Group Treatment in Psychotherapy*, Minneapolis, University of Minneapolis Press, 1951.

5. —— College mental hygiene and group therapy, *Internal Journal Group Psychotherapy, 3:88.* 1953.

6. Keeler, Martin H.; Fortin, John N.; and Abse, D. W., A trial of group psychotherapy of aprosexia with university students (read at the Annual Meeting of the American Group Psychotherapy Association, New York, N.Y., Jan. 11, 1957); unpublished manuscript.

7. Sheldon, William D., and Landsman, Theodore, An investigation of nondirective group therapy with students in academic difficulty, *Journal of Consultative Psychology, 14:210.* 1950.

8. Wedge, Bryant M., Group therapy for college students, Proceedings of the 29th Annual Meeting of the American College Health Association (Chicago, Ill., May 3–5, 1951), Bulletin 31.

CHAPTER 10

The Borderline Patient in the College Setting

BY ROBERT L. ARNSTEIN

This clinical psychiatric study deals with students in college who demonstrate unquestionably severe disturbances of personality structure. Using flexible methods aimed at strengthening the ego, the author is able to emerge with "an attitude of tempered optimism" concerning the outcome. It appears that growth and synthesis is possible even for poorly integrated students in college, at least with some special help.

MY INTEREST in the "borderline" patient in the college setting resulted from my impression that a rather significant number of the approximately 100 patients seen by me during a two-year period at the University Mental Hygiene Clinic were extremely disturbed but neither clearly psychotic nor classically neurotic. Moreover, because this segment of my case load required a considerable portion of my energy and thought, it seemed worth while to attempt to understand the psychopathological position of these patients in order to develop a more systematic therapeutic approach. The wisdom of using the word "borderline" as the key term in this effort may be questioned, inasmuch as it has been in some disrepute as a technical entity, although it recently has been given considerable prominence in panel discussions of the Psychoanalytic Association meetings. The term, however, does seem to be descriptive and at the present state of our knowledge one that is hard to displace clinically despite the fact that the diagnostic, prognostic, and therapeutic implications of such a concept are not always clear.

Inevitably, any discussion of "borderline" patients must start with a consideration of the meaning and use of the word "borderline," which is at best an imprecise diagnosis and is at worst a diagnostic wastebasket. A review of the literature reveals a series of terms which, if not synonymous, seem at least roughly equivalent. These include borderline state, borderline schizophrenia, borderline neurosis, borderline psychosis, ambulatory schizophrenia, oneirophrenia, preschizophrenia, pseudoneurotic schizophrenia, latent schizophrenia, incipient schizophrenia, and potential schizophrenia.

The number and variety of the names which have been employed to cover the general area suggests, on the one hand, a need for some systematic understanding and definition, and testifies, on the other hand, to the difficult and elusive nature of the problem. As long ago as 1919 L. Pierce Clark was concerned with treatment of the "borderline neuroses and psychoses," and periodically ever since, this has been a subject for discussion as to classification or management (6). In description and definition there have been almost as many approaches as there are names. Fenichel defines "borderline cases" as "neurotic persons who, without developing a complete psychosis, have certain psychotic trends or have a readiness to employ schizophrenic mechanisms whenever frustrations occur" or "persons who have channelized their schizophrenic disposition . . . into one more or less circumscribed area. . . ." (11). Stern defines the "borderline group of neuroses" as containing ten clinical symptoms including "narcissism, psychic bleeding, inordinate hypersensitivity, psychic and body rigidity . . . negative therapeutic reactions, . . . deeply rooted feelings of inferiority, masochism, . . . deep organic anxiety, use of projection mechanisms, and difficulties in reality testing, particularly in personal relationships." Generally he feels they are similar to the narcissistic neuroses (25). Eisenstein also places the "borderline state" in this category, but further describes such patients as "superficially appearing to function at the neurotic level . . . but suffering from deficient emotional contact and from a seriously impaired sense of reality" (8). Schmideberg states that these patients are "for the most part defective in object relations, reality sense, judgment, etc. and in their poor control of the id" (20). Robbins comments that characteristically there is "inability to tolerate frustrations and anxiety and the presence in consciousness of certain primary process mechanisms" (21). Rapaport, Gill, and Schafer use the term preschizophrenia and define this "as schizoid personalities whose adjustment was so precarious that schizophrenic-like withdrawal tendencies in the guise of anxiety and inhibition, or schizophrenic-like ideational productions in the guise of obsessive-phobic thought, had already penetrated into their everyday life." It should be noted that they also describe "paranoid conditions," which are differentiated from acute schizophrenia by the ability to continue to function and by an absence of primary schizophrenic thought-disorders and dissociation or flattening of affect (23). Bychowski stresses ego weakness and fluidity of ego boundaries (4), which is similar to Federn's theoretical approach to the psychoses as described in his paper on latent schizophrenia (10). Buxton feels that identity problems are basic with blurring of the ego boundaries occurring (20) and Carlson, in describing a particular group of patients, stresses confusional aspects, and thinks of the problem in terms of a disrupted self-perception (5). Frank states that "the synthetic function of the ego has been broken" (20), while Gitelson regards the borderline category in terms of gradations of defenses, feeling that in borderline conditions "there is a mixture of the more advanced postoedipal defences with primitive pregenital ones" (20). Hoch and Polatin use the term "pseudoneurotic schizophrenia" and define it in terms of the presence of Bleuler's basic schizophrenic symptoms of disorder of association, rigidity of affect, ambivalence and dereistic thinking but feel that gross thinking disorder is not present. They make the final diagnosis dependent "on the constellative evaluation of a group of symptoms even though in any given case it is not necessary to have all the symptoms present . . ." (16). Axel elaborates on this concept and describes it as "a fluid transition stage from the psychoneurotic to the schizophrenic type of reaction" (1). Knight in his review quotes various authors as applying the term to patients who are "quite sick but not frankly psychotic," or patients in whom both neurotic and psychotic phenomena are observed, or to a patient who has not yet "broken with reality" but in whom "the severity of the maladjustment and the presence of ominous clinical signs preclude diagnosis of neurosis" (17). He concludes that the diagnosis tells more about the "uncertainty and indecision of the therapist than it does about . . . the patient." Knight, as does Rangell (20), states that the diagnosis must be made on the basis of an evaluation of total ego functioning, which suggests he thinks in a kind of quantitative approach, using multiple factors, although he never states this in these words (17). In addition to those who are moved to state what

"borderline" is, several men have been quite emphatic about what
it is not. Glover in a paper on classification denies the existence
of such a categorical concept and says that psychotic mechanisms
should be labeled when present (15). Zilboorg prefers to think
of all cases as "borderline" in the sense that all psychopathology
is a continuum but feels that the borderline concept as usually
used is dated (20, 30). He prefers the term ambulatory schizophrenia and in his latest paper "favors the opinion that it is the
superego that is hypertrophied and overwhelms the more or less
usual, if not normally strong, ego" (31).

To think about the term in any theoretical way one would presumably have to start with the fact that, whereas the word "borderline" may be the dividing zone between two areas of any sort in
psychiatry, most simply and as most commonly used in the sense
under study it means the area between neurosis and psychosis.
Immediately, then, one must be concerned with the relationship
of these two pathological entities. A cursory review of the literature suggests that almost everyone who has considered this problem makes some distinction between the two and almost all imply
that clinical diagnosis and differentiation is not necessarily difficult. There seems, however, to be considerable disagreement as
to the difference expressed in theoretical terms. I do not feel that
an exhaustive study of this problem can be handled here, but
some scrutiny seems in order because it soon becomes apparent
that part of the confusion about the "borderline" concept is re-
ferable to more basic confusion about "neurosis" and "psychosis."

Approaching the problem most simply and directly, the *Diagnostic and Statistical Manual on Mental Disorders,* published by
the American Psychiatric Association, has a basic division into
"mental disorders associated with organic brain disturbance, and
those occurring without such primary disturbance of brain function" (19). Secondary to the latter division are such categories
as psychotic disorders, psychoneurotic disorders, and personality
disorders.

> Grouped together under psychotic disorders are: (1) affective
> disorders, characterized by severe mood disturbance . . .
> (2) schizophrenic reactions, characterized by fundamental dis-
> turbances in reality relationships and concept formations,

with associated affective, behavioral, and intellectual disturbances, marked by a tendency to retreat from reality, by
regressive trends, by bizarre behavior, by disturbances in
stream of thought, and by formation of delusions and hallucinations; (3) paranoid reactions, characterized by persistent delusions and other evidence of the projective mechanism. From this grouping, a psychotic reaction may be
defined as one in which the personality, in its struggle for
adjustment to internal and external stresses, utilizes severe
affective disturbance, profound autism and withdrawal from
reality, and/or formation of delusions or hallucinations.

Under psychoneurotic disorders "are those disturbances in which
'anxiety' is a chief characteristic, directly felt and expressed, or
automatically controlled by such defenses as depression, con-
version, dissociation, displacement, phobia formation, or repetitive
thoughts and acts." Interestingly enough, the closest that the manual comes to categories akin to "borderline" are the "schizoid
personality" and "paranoid personality," which are carried under
personality disorders. These "are characterized by developmental
defects or pathological trends, in the personality structure, with
minimal subjective anxiety, and little or no sense of distress"
(19).

In summarizing these categories for a basic psychiatric text
based on dynamic principles, English and Finch state that "if the
ego's attempts to deal with [infantile instinctual impulses] result
in the development of conflicts, of anxiety, inhibitions, or perversions of physiological rhythm, the result is called a neurosis
or psychophysiologic disorder. At times the entire struggle of the
ego to maintain psychic equilibrium is given up and the ego itself
begins to disintegrate, in which case the result is called a psychosis." It goes on to say that "the psychotic reaction is a much more
thoroughly and severely abnormal type of personality reaction
than is the psychoneurosis" with a loss of "reality-testing functions" (9).

In a discussion of current thinking on the terms "psychosis"
and "neurosis" Bowman and Rose review the historical development of the concepts. They state that "neurosis" was used first
by William Cullen "to designate a functional disease of the nervous

system," whereas "psychosis" was introduced by Feuchtersleben "to refer to the psychological manifestations of a mental disorder in contradistinction to the underlying physiological condition." There followed a parallel development of psychiatric nosology and classification by Kraepelin, on the one hand, and "an expansion of psychiatry to include the non-insane" on the other. The latter movement led to attempts to work out some purely psychological theory for understanding mental disorders and this "psychodynamic" approach was spearheaded by Freud and Meyer (2).

Freud states that "neurosis is the result of a conflict between the ego and its id, whereas psychosis is the analogous outcome of a similar disturbance in the relation between the ego and its environment [outer world]." He further states that the "factor of frustration" is "a common feature in the etiology both of the psychoneuroses and the psychoses." He then introduces the term "narcissistic psychoneuroses" for those diseases "founded on a conflict between ego and super-ego" (12). In a later expansion Freud describes two steps in the process, in each case an outcome of the continuing "struggle for power" of the id. In the neurosis this pressure leads to a symptom formation which causes a certain loss of reality, whereas in the psychosis a new reality is created (13). In speaking of paranoia he also introduces a quantitative factor involving the "degree of attention, or more correctly the measure of cathexis that these formations engage" (14). He uses the terms "neurotic mechanism" and "psychotic mechanism" in these papers, but their precise definitions were not clear to me. In his later writings he applied the term "neurosis" to all mental disorders not of toxic-organic origin. He subdivided these into transference and narcissistic neuroses and frequently used the term "psychosis" for those narcissistic neuroses in which there was a break with reality (2). Meyer developed the "psychobiological" system as the sum total of the interaction of multiple forces. It was divided into "major reactions," which included psychosis, and "minor reactions," which included neurosis (2).

The theories of these men separately or conjointly influenced the majority of later theoreticians. Fenichel feels that Freud conceived of schizophrenia * as being characterized by regression "to much earlier times than . . . any regression in neuroses, specifically, to the time when the ego first came into being." Fenichel feels that "the schizophrenic has regressed to narcissism; the schizophrenic has lost his objects; the schizophrenic has parted with reality; the schizophrenic's ego has broken down." He goes on to say that "many phenomena seem to indicate that a schizophrenia is something basically different from a neurosis; still they have many features in common. It remains to be learned whether the differences are due to difference in depth and severity of principally similar processes or whether neurosis and schizophrenia have an altogether different etiology . . ." (11). Pious takes issue with Fenichel and states, "[the essential process] is not so much [related] to regression as to a peculiar fluidity in object- and ego-libido." He goes on to say that "the psychotic process follows immediately on a traumatic experience and its nature is enigmatic; all observable manifestations in the patient are attempts at restitution" (22). Glover thinks in terms of "fixation" and states that psychoses are the result of the breakdown in the "auxiliary repression system" (15). Federn states that "every psychosis is a mental disease of the ego itself, while in neurosis only some functions of the ego are impaired." He further states that "in psychosis the main damage consists of the loss of cathexis of the ego boundaries. . . . In every case of neurosis, some ego boundaries are too much cathected" (10). Knight simply states that "neurotic mechanisms are different from psychotic mechanisms, and that psychosis is not simply a more severe degree of neurosis. However, it is quite possible for both psychotic and neurotic mechanisms to have developed in the same individual." He does not define these mechanisms precisely. He is critical of the criterion of "a break with reality" as the major diagnostic concept and also of diagnostic classification based exclusively on regression to stages of libidinal development (17). Zilboorg, along with other writers,

---

* It is, of course, technically imprecise to use "schizophrenia" and "psychosis" synonymously. They are, however, used more or less interchangeably in this section, inasmuch as they seem to be used rather generally in this way by various writers.

without defining neurosis or psychosis gives certain symptoms, such as ideas of reference and auditory hallucinations, as belonging to well-advanced schizophrenia (30). In concluding this discussion it is appropriate to return to Bowman and Rose, who feel that "even though attempts are made to interpret the diagnostic 'psychosis' and 'neurosis' according to various theoretical concepts of mental illness, there has never been established a precise and universally accepted definition of the terms. It remains as it began, an administrative distinction based upon rough descriptive differences in symptomatology." They refer to Janet and Cobb as espousing this viewpoint and recommend that because of the confusion both "psychosis" and "neurosis" be dropped as diagnostic terms (2).

My feeling is that this rather drastic measure seems somewhat impractical in view of the widespread usage of the terms, although the foregoing review documents the degree of confusion about them. An attempt to understand the "borderline" position in relation to these problems will be described below, after considering the group of cases under study.

Inasmuch as the impetus for this study arose from clinical work, the attempt to select and organize relevant case material was accomplished retrospectively. As has already been noted, traditionally the borderline concept suggests uncertainty on the part of the therapist, and the present study is in part an effort to clear my own confusion about a series of cases that I had encountered. Initially (and before I had reviewed the literature) I wrote down the names of patients seen during a two-year period who, I felt, might be called "borderline." This list totaled twenty-nine. In simplest terms, I chose those patients who, by their clinical appearance or reported behavior outside the psychiatric interview or both, gave some evidence of rather severe disturbance of functioning. More specifically, these were patients who had severe interpersonal difficulties involving withdrawal tendencies or paranoid thinking, severe "neurotic" symptoms that seemed more than just that, or definite "psychotic" symptoms such as delusions or disturbances in reality testing. All were patients who did not seem to fit well into either neurotic or psychotic classifications. After some thought (and some reading) I pruned this list to twenty.

Of the nine who were dropped, six seemed to me to display symptoms which could be explained satisfactorily as adolescent adjustment reactions, two were foreign students and I felt unqualified to assess with any accuracy their pathology, and one seemed more clearly neurotic on closer examination. I was satisfied that the remaining group belonged to the general borderline category, but because there was considerable variation within the group I felt that a subdivision could be made. After additional study it seemed possible to classify these cases into four groups, each with some internal homogeneity, and I did this with the hope that such a classification might lead to some clarification of the whole problem.

Prior to describing the subgroups a few general comments can be made about the study group. Because these cases were chosen retrospectively, no standardized approach existed other than that incidentally imposed by the usual clinic routine; consequently, available data for each patient varies somewhat. All did not have psychological testing, intake interviews were not always conducted, and no special schedule of questions was used in the intake interviews when they were done. Referrals came principally from the medical service and from various administrative personnel. Only two were self-referred, which is an unusually small number in comparison with over-all clinic referral statistics. The presenting complaints were variable, and in one instance the presenting complaint seemed inappropriate to the clinic and the patient applied twice before he was placed in therapy. Nine out of twenty presented themselves in a manner which was adjudged sufficiently acute by intake worker or medical personnel so that I was called to see them immediately. The remainder were seen in the normal course of clinic intake procedure.

As has been remarked, these patients were not subjected to any special or consistent processing; consequently, only seven of the twenty patients in the groups were given psychological tests. The testing, which consisted usually of Wechsler-Bellevue, Rorschach, and TAT, was done in five cases by Dr. Roy Schafer and in two by Dr. Ernst Prelinger. Actually the percentage of those tested is remarkably high in comparison with the clinic as a whole and is testimony to the confusing and disturbing nature of the impression presented by these patients. A survey of the reports does not reveal any striking agreement in detailed findings, although diagnostic impression was generally similar. A variety of attributes are noted, including distortions of body image, poor reality testing, depression, homoeroticism, thinking disorder, grandiose strivings, obsessional features, unreliable judgment, disruptions of intellectual efficiency and integration, paranoid trends, difficulties of interpersonal adaptation, withdrawal of emotion, autistic activity, pathological sexual concern, poor integration of affective responses, inadequate defense against primitive fantasy, fluidity of thought, and openness of consciousness to normally unconscious content. The range of I.Q. was from 115 to 131, with four individuals scoring over 15 points higher on the verbal than on the performance scale. Although there was some suggestion of intellectual impairment on the tests, in no case was the I.Q. estimated to be greatly lowered by a temporary pathological condition.

Of the subgroups, Group I consisted of five individuals. These were patients who manifested rather serious disability socially, internally, and, with one exception, academically, although all had rather high potentials. I have grouped these patients together because they were the most clinically disturbed over a long period, because they created crises (in fact, life was one continual crisis), because they had some awareness of their own desperation, and because there was considerable drive for aid from the clinic. These patients displayed a wide variety of serious symptoms including phobias, obsessions, eating disturbances, sexual disturbances, high anxiety, and severe regressive behavior. There were probably moments of "psychosis" in all, but these moments were so similar to the average functioning of the individual that they did not appear to constitute a "break." Of these patients three had psychological testing; in two instances the diagnostic impression was borderline psychosis, and in the other psychotic trends were noted. This group will be identified as the continual crisis group.

Group II consisted of six patients. In general, all of these patients had a rather distinct psychic crisis from which movement was relatively rapid toward some resolution. Four had perceptual distortions that can be described as ideas of depersonalization or estrangement. One had transitory but severe impairment of judgment, and one made a suicidal attempt. In each case there was a relatively rapid change in the intensity of these acute difficulties, sometimes even prior to being seen in therapy. One case should probably be considered a true psychosis, as the symptoms were more clearly defined and of longer duration, but there were certain aspects pertaining to the amount of ego preservation that suggested a diagnosis not far from borderline. In trying to describe my feeling about the course of these patients, I am tempted to use the phrase "sealing over," and it is perhaps significant that of this group only two showed any positive interest in therapy, one of whom was the patient who "sealed over" most slowly. Of this group three patients had psychological testing; one was diagnosed as a schizophrenic reaction which had not at that time led to any large-scale ego destruction or regression, one was considered to have psychotic trends, and one was called borderline psychotic. This group will be identified as the delimited crisis group.

Group III contained three individuals. In these cases there was an apparently classic psychotic symptom which was quite circumscribed. One patient had frank auditory hallucinations of the classical paranoid nature, one displayed a kind of delusional jealousy, and one showed more general but still circumscribed projections. In one sense this group had the best level of over-all functioning in college of the four groups and gave the impression of being less disturbed than the other groups, although the symptoms are almost the most bizarre. This group was extremely intelligent and intellectual and maintained very high academic functioning concomitant with their symptomatology, although academic failure had been the leading manifestation of a previous period of upset for one individual. This group will be identified as the isolated psychotic symptom group.

Group IV consisted of six cases who seemed to have as their main symptomatology a withdrawn quality that made the forming of peer relationships difficult. They appeared diffusely anxious, ineffectual, and constricted. They formed a group that is akin to the diagnostic category "schizoid." The pathology seemed relatively stable and chronic, and although it was of a severity that seriously impaired functioning, it did not seem alarming in the way that the symptoms of Group I seemed. Depression appeared to be a more significant component. One individual of this group was given psychological tests and was found to have depression and schizoid personality. This group will be identified as the schizoid group.

Needless to say, these groupings are not pure in any sense, and as most superficial classifications in psychiatry, they are basically descriptive. Many of the individuals had symptoms in common with members of other groups but the above seems to me a reasonable division. After forming these groups, I attempted to study them in the light of the foregoing remarks about the diagnosis and concept of the borderline state. This led to the conclusion that, in general, each group can be understood theoretically in the terms of one or another of the writers quoted but there does not seem to be a single conceptual system that covers all four groups. In the formal sense, the first group seems best to fulfill Knight's criteria in that more than one ego function was impaired in each case and I had the feeling that the ego was "laboring badly" at times (17). Descriptively this group had many of the characteristics delineated by Eisenstein, Schmideberg, and Stern (8, 24, 25). The second group seems somewhat different in the sense that the dysfunction was delimited in time and appeared to be a more severe disruption of a single ego function. This group seems more like the confusional syndromes presented by Carlson (5) and the benign psychotic episodes which were described by Wedge in terms of developmental crises (28). The third group fits into the description by Fenichel of a channelization of psychotic mechanisms into one "crazy" area (11) and is quite similar to the "paranoid conditions" described by Rapaport, Gill, and Schafer (23). Several authors suggest that anyone with an advanced "psychotic symptom" such as an hallucination or delusion should be called psychotic and, therefore, one could question the inclusion of this group at all. However, the individuals in this group really seemed less disorganized in their general function than others of the groups, and classification would depend on the theoretical concept of the word "psychotic." Classifying them as less than psychotic borrows from the Meyerian principle of diagnosis on the basis of involvement of the personality. The fourth group fits well into the preschizophrenia description of Rapaport except that it is not really clear in the cases chosen that the process is "pre" in the sense of progressing to schizophrenia (23). In some ways this group seems to display the most stable pathology and the most chronic.

My own attempt to explain all four groups in some systematic way is basically eclectic, but it borrows most heavily from concepts of Knight and Rangell. Knight states that one must make an "appraisal of the balance in each patient between the ego's defensive and adaptive measures on the one hand and the pathogenic instinctual and ego-disintegrating forces on the other . . ." (17). This underlines the fact that one must consider all parts of the psychic apparatus in any theoretical approach. It is my feeling, however, that the major area of deficiency is relative to ego functioning. If this is the case, then the different subgroups of the borderline group might be explained by presuming that the separate ego functions undergo partial and differential deficit, as Rangell suggests (20). It would appear that the continual crisis group had particular difficulty with the integrative function and adaptation; the delimited crisis group, fluctuating difficulty with reality testing; the isolated psychotic symptom group, gaps in the defensive system against primitive, unconscious impulses; and the schizoid group, difficulty with the establishment and maintenance of object relationships. Knight, in stressing evaluation of the total personality, suggests a kind of rough quantitative approach (17), and I feel that some such quantitative factor, not unlike Meyer's principle, is really basic to the concept of "borderline" (and probably to psychosis also) at the present stage of our knowledge. Thus the diagnosis of "borderline" may be made because several ego functions are impaired slightly or one ego function is impaired severely. In the continual crisis group there seems to have been limited impairment of more than one ego function while the delimited crisis group and the isolated psychotic symptom group had relatively severe impairment of one function. Presumably any degree of spread of deficit in the delimited crisis and isolated psychotic symptom groups, or an increase in the severity of the deficits in the continual crisis group would have led to the presentation of a clearly psychotic picture. It would be helpful to be able to assign numerical categories to these combinations, but unfortunately it is very difficult to measure such matters precisely and in the end the diagnosis may still be made because the patient is very sick but neither clearly psychotic nor classically neurotic.

Prior to discussing the problems of the management of this patient group, the setting, and in particular certain aspects thereof, must be described. First, all the individuals under discussion were students at Yale, some graduate and some undergraduate. There tended to be implicit, therefore, the assumption that one of the goals of the patient in seeking therapy was to further his functioning within the University, although of course it became clear in certain cases that this was impossible, inadvisable, or not really desired by the patient. Actually, a majority of the group did continue to function in college, and almost all achieved their immediate academic goals. It should be noted, however, that the ability to continue in college and thereby to make possible the achievement of such goals is not entirely controlled by either the patient or the therapist. The academic position of the student in many cases determines the amount of administrative pressure that the student will be under and consequently the amount and duration of temporary disability that can be tolerated. Thus a graduate student in the process of finishing his thesis may be able to be totally disabled for a given period of time and still manage to recover and finish on schedule, or at least finish without any disruption other than the time that was lost during disability. On the other hand, an undergraduate may find it difficult to suffer even brief total disability or any prolonged partial disability and remain in college. Of the individuals in the first group, for example, there were three graduate students and two undergraduates. The administration was remarkably tolerant of their derelictions in all cases, but unquestionably there were differential pressures. It seems quite clear that it would not have been possible to carry one of the undergraduates in therapy for any length of time if he had been in trouble academically. With the other undergraduate who was having academic difficulties there was a certain amount of communication from the Dean's Office concerning academic deficiencies and possible administrative measures necessary; whereas with the graduate students who were having at least as much, if not more, difficulty there was no official communication, although the students themselves were aware of their deficiencies and were conferring with their respective deans regularly.

Secondly, as has been explained elsewhere, the clinic is a free facility if the health fee has been paid (and it is compulsory for most students), and the student is in addition entitled to ten days of care in the medical infirmary without charge. This allowed considerable flexibility in arranging for extra appointments, short interviews, and brief stays in the infirmary. Although presumably one would never omit for financial reasons a measure that was indicated therapeutically, it made the execution of such measures considerably easier. The general practice of the clinic as outlined elsewhere is brief therapy on a once-a-week basis. My aim in all cases was to hold the line of once-a-week appointments because of the pressure of other clinic commitments, but it was possible to modify this policy when necessary, and particularly with the patients included in this study it frequently seemed indicated. Many of the extra appointments were brief ones, and one patient was carried for a period of time on a regular basis of one full hour and two brief visits a week. In only one instance was therapy conducted regularly with more than one full hour a week.

Thirdly, a discussion of the management must take into account my training and general therapeutic approach. Inasmuch as the treatment was psychotherapy, all interviews were conducted face-to-face. The major focus of the therapy was on the current situation with solution of immediate problems the goal rather than the resolution of basic personality conflicts. Thus, although it was possible to carry a patient in therapy for a long period of time, and this was frequently done, I was always willing to terminate if the patient felt sufficiently improved. Interpretations tended to stress current reactions and the realistic patient-therapist relationship rather than "transference" elements in the technical sense of the term. The orientation was basically dynamic and the approach nondirective. Within this framework my personal behavior as a therapist tends to be conservative, inactive, gentle, and permissive.

In dealing with the specific case groups, some modifications of the general approach were made empirically. With the continual crisis group, I was extremely supportive, not so much out of theoretical design but out of what seemed at the time like necessity. I gave extra appointments quite freely in all cases, sometimes on "emergency" request, sometimes on plan, although I was not above turning down a request for extra time. I gave relaxing medication or sleeping pills in four cases and used the infirmary as a temporary haven in three cases. I was rather permissive about lateness and missed appointments. I was very impressed by the degree of illness and I do not think that it was ever far from my mind that any one of these patients might need to be hospitalized. As has just been stated, I actually did place three in the infirmary at moments of extreme disability and at moments, I suppose, when I was not willing to endure the anxiety or accept the responsibility of having them in the community. In four out of five there were very limited financial resources, so that the idea of elective placement in a private institution was out of the question except possibly temporarily prior to disposition. I feel that I might have suggested this quite strongly if it had been possible. My therapeutic approach was quite low-pressure. I made some interpretations but never made any attempt to stress them if they did not seem acceptable. I was rather chary of emphasizing possible negative reactions to me, although from time to time I took up missed appointments and lateness. In each case continuance in college was an issue, although for somewhat different reasons. With three patients academic problems involving difficulty in completing work were basic issues, although all three had apparently done quite satisfactory work prior to their psychological difficulties. With three patients the chief issue was motivation for continued study. On these matters I tended to take the attitude that it was important to finish the work. I did this with some misgivings, for in all instances I felt that there might be some very good unconscious reasons for not wanting to complete the work and I was somewhat reluctant to align myself with what I suspected was a pressuring parent figure. I explained my position, however, with the statement that I wanted them to complete their work not for any abstract or moralistic reason but because they consciously appeared to want this. Whether this kind of statement was accepted as sincere and really avoided the parental position, I am not sure. It is of interest that in this group three have graduated, one has withdrawn in relatively orderly fashion to undertake more intensive therapy, and one has completed the year successfully. Another important factor in the handling of this group was the interest of the patients in therapy and the therapeutic relationship. In all the cases there was distinct pressure for increased contact during some portion of the therapeutic course, and only rather firm measures held the contact down to practical limits. With only one individual was there a period in which almost no interest in the relationship was displayed. No summary of the management of the continual crisis group can be complete without some mention of the fact that I think, unquestionably, the patients in this group were particularly interesting to me. Whether this was a response to their desire for contact with me or because, more simply, I found them attractive personally or psychologically is difficult to say. There were certainly times when I found them difficult or when I was discouraged to the point of desperation, but they never failed to hold my interest, and I am sure that I had such a considerable investment in the ultimate outcome that I made extra efforts at times.

The delimited crisis group was handled somewhat differently, mostly because their demands were considerably different. Four of these patients were actually seen first in an acute emergency situation during which they had gone to the infirmary in the middle of the night or had come to the attention of the medical personnel during the day and been referred for immediate attention. Two came through regular intake channels. Of the four who were seen in emergency, considerable time and attention was given at the outset because of the critical nature of the situation. This attention was, of course, focused on understanding the crisis, terminating it if possible, and arranging for some satisfactory disposition thereafter. As has been described, the infirmary is at best a temporary haven and active consideration of mental hospitalization or return home was necessary if the symptoms continued. Three of these patients emerged from the situation rather rapidly and showed little interest in further therapy, although they returned for follow-up interviews on request. Of these, two apparently recovered sufficiently so that they were able to complete the year without further known incident and one withdrew from college to seek a solution elsewhere. The fourth, who should perhaps be considered psychotic, was anxious for therapy and was seen regularly over a prolonged period. Of the two who came through regular channels, both seemed to have recovered from brief episodes with psychotic symptoms by the time they were seen in their first "therapy" interview. One decided not to continue therapy and the other wanted to continue to work on certain personality problems. The therapeutic approach in these six cases was rather diverse because of the varying length and conditions of therapy. In general, it was directed toward achieving some sort of rapport as a necessary preliminary to understanding more fully the circumstances leading to the acute decompensation, and to supporting the patient through the crisis.

The isolated psychotic symptom group was handled in much more orthodox fashion in regular once-a-week psychiatric interviews. All three patients came through routine channels, and all three had been seen by a prior therapist. The delusional symptoms were neither ignored nor stressed, but some attempt was made to investigate the feelings and events leading up to the appearance of the delusional symptom in order to understand the manner in which the symptom was being employed. Again, the emphasis was on current situations and feelings rather than on the developmental origin of difficulties. There was relatively little need in this group of additional supportive measures, although some direct reassurance was used.

With the schizoid group my major attempt was to establish some sort of relationship with the ultimate aim of increasing the patient's confidence in himself and his ability to handle interpersonal relationships. An attempt was made to focus on day-to-day events and feelings, but this sometimes failed because the patients were interested in discussing more intellectual attitudes. Actually, the results were so uniformly unsuccessful with this group that it is hard to present the program as purposeful, although in one case the establishment of a supportive, friendly, moderately exploratory attitude achieved apparently good results. In this instance the patient was seen for over a year, whereas the others were all seen for shorter periods and it is possible that the unsuccessful cases simply were not carried long enough.

In general, for all groups I feel that my therapeutic approach was in line with the principle that a real ego weakness existed. My efforts, then, in all cases were devoted to somehow strengthening the ego. For the achievement of this goal I think the most useful measures were reassurance, support, acceptance, and interest. Insight into developmental processes seemed of limited usefulness. I tended to point out feelings of low self-esteem, feelings of being criticized, and feelings of being different, rather than to stress the more dynamic aspects present in a situation. Although these interpretations might qualify as "insight," I think that this type of interpretation had a largely supportive and reassuring effect. I attempted to avoid exploratory remarks that might be interpreted as criticism. Thus, although I was aware that lateness and missed appointments might be an expression of hostile feeling toward me, I was quite permissive about irregularities and did not stress them during the hour because I had the feeling that taking them up would be understood as criticism. Although there were definite limits to my permissiveness—set partly by my preference, partly by theoretical considerations, and partly by practicality—there was relatively little attempt to analyze demands made by the patient. Furthermore, there was very little attempt to press interpretations against denial by the patient. Thus a kind of low-pressure therapeutic situation existed from the therapist's viewpoint, although the patient often exerted considerable pressure. Much of the patient pressure was to obtain advice, and this was almost never given. The exceptions were occasions when the situation verged on emergency and I felt some active, positive management was necessary. I made every effort to encourage the patient to remain in control of himself and I rather openly stated this aim even when I did not always feel great confidence in the patient's ability to do so.

In reviewing the literature on the management of similar cases, the experiences and thinking of a considerable number of therapists may be found. Many of these therapists are psychoanalysts and consequently much of the theoretical discussion of technique is concerned with modifications of classical psychoanalytic procedure, and most of the theoretical discussion of aims uses the psychoanalytic model. Knight feels that the therapy should attempt to strengthen ego controls over instinctual impulses, and he, therefore, discourages free association, which he feels causes invasion of the ego by autistic thinking with implicit breakdown of normal ego defenses. He also feels that "deep" interpretations are contraindicated and that an overpermissive attitude should be avoided. He stresses the necessity for gratification rather than frustration of needs within limits and warns against trying to undercut neurotic defenses. He feels that the therapist should attempt to maintain the patient's self-esteem, responsibility, and inner controls, and as an adjunct to individual therapy recommends the use of an open hospital. He feels that the patient may need more group support than outpatient therapy can provide but feels that an open hospital may be preferable to a closed hospital because the latter tends to take too many controls away from the individual who is fighting to maintain his autonomy (18). Stern feels that attempts should be made to remove "mystery, unapproachability, and taboo" from the therapist and recommends face-to-face therapy with emphasis on the reality aspects of the relationship rather than the transference (27). He feels that the patient should have the therapist's respect, sincere interest, protection, and support, all of which he feels were absent in the childhood experiences of these patients, and he feels that the therapist must be willing to accept at least at the outset a fair degree of dependent striving on the part of the patient (26). Schmideberg feels that the important factor is the "establishment of contact" and she feels that appearing as "nonprofessional as possible" is effective. She uses reassuring interpretations to reduce anxiety and often explains how observations were arrived at in order to reduce paranoid ideation. She avoids threats or disapproval and uses the patient's terminology wherever possible. The negative transference is analyzed to reduce anxiety and hostility, but when analyzing the positive transference care is taken not to devalue genuine feelings. She advises and helps in practical difficulties and does much work over the telephone. She talks to relatives when necessary as a support (24) and states that all these measures are used "to strengthen the ego" (21). Eisenstein feels that the therapist must assume an "active and benevolent role of parent . . . but must provide more than supportive or educational help." He states that the first therapeutic aim is the reduction of negative feelings and states that silences, questioning latenesses, and evading certain types of questions may engender mistrust. He focuses on the weak ego state with an attempt to reduce guilt and anxiety and attempts to bolster the ego by commendation and by "interpretation of the patient's adaptive difficulties and their origins in his history." He avoids interpretation of deeper emotionally charged material and attempts to foster re-repression through improvement in reality testing. He feels that discontinuous therapy is appropriate and recommends work with the family (8). Bychowski comes to generally similar conclusions and specifically recommends a careful dosage of interpretations (4). Wolberg feels that the therapist must "function in a role reminiscent of a parent figure" and be prepared for a long period of therapy. Interpretations should not be forced and the patient "should be allowed to 'control' the situation to a great extent" but with limitations on acting out. Questions about the therapist's life should be answered as one would answer a child rather than explored as resistance (29). Greenson feels that the therapist must be a model for identification and help the patient to achieve better reality testing (20). Robbins feels that the patient borrows ego strength from the therapist (20). Douglas feels that therapy should aim at relieving tensions but not "by removing the protective armoring of neurosis." He feels that one must give ego support and respond to dependency needs (7). Lipton stresses insight into the unconscious ego rather than insight into id mechanisms, which he feels may be dangerous (21). Federn feels that the aim of therapy is to prevent the breakthrough of unconscious material by supporting healthy parts of the ego and preserving a positive transference. He recommends cautious attempts to rectify falsifications not by criticism but by exploration, and states that one must respect and support defenses. He feels that the therapy of latent schizophrenia should last indefinitely (10). Pious, in speaking of an incipient psychosis that developed and receded during analysis in an individual with obsessive-compulsive symptoms, says that the therapist must aim to retain the positive feeling of the patient and must make himself accessible and visible to the patient (22). Zilboorg feels that a preliminary period is necessary "for ego-testing and . . . observation of libido orientation," after which "regular analysis . . . is always indicated. During the preliminary period improvisations are the rule . . . and the treatment is an art" (20). He feels that "the problem is that of affective re-integration" (30). Gitelson also feels that "one should move toward the goal of eventual psychoanalysis" and states that in this endeavor it may be necessary to establish parameters. He feels that "one should try . . . to introduce as few parameters as possible and yet be ready to introduce as many as may be necessary" (20). Fleischmann feels that more parameters are necessary when the patient is closer to psychosis (21). Rangell, however, warns against throwing out "the analytic attitude" too readily, for he feels that one must distinguish between deviations in behavior, such as free association, expected from the patient and what is called for from the therapist in abandoning the neutral therapeutic position (21).

A comparison of the general principles of management attempted by me and the excerpts from the literature makes it evident that my more or less impromptu handling of the college group is in general agreement with the experience of some others in handling similar patients in various settings. The general aim of therapy was strengthening the ego, and to this end various measures were taken involving additional support when necessary, avoidance of criticism, encouragement of patient autonomy, a limited type of insight, and indirect reassurance. Many of the technical suggestions in regard to therapy with borderline patients in the literature were modifications of classical psychoanalysis. Frequently these modifications led to practices which are more or less routine in psychotherapy. Thus, face-to-face interviewing, modified free association, and stress on the reality aspects of the patient-therapist relationship rather than the transference were employed automatically by me in the normal procedure of clinic work and did not represent a change from therapy with patients in nonborderline categories. Perhaps the greatest difference between my approach and that of others was my unwillingness to give advice and assume a really parental role. I departed from the nondirective psychotherapeutic position only reluctantly, although there were times when it seemed inescapable. In the use of adjuncts to individual therapy, such as an open hospital, available facilities were limited, but at times the infirmary was used as a somewhat comparable installation. I contacted the family only in emergency situations, but the college community provided a kind of group support which was unquestionably helpful in sustaining the patient during crises. The presence of roommates, counselors, and faculty advisers made it possible for the patient to gain support between therapeutic hours, and this was frequently used. Furthermore, the necessity for dealing with studies, while sometimes a stress, was probably often a factor in allowing the patient's ego to maintain a hold on reality.

No study of such a group probably should be concluded without a brief look at the results. As with all psychotherapeutic results, it is difficult to describe them quantitatively and it is particularly difficult to evaluate the role played by the therapy. In all the cases of the continual crisis group I feel that the psychotherapy played an important part in aiding the student during his stay at college. On the other hand, I do not feel that the therapy was definitive in any case and I would be surprised to hear that the individuals had adjusted smoothly without further therapy. As has already been stated, three graduated, one withdrew at the end of the year and one will continue in college. I cannot say whether their successful completion of work was directly attributable to the therapy, but I would estimate that the therapy played a significant part in improving their total adjustment. With the delimited crisis group it is much harder to estimate the significance of the therapy. Four are continuing college with some sort of adjustment that seems to be fairly satisfactory to them, one has withdrawn, and one is returning after a period of more intensive therapy. Two of the first four have been seen again during similar brief episodes. About the most that one can say for this group is that the therapeutic experience may have been helpful in weathering a period of acute crisis, although two individuals seem to have entirely recovered from the crisis prior to therapy. With the isolated psychotic symptom group all three have graduated successfully and two stated quite definitely that they had found psychotherapy helpful. There was a distinct diminution of symptoms for these two but with the third the case was not so clear. In the schizoid group the over-all results were by all odds the most equivocal. One individual appeared to respond quite well and stated that the therapy had been very helpful. Two patients stated that they felt that the therapy had been of no aid and I agree. One individual was seen discontinuously over a period of three years with some improvement but with no feeling on my part that his problems had been satisfactorily solved. One patient was seen for a year and then withdrew to seek more intensive therapy, and it is the impression of the psychiatrist to whom he was referred that the therapy with me acted as an essential preliminary, although it was my impression at the time of referral that he had not found the experience particularly rewarding. One individual was seen for a term with uncertain results. He did not feel that much had been accomplished and neither did I, but there was some improvement during the term in his grades, which had been a major area of malfunction. In summary, I would say that approximately eight out of fifteen who were in therapy for more than a month showed some improvement: in their feeling about themselves, in their sense of well-being, in their functioning, or in their symptomatology. This is roughly the same percentage of improvement that I have estimated for my case load as a whole over the same period. For those who were seen for less than a month, four out of five improved, but the function of the therapy in relation to this improvement is probably of a rather different nature, as already described. It is hard to say whether therapy was ever detrimental, although I have some feeling that it may have been in one case. No comparison of my results with those of others is possible because attempts at quantitative evaluation were absent from the literature. There were accounts of successful cases, and it was implied that improvement was quite common, but there is no way of estimating percentages.

In conclusion, it seems relatively clear that the "borderline" patient as described is not a rare occurrence in the college community. Furthermore, and in view of this, it would seem reasonable that a well-established college mental hygiene clinic should be prepared to deal with individuals who present this clinical picture. My experience suggests that limited therapeutic success and partial recovery without leaving the college setting is by no means unlikely. While little can be adduced from the current study about the over-all prognosis for life adjustment or the effect of psychotherapeutic intervention at this time on this adjustment, two factors imply at least a possible importance of such action. First, and generally, the college student is in a transitional period during which some important and perhaps final decisions are in the process of being forged. Support and help at this period might conceivably make the difference between, on the one hand, a more or less satisfactory resolution of the inevitable conflicts and, on the other, disorganization in the face of the inevitable stresses and uncertainties. Secondly, and more specifically, if the major over-all problem of the borderline state is a problem of ego weakness, as seems most probable, successful completion of the prestigeful college course may do much to strengthen the individual's general adaptive abilities, in contrast to a failure which may have consequences far beyond the "reality" factors involved in not finishing college.

In the foregoing I have attempted to describe measures which may be useful in the course of psychotherapeutic intervention. Whether my tentative subclassification of the patients in the borderline group illuminates in any way either therapy or prognosis is debatable. My lack of success with the fourth group suggests either the need for a new approach or a recognition of the length of time necessary for improvement in these cases. This should probably be a subject for further consideration, as should exploration of family and developmental patterns typical of the group in an attempt to clarify psychodynamic and etiologic factors. The present study as a whole, however, suggests that an attitude of tempered optimism is not unreasonable providing one has considerable time available for meeting the needs that may arise.

REFERENCES

1. Axel, M., Ten borderline cases, *Psychiatric Quarterly, 29:*555. 1955.

2. Bowman, K. M., and Rose, M., A criticism of the terms "psychosis," "psychoneurosis" and "neurosis," *American Journal of Psychiatry, 108:*161. 1952.

3. Bychowski, G., The preschizophrenic ego, *Psychoanalytic Quarterly, 16:*225. 1947.

4. ———— Therapy of the weak ego, *American Journal of Psychotherapy, 4:*407. 1950.

5. Carlson, H. B., Characteristics of an acute confusional state in college students, *American Journal of Psychiatry, 114:*900. 1958.

6. Clark, L. P., Some practical remarks upon the use of modified psychoanalysis in the treatment of borderline neuroses and psychoses, *Psychoanalytic Review, 6:*306. 1919.

7. Douglas, D. B., Jr., Management of borderline schizophrenia, *American Journal of Psychotherapy, 6:*245. 1952.

8. Eisenstein, V. W., Differential psychotherapy of borderline states, *Psychiatric Quarterly, 25:*379. 1951.

9. English, O. S., and Finch, S. M., *Introduction to Psychiatry*, New York, Norton, 1954.

10. Federn, P., Principles of psychotherapy in latent schizophrenia, *American Journal of Psychotherapy, 1*:129. 1947.

11. Fenichel, O., *The Psychoanalytic Theory of Neurosis*, New York, Norton, 1945.

12. Freud, S., Neurosis and psychosis, in *Collected Papers* (London, Hogarth, 1946), *2*, 250.

13. ——— Loss of reality in neurosis and psychosis, in *Collected Papers, 2, 277.*

14. ——— Certain neurotic mechanisms in jealousy, paranoia, and homosexuality, in *Collected Papers, 2, 232.*

15. Glover, E., A psychoanalytic approach to classification of mental diseases, *Journal of Mental Science, 78*:819. 1932.

16. Hoch, P., and Polatin, P., Pseudoneurotic forms of schizophrenia, *Psychiatric Quarterly, 23*:248. 1949.

17. Knight, R. P., Borderline states, in *Psychoanalytic Psychiatry and Psychology*, New York, International Universities Press, 1954.

18. ——— Management and psychotherapy of the borderline schizophrenic patient, in *Psychoanalytic Psychiatry and Psychology*, New York, International Universities Press, 1954.

19. *Mental Disorders: Diagnostic and Statistical Manual*, American Psychiatric Association, 1952.

20. Panel Report: the borderline case (Scientific Proceedings of the American Psychoanalytic Association, May 1954), *Journal of the American Psychoanalytic Association, 3*:285. 1955.

21. Panel Report: the borderline case (Scientific Proceedings of the American Psychoanalytic Association, December 1955), *Journal of the American Psychoanalytic Association, 4*:550. 1956.

22. Pious, W. L., Obsessive-compulsive symptoms in an incipient schizophrenic, *Psychoanalytic Quarterly, 19*:327. 1950.

23. Rapaport, D.; Gill, M.; and Schafer, R., *Diagnostic Psychological Testing* (New York, Yearbook Publishers, 1945), Vol. *1.*

24. Schmideberg, M., The treatment of psychopaths and borderline patients, *American Journal of Psychotherapy, 1*:1. 1947.

25. Stern, A., Psychoanalytic investigation of and therapy in the borderline group of neuroses, *Psychoanalytic Quarterly, 7*:467. 1938.

26. ———Psychoanalytic therapy in borderline neuroses, *Psychoanalytic Quarterly, 14*:190. 1945.

27. ——— Transference in borderline neuroses, *Psychoanalytic Quarterly, 17*:527. 1948.

28. Wedge, B. M., personal communication.

29. Wolberg, A. R., The "borderline patient," *American Journal of Psychotherapy, 6:*694. 1952.

30. Zilboorg, G., Ambulatory schizophrenia, *Psychiatry, 4:*149. 1941.

31. ———The problem of ambulatory schizophrenics, *American Journal of Psychiatry, 113:*519. 1956.

CHAPTER 11

Fear of Homosexuality in College Students

BY HENRY HARPER HART

The author makes use of case comparison methods to show that a major common factor in students sharing a common presenting symptom is a relative failure of integrative mechanisms. He suggests that this ego weakness results from growing up in an atmosphere of parental discord. While final outcome is not the issue ·of this exposition it seems implicit that a variety of integrative solutions are open to such students.

THE TERM acute homosexual panic introduced by Kempf in 1920 (2), has been in general psychiatric usage ever since, although not much further study of the phenomenon has been made. The commonness of the fear of homosexuality among college students, and our growing knowledge of the ego and its defenses against anxiety, makes further evaluation of this problem of timely importance, particularly since the symptom has so often been the prelude in an adolescent to a psychotic breakdown.

Kempf first defined homosexual panic as "due to the pressure of uncontrollable perverse sexual cravings" which threaten to overcome the ego. "Weakness of the ego is usually due to fatigue, debilitating fevers, loss of love object, misfortune, homesickness, and the seductive pressure of some superior and erotic companions."

Karpman (3) in 1943 declared that "it is latent homosexuality that is pressing to the surface for open expression, but is held in check by the dictates of the super-ego, with its sense of guilt. Finding himself between these two conflicting trends which he is unable to reconcile satisfactorily, the patient is thrown into an acute conflict of which the panic is the clinical expression, and preoccupation with paraphilia, the mental content."

Kempf and Karpman see the acute homosexual panic as essentially an ego squeezed between id and super-ego. Why certain egos only are thus threatened is not explained. Bychowski's article

"The Ego in Homosexuals" (1), while not dealing with homosexual panic, reveals many factors making the homosexual ego weak and which can be found in many adolescents in whom the panic can denote a shattering ego disorganization.

A number of questions should be answered to clarify our confusion on this subject. First, is the fear of homosexuality in the degree of its intensity proportional to weakness of ego structure? Does such fear presage an ultimate career of homosexuality? Does overt homosexuality increase or diminish this panic? If homosexuality is a defense against fear of castration, why does it provoke it? Can we speak with equal validity of heterosexual panic?

Many psychiatrists long for a statistical survey of Kinsey proportions on such problems and will rest content only when they can read something like this—"Of 10,000 university undergraduates between eighteen and twenty, 20 per cent admitted a fear of homosexuality, while only 10 per cent admitted overt homosexual experience, and of these only 500 subsequently became psychotic," etc. With our present guilt, concealment, repression, and fear of social rejection, how much validity could be found in such percentages? Psychoanalysts well know that many patients will often reveal after a year or two of analysis a sexual trauma which they emphatically denied at the beginning. There is no valid statistic of the unconscious. Yet it is only by allowing the repressed polymorph perverse sexual cravings to gradually come to consciousness that we can estimate their dynamic importance in the character of the individual. The denial of such cravings is notoriously poor evidence of their nonexistence, since emphatic denial often precedes reluctant admission. So we are forced back to the painstaking, time-consuming study of only a few cases, recognizing full well that a small number of cases thoroughly studied cannot pretend to establish universal factors.

With these facts in mind I present the following six cases selected entirely on the basis of the amount of material available on them. I have excluded many cases of students who having had homosexual experience wanted intensive psychotherapy to transform them into normal heterosexuals, although this group would numerically equal if not exceed the panic-stricken group.

CASE A. This timid, small, unprepossessing, 20-year-old junior, seen twenty times by the department and subsequently over a period of seven years in intermittent psychotherapy, came for treatment with feelings of depression, thoughts of suicide, spells of weeping, and inability to concentrate consequent to the discovery of mutual erotic excitement in a roommate who had shared his room both at prep school and at college. They solemnly swore "not to pursue this meaningless kind of experience which was a waste of time but would fight it out together." When the patient discovered this roommate engaged in mutual masturbation with a third fellow, he was "greatly shocked and insisted on a showdown." He disclaimed any homosexual interest before this event, even though he had slept with an only brother four years older. The latter talked to him about an actual homosexual experience which he had at college and which the brother thought had impaired his marital satisfaction. Although *A* experienced erotic excitement in the caressing of girls, his severe acne which scarred his face and back caused him to feel no girl would want him. When some did, he became frightened. On a bicycle trip to Europe away from his overprotective, infantile mother he had heterosexual opportunities enough but never dared avail himself of them.

Although fear of homosexuality appeared the precipitating factor in his initial depression and release from college, many other ego-weakening factors so well described by Bychowski in the homosexual ego were found; for example, infantile ego states in which he would whimper inarticulately like a scared little boy who wanted to be both nasty and caressed lovingly at the same time. He would identify with the person he clung to in his panic, such as his mother—herself an infantile, confused, incoherent person—but his maturer self rejected her. He felt his businesslike, matter-of-fact, successful, and practical father was hostile, insensitive, and materialistic. These subsequently were seen to be largely projections of his own oedipal needs, but like his brother the patient strove to defy, despise, and disappoint his father by eschewing his father's "middle class, Jewish values," by failing in medical school and threatening to enter the mother church while economically dependent on father. Concealed beneath the defiance was a passive wish to be loved and caressed by the father who whenever his son took a plunge into his recurrent suicidal depressions rushed by plane or car to rescue him. *A* cherished for himself the ascetic, self-denying career of Albert Schweitzer or that of a Trappist monk because American materialism meant to him his parent's Bronxlike values.

As the years went by this patient learned to support himself with masochistic frugality teaching in an Indian reservation, though by twenty-eight years of age he had not been able to consummate a physical relation with a girl which he rationalized on the basis of its immorality. His search for peace in a Catholic monastery seemed to be a sublimated substitute for mother, whom he despised, and his return to the therapist as a search for father-identification to counterbalance it, although he was mortified to find that monasteries demanded higher standards of mental health before encouraging such retreat.

The deepest injury to his ego was the hostile identification with the helpless and overprotective mother, who gave him warmth and nearness in infancy and yet who was inwardly hated by him and in his suicidal moods was the internal object to be destroyed. Thus his homosexual yearning in earlier adolescence which had provoked the panic at college expressed the regressive need for and identification with the hated mother, when adult masculine responsibilities were being placed on him. Neither parent had prepared him for this, so he revenged himself upon them by failure and breakdown. Whenever he was able to express open hate and anger, his depression would lift and his work would improve. Thus the fear of homosexuality beginning at twenty became rapidly lost in the onrush of more serious symptoms and deeper conflicts associated with recurrent depressions of a Manic Depressive Psychosis. It did not presage either homosexuality or complete ego disintegration but a deeper fixation to the mother with a desire to get rid of her, which seems to be at work in many homosexuals.

CASE B. A nineteen-year-old, rather awkward, confused freshman, an only child, came to the clinic because of failure to concentrate on his studies, marked self-consciousness, and the fixed obsession that he was a homosexual. His speech was hesitant, often blocked, and punctuated with "I don't know." He considered himself skinny, ugly, jerky, too unattractive for girls, and too unsophisticated to be socially popular, yet he demanded of himself that he be socially charming, athletically strong, and a competent student at the same time.

His obsessive fear of homosexuality developed when a homosexual actually made a sexual advance to him when he was renting
a room for piano practice. He never had any overt homosexual
experience nor any sexual excitement with males. His masturbation fantasies and sexual dreams all had heterosexual content.
There was nothing girlish in his bearing or mannerisms, which
were really those of an awkward adolescent male. He rejected himself with a contempt that expressed overexpectation of himself.
Thus in order to achieve independent finger movement on the
piano, he would practice as much as seven hours daily. Like case
A there was an unconscious identification with his mother, who
was a dainty, infantile, naive, but artistic lady out of the nine-
teenth century, largely ignored by her creative, successful, but
absent-minded husband. Their only child, in the absence of much
social life, had become the object of disproportionate attention,
concern, and protection, which he tried to counteract by trying to
talk and act tough like the Italian boys in the school. Indeed, the
use of good English diction and the expression of his extremely
capable artistic gifts were both rejected by him as "sissy." Just as
in case *A* the emotional distance between the parents seemed to
reflect itself in the gap of the boy's ego fabric. Logical thinking
required much effort, apparently, because autistic thinking had
been only too absorbing. He despised both his parents as he
despised himself and that which he despised in himself was apparently his regressive infantile need to be dependent on them.

He avoided girls of charm and intelligence because he could
not impress them. In their presence, compared to the more so-
phisticated fellows from the prep schools, he appeared awkward,
boorish, inarticulate. With less intelligent girls of a lower social
class he felt more at ease. He professed no guilt or self-depreciation
over masturbation, considering this the only practical sexual out-
let available to him, and when in Paris he had sexual contact with
a prostitute; but in general he seemed contented with passionate
petting short of penetration.

In *B*'s case the fear of homosexuality was related not to any
deep homosexual trend but to something more profoundly dis-
organizing and which bordered on the schizophrenic. When accepted by another college where scholastic standards were high,
he developed panic, not over homosexuality but over inability to

think clearly. As in *A* there was a very immature ego unable to accept the burdens of independent thought, self-support, hetero-sexual gratification, and social responsibility. He returned not to a whimpering, helpless little boy like *A* but to a confused, in-articulate, slow-thinking, awkward boy, who found work of a physical outdoor nature less disturbing to his narcissistic equi-librium.

Both *A* and *B* were boys whose parents had little in common and were actually indifferent to one another. Both boys failed to identify with the father, who preferred work to the companionship of the overprotective, infantile mothers. Lack of interest on the part of the father threw both boys into the mothers' zone of in-fluence. Both were ambivalent to all male authority even when they sought to emulate father-substitutes, probably as a defense against the wish to be loved passively. Both despised the parts of themselves they recognized as parts of their mothers. Both were extremely perfectionistic and overdemanding of themselves; hence it is not surprising that their feeling of self was depreciatory. Neither *A* nor *B* had been trained by the parents to adjust grace-fully to complicated social demands of leadership. Both despised themselves for a showing-off tendency and a feeling of sham. Both found work of a less socially taxing character their best support for their self-esteem and tended to identify themselves with the underdog. The fear of homosexuality was developed in the all-male university environment under the influence of both internal and external barriers to heterosexuality, which an exaggerated per-fectionism did nothing to dissolve.

CASE C. This twenty-one-year-old senior was seen twenty-nine times in the clinic complaining of a "terrible bodily feeling, like a general body tension," and manifested extreme restlessness, talka-tiveness, irritability, and fear of homosexuality, and of going in-sane, and was suspicious of his remarks being recorded. Given to excessive fantasy, he talked of living in a dual world; and lacking social confidence, he drank to excess to give himself the feeling of belonging. His thinking was rapid but jumbled, rather flighty and shallow. Inappropriate laughter and feelings of suspicion would occur suddenly. In his studies he was failing to concentrate and could not sleep without drinking whiskey.

Since permitting, under the influence of alcohol, a homosexual classmate to caress him physically, he developed a fear of becoming a homosexual. About all his sexual experience he was very evasive and full of shame and tension, regarding masturbation as both immoral and disgusting and leading to insanity. He made the odd remark "that discussing sex was against my system." Like *A* he had come to college and roomed with a friend who had been his roommate at prep school and then had quarreled with him. It was after this that he turned to the smart, alcoholic, social-climbing set. His value system was chaotic and took on the cast of those around him. He confessed he felt he never "belonged" even at prep school. He compensated for this by extensive day-dreaming of being a captain of industry. He felt himself in childhood skinny and unattractive but at college he derived considerable prestige as a good squash and tennis player and was physically quite well built and muscular.

At the age of five his parents began divorce proceedings. His father had a psychosis of a paranoidal nature in which he projected his own infidelities upon his wife. There must have been a strong homosexual trend in the father who seemed to like to take the little boy to bed with him and hold him in his arms. The boy still called him Daddy, and the father did not scruple to drink heavily with his son, enjoining him to avoid psychiatrists, and running down the boy's mother. He wanted his son to assist him in his industry, where he was apparently quite successful. This the patient preferred to visiting his mother, who lived with his sister and grandmother, where on his visits he was pampered and waited on. With neither of his parents was this student on terms of sufficient intimacy to discuss frankly his own personal problems.

In the course of treatment, *C* revealed that he had numerous incestuous dreams about his sister, four years younger, which seemed to him hideously immoral and abnormal. He could not be honest with himself even though he admitted he was a phony, associating with phonies; but they seemed to need him as he needed them. His snobbishness, sham, and strikingly illogical thinking revealed the dearth of parental harmony and understanding, since from neither could he get anything but the most superficial insight into adolescence and the most superficial values.

Like *A* and *B* he showed not only a conflict of identification but an identification with conflict, in that his shaky integration dated from the separation of his parents. While *A* compensated for his lack of self-esteem by philosophic idealism, and *B* compensated by trying to be tough, *C* compensated by athletic prowess. Psychotherapy and the use of thorazine enabled him to reach enough stability to graduate and to be chosen to represent his college in an intercollegiate tennis tournament, but the profoundly self-destructive alcoholism, extravagance, and procrastination had in it the meaning of revenge against his parents, for having abandoned him. His fear of homosexuality abated, but his shaky ego integration makes it probable that this lad will have a serious breakdown later on in life.

CASE D. This student, age twenty-one, was an effeminate architectural student of Jewish background, with an affected Oxford accent, who was seen twenty-tix times in the clinic and diagnosed psychoneurosis, mixed type. His chief complaints were severe anxiety approaching panic, tremulousness, fear of sexual contact with girls, blinking of the eyes, twitching of the cheeks, fear of being attracted to the male body, and feeling of his own body being inadequate and "all messed up inside." He told his story with tears in his eyes and the precipitating event of his anxiety was his first exposure to homosexuality in a Bohemian group of students. He feared that he did not respond to his girl friend as he should and that he might be a homosexual. The fear that she might want him to sleep with her frightened him, perhaps because of the fear of impotence. He was concerned over friction in his family, which he visited weekly, even though he "had nothing in common with them." Like *A, B,* and *C* he felt a certain falsity or phony quality in his narcissistic equilibrium. He felt inferior to his athletic brother, who, however, did not have the patient's artistic or intellectual ability.

D's father was a poorly educated, passive little shopkeeper who rebelled in violent outbursts of wrath against the domination of his wife and her two unmarried sisters, a matriarchal trio who compensated for their inferior intelligence by depreciating others. They interfered with *D*'s independence and dating by the threat of withdrawal of money if he did not submit.

D became involved in a sexual affair with a very masculine girl in his class who had been the mistress of an older father-figure. His first sexual intercourse with her reassured his masculinity only temporarily, for he broke it off to become preoccupied with homosexuality, particularly as the matriarchy at home tried to make him more submissive. His mother consistently strove to keep him from identifying with the father. After twenty-six interviews his anxiety was considerably reduced and he traveled abroad for a year. Subtle changes, identification, and the spirit of equality entered his feelings toward his father which his mother unconsciously perceived and sought to destroy.

Conflict of identification occurred therefore in *D* as in *A, B,* and *C*. In neither father nor mother could he find a model of psychic integrity. Fear of castration at the hands of both, the butcher and the purser, induced passive, submissive dependence, in turn intensifying the castration fear. But his ego was better integrated than that of the first three patients and his thinking more coherent and logical. He could free himself from his maternal super-ego pressure by defying mother and her money. His work gave him increasing security. *D* differed from the three foregoing patients in that the maternal figure played a more dominating role. Whatever identification he could form with her would strengthen his capacity for defiance and assertion. With *A* and *B* identifying with the infantile maternal ego, the regressive tendency was strengthened.

CASE E. This polite but somewhat formal and compulsive senior of twenty came to the clinic because he had a fear that he was a homosexual. In the presence of girls he was self-conscious, ill at ease, and overintellectual. He confessed that he had no sexual interest in women and that all his sexual fantasies and excitement were about men. The male body seemed more attractive to him and boys who were "elfish" attracted him sexually. Yet he had never had any homosexual experience. Reading about the homosexual orgies of delinquent youths excited him into masturbation with a fantasy of inserting his penis between the legs of his partner. However, his first sexual arousal had been with his sister when he was five years of age when he became aware of their anatomical differences. At nine years of age he proposed intercourse with his sister, i.e. rubbing their genitals together, but her refusal made him feel guilty and he feared she would report the matter to their parents. At ten he was impressed by the fact that his sister had only a slit. At twelve he began masturbating with great guilt, and despite the fact that his mother was an executive social worker of a child welfare agency, he had never been able to discuss sexual anatomy and physiology or psychology with her or his father. His mother made the decisions in the family, and the patient almost never mentioned his father. However, despite his mother's opposition the patient at sixteen had independence enough to go to a university distant from New York City. His notion of women was confused, illogical, and contradictory. They were delicate pieces of Dresden china, yet they were entitled to govern men. He did not know what girls expected of a man, and when they said no he took this as final rather than introductory.

Actually, considering his family background, he was amazingly and defensively ignorant of male and female anatomy, the process of conception and contraception, pregnancy, childbirth, and menstruation. His treatment became a course in sex education in which one by one of his distorted notions were explored and relinquished. The basis of his homosexual preoccupation seemed to be rooted in the feeling that heterosexuality was more taboo, inaccessible, less pleasant, and liable to lead to the immediate imprisonment of marriage, as well as fraught with social and biological responsibility which he sought to avoid. Fear of the vagina and of castration led to the sexual pleasure in the object with a penis, which underlay his feeling that the male body was more beautiful than the female. However, when male and female genitals were compared in charts, he decided that neither was lovely. Gradually, with weekly interviews over six months, it was possible to relieve his mind of his fear of the female. His week ends with his girl friend became more enjoyable as he was able to be freer and franker in their discussion about sex. He began to feel that the female body was actually more beautiful than the male and his sexual arousal in petting was intense and reassuring. When treatment was discontinued, he had three girl friends and felt quite happy socially. He said he had had no homosexual dreams for six months.

This boy showed a striking contrast to the previous four cases in that he was so much better integrated and the conflict had not reached into the depths of his ego. There was little apparent conflict of identification. There was no incoherence of thought, no intense panic, no fear of insanity. At the threshold of sexual life

E had the feeling that homosexuality was less threatening than heterosexuality. Probably the phallic-dominating, directing mother made this possible, being an object of respect rather than sexual arousal. Cases *D* and *E,* accustomed to maternal domination, enjoyed at least the better ego organization that comes from directive interest as compared with absence or indifference. A strong maternal super-ego may intensify the homosexual's tendency without producing ego weakness.

Case F. A nineteen-year-old sophomore, one of two brothers from a Texan family of moderate income, became depressed—unable to concentrate or to take his examinations—and finally confessed his struggle against homosexuality to the psychiatrist. When he was one year old his father divorced his mother "because she was bad" and the boy never saw her again. He was raised by a stepmother who wanted him to be a sensitive artist, in contrast to his more masculine brother, the favorite of the father. It seems probable that the father regarded the patient as morally and sexually weak like his mother, whom he despised. At fourteen the boy was approached by a sailor while working at a hotel and had a homosexual affair which father discovered. Three years later another homosexual affair lasting three months with a big athletic type of his own age was discovered by father. At eighteen when he entered college he was involved in an accident in which his boy friend, at whose side he had been sitting, was killed while the patient was saved by having changed his seat. He felt guilty over this boy's death because he had persuaded him to return to college against his will. His panic was sufficient to make him fear insanity, but he did not consult the department until a dormitory prank in which he had been hypnotized by a classmate caused him to become violent, destructive, and unable to concentrate. Apparently the hypnosis revived passive homosexual urges he had striven to suppress. At a religious meeting he got excited and talked about the H-bomb and the end of civilization.

He left college on advice, took a job in a garage, but afterward entered the army and was caught in another homosexual relationship and was discharged. He returned to college to graduate, reconciled to both his homosexuality and its risks. The period of psychiatric observation consisted of thirteen interviews, and during this time he wrote much poetry, apparently in the attempt to sublimate his homosexuality, but the poetry was abandoned on entering the army and into contact again with male bodies. Reference to emptiness, castration, chaos, and surrender suggest that the final decision to become a homosexual involved much painful conflict.

Examination of the panic here seems to point to an identification with the weak, promiscuous, or "bad mother," rejected by the father, which was not at first acceptable to the boy's ego. Presumably, at the time of the airplane crash he was trying to free himself from homosexual bonds. The psychiatrist who saw him felt that he was being threatened by a band of experienced homosexuals who were subjecting him to more perversions than he could accept. In his homosexuality he seemed to be asking for the love of the father and at the same time to be punishing father for his rejection of him. Likewise, by discarding women altogether he revenged himself against the mother who abandoned him in infancy. Even with the psychiatrist he could not be honest and like many college homosexuals he preserved the common triad of deceit, perversion, and precious attitude toward English literature.

A complete study of *F* would bring us into the dynamics of homosexuality itself; this is not our task, which is, rather, the significance of the fear of homosexuality. Apparently when *F*'s fear of social rejection, guilt, and castration anxiety were reduced, he felt accepted by his kind and he escaped a psychosis by a perversion, a solution that would have horrified *A* and *B* with their idealistic, conscientious, moralistic super-ego structure. The super-ego's irrational demands were likewise decisive in *C*, who could not even accept masturbation comfortably. In the cases *D* and *E*, where the mother was of directive importance, there seemed to be a stronger fabric of ego integration, whereas in *A*, *B*, *C*, and *F*, where the father was distant and dominant, there was a passive wish to be loved rather than an identification with his masculine aggression. Thus the nature of the super-ego and the identifications that compose it seem to be decisive as to the nearness to psychotic disintegration the ego feels. Why the passive need for father's love prevailed over identification with the strong father is not clear, unless furthered by identification with the weak, passive mother made passivity more rewarding than independence and aggression. Certainly in all the above six cases the paternal super-ego elements and identification were less notable than the maternal. Why was the capacity to identify with the mother rather than with the father so consistent in all these cases? Could it have been that the father in none of these cases played a close, companionate, understanding role?

What makes homosexual panic a concept of questionable dynamic validity is the fact that homosexuality often, as in case *F*, relieves anxiety. The intensity of the panic in cases *B* and *C* seemed to depend not on the intensity of an inverted desire but upon the weakness of the ego and its integrative capacity to master the sexual urge in any of its manifestations. There is nothing to indicate in these six young men that sex was ever comfortably talked of or understood by the parents, nor did they have any consistent, logical philosophy about sex. The prompt response of *D* and *E* to the exploration of sexual psychology and physiology suggested that the fear in these cases was not a deeply rooted ego insecurity based on a poor synthetic capacity. Both these boys managed their college work well, and their thinking showed no disturbance. Neither yielded to homosexual temptation, and when the way was clear for heterosexual pleasure they took advantage of it. But in cases *A*, *B*, and *C* the fear of homosexuality was the superficial indication of a much deeper ego-shattering process, with a deeper injury to narcissistic equilibrium, requiring at times almost megalomanic props.

An important factor in ego strength is the degree of harmony between the parents. This seems to have been greatest in *E*, who presented the least serious disturbance of ego and who reported no serious conflicts between his parents despite the decisive directiveness of his mother. Where parental cleavage was most profound and prolonged, as in case *C*, there was the most serious probability of a psychosis. He could find no peace or understanding in either camp. Little wonder that he felt in no-man's land. His turning to alcoholism implies a more profoundly regressive need than could be satisfied by homosexuality.

Thus we may answer our first question confidently in the affirmative, that the fear of homosexuality in the adolescent is proportionate to the weakness of ego integration. The six cases studied indicate that a career of homosexuality need not be the ultimate result. The ego may regress to a psychosis or progress to heterosexual adaptation. We have included only one student who ultimately turned to homosexuality, and seemed thereby to lose his panic, but the last chapter has not been written about him. The fact that homosexuality itself is not a source of panic is seen in the use made of it by males fearful of their biological responsibilities. Many homosexuals relieved of these responsibilities seem able to achieve some social efficiency and preserve their narcissistic equilibrium by esoteric exclusiveness. The fact that homosexuality is used as a defense against "castration anxiety," as well as a stimulus to it, differentiates it in no way from other ego defensive mechanisms such as identification, projection, repression, reaction formation, etc. When it breaks down as a defense against anxiety, homosexuals often seek cure through psychoanalysis.

In conclusion, I do not wish to give the impression that cultural, social, and hormonal pressures on our adolescents are to be ignored. Because of guilt and anxiety, it is practically impossible to gather valid data on the incidence of homosexuality and the degree of exposure to it. Hence we cannot claim that casual companionship with girls in co-educational colleges reduces the incidence of homosexuality or not. The modern college is far from being the ascetic monastery from which it sprang. The opportunities for wholesome heterosexual experience are increasing, and do not appear to be inimical to good scholarship. When sex becomes less and less an object of dread, guilt, and shame, fears connected with it will diminish. Many more objective studies in the future will help to bring this about.

REFERENCES

1. Bychowski, Gustav, The ego in homosexuals, *International Journal of Psychoanalysis, 26*:114–27. 1945.

2. Kempf, Edward, *Psychopathology* (St. Louis, C. V. Mosby, 1920), p. 477.

3. Karpman, Benjamin, Mediate psychotherapy and the acute homosexual panic, *Journal of Nervous and Mental Disease, 98*:493–506. 1943.

CHAPTER 12

Identity Diffusion and the Synthetic Function

BY ERNST PRELINGER

The author utilizes clinical psychological methods to explore the synthetic function of the ego. The intensive study of a single case is used to develop criteria of the efficiency of synthetic functioning. This represents a beginning effort to formulate the fundamental concepts and tools which are necessary to describe and study developments within the psychological structure of the college student. The author is indebted to Dr. Roy Schafer, consultant of the Division of Student Mental Hygiene, Yale Department of University Health, for many stimulating discussions of the points in this paper.

1

THE CLINICAL PHENOMENON of identity diffusion, recently described in some detail by Erikson (3), presents a curious diagnostic problem. In clinical work with late adolescents and young adults identity diffusion can frequently be observed as a characteristic picture. If such patients are seen in clinical psychological examination, however, one finds in their test records, if conventionally evaluated, the familiar patterns of neurotic disorders, character difficulties, or borderline and even latent psychotic states. Experience seems to have shown that patients with identity diffusion are on the basis of test records so frequently classified into the last two of the mentioned categories that their prognosis would often seem rather unfavorable. Actual clinical observation, on the other hand, suggests that in many cases of identity diffusion stabilization sooner or later occurs, so that the outcome is frequently more favorable than suggested by their test records. Thus it would seem useful to search for some distinguishing characteristics in test behavior which might differentiate patients with identity conflict from patients with more permanent or more serious disorders.

In the present chapter we shall attempt to point out a possible direction in which such differentiating test criteria might be found. Unfortunately, so far no well-validated or even well-studied set of test indications typical of cases of identity diffusion can be offered. In the following the definition of the syndrome of identity diffusion shall be exemplified by the case history of a rather striking patient. After hypothesizing that the critical feature in the ego of persons with identity conflict or identity diffusion may be an insufficiency of synthetic functioning, tentative test criteria for the adequacy of synthetic functioning will be developed. This will be done by relating theoretical descriptions of the synthetic function as currently conceptualized to certain aspects of Rorschach responses. Then the Rorschach record of our patient will be scrutinized in the light of the preceding discussion. The serious limitations of this study, which is based on deductions from a still loosely developed theory and exemplified by only one case description, are of course recognized.

2

First a definition of the terms "identity" and "identity diffusion." A person's identity is a fairly harmonious configuration of a number of psychological structures and functions within the ego which allow a person to define himself and to be defined by others in his present and future adaptive relations to a social environment. It is the product of a great number of psychosocial and psychosexual processes which during their development are, in interaction with the social environment, continuously synthesized and modified into always new forms of identity until by the close of the adolescent period a fair amount of stability and internal consistency of a person's ego identity has been reached. An ego identity is more than a person's childhood identifications. Childhood identifications are modified by the demands of reality and are reconciled in their contradictory aspects as well as integrated with the individual characteristics and assets of the particular person. Changing social roles, furthermore, which are attributed to the growing child at various ages by the surrounding society are constantly integrated into the growing ego identity of the young person. In all this, processes of integration are supple-

mented by processes of rejection and selection of identity frag-
ments. As Erikson (3, p. 71) summarizes it, ego identity is "a
configuration gradually integrating constitutional givens, idiosyncratic libidinal needs, favored capacities, significant identifications, effective defenses, successful sublimations, and consistent
roles."

Identity formation may proceed smoothly in certain persons
or it may be delayed or disturbed. There are many possible causes
for delays and disturbances of identity formation. Strong unifying
factors facilitating synthesis of all the many elements just mentioned may be weak or absent for some reason; fixation or arrest
at an earlier developmental level may have occurred as the result
of an earlier unsolved psychosocial crisis, so that other problems
than those of identity formation confront the adaptive resources
of the ego; almost equally strong, conflicting identifications may
be present; clearly and consistently defined roles within the surrounding society may be unavailable; a particularly strong childhood identification may resist reconciliation with other, newly
possible identifications or with new role definitions from outside
which may become available—to mention some alternatives. Sometimes a prolonged period of usually unconscious experimentation
with various forms of synthesis may be sufficient to allow the individual to arrive at a workable formation of an ego identity
without outside help or deeper disturbance. This is a possibility
when the social environment allows a person to enter a state of
what Erikson calls a psychosocial moratorium (3, p. 66). However,
it may happen that a person fails to develop a relatively harmonious solution by himself and in interaction with the social environment and in such cases identity diffusion may result. Individuals
then may vacillate between a number of roles and contradictory
sets of values, and remain in a state of constant and severe doubt
about their place in the world. They may choose radical and rebellious positions hostile to any identification or social role, or
they may fall victim to a sense of empty nothingness, of not belonging anywhere in the world, and in extreme cases they may
withdraw severely or commit suicide.

The *content* of needs, defenses, identifications, values, and roles
involved in such a picture of confusion may be expected to be
extremely variable from person to person. It seems therefore that

in the search for characteristics of test responses typical of identity diffusion, one cannot primarily rely on an analysis of response contents. It seems more promising to search for *formal* variables which might be of significance. Since the foregoing description of identity diffusion already seemed to point to a characteristic lack of integration or synthesis of varied and powerfully divergent factors within the ego, an attempt shall be made to evaluate by means of formal criteria the efficiency of synthetic functioning. In this chapter such criteria shall be applied to the test responses of one subject. This is done with the hope, however, that these criteria will be further studied on other known cases of identity diffusion and thus perhaps be perfected in the direction of greater diagnostic utility.

3

Let us study the history of a case of identity diffusion: A twenty-five year old student from India, *N*, comes to the student mental hygiene clinic complaining of inability to study, although he thinks of himself as a very bright person. He feels empty and lonely and states that in spite of his efforts to lead an entirely rational life he continues to have intuitive feelings of likes and dislikes and that this fact disturbs him. He is the only son of an Anglo-Indian family living in Calcutta and is the youngest of four children. He has little to say about his father. He has hardly known him but remembers that for years before his death in 1949 father had always been ill. He recalls that father together with the sisters always had created an oppressive atmosphere at home. Ideologically they have always been "traditionalists." While his father seems to have been at least partly European, his mother is an Arabian Jewess. *N* describes her in glowing terms. She has always been much closer to Indian culture than the father and was a warm person as well as always intellectually open-minded and curious. He describes her as "an aristocratic democrat, refined, sensitive, yet completely open." "Like Jesus Christ" she could see through one's soul, and she loved everybody. The relationship between *N* and his mother seems to have been intense. He recalls that she always adored him and even stated that she didn't need any god because "you are my god." About eight years ago, at the

age of eighteen, *N* came to the United States to study. This he did
because he expected a great deal of liberty, freedom of learning,
and he hoped to have the opportunity to "wrestle with philo-
sophies different from the father's and the sisters'." However, he at
first followed one of his father's wishes, namely to study engineering. This he did for four years at a large midwestern university,
being thoroughly miserable. He did not like engineering and
graduated with very poor grades. He describes himself as being
at that time in acute "spiritual, religious, and philosophical conflict." This motivated him to see a counselor for a while. After
graduation and apparently fulfilling what he felt to be a commitment to his father, he went to another midwestern university
and began to study economics. There he arrived with hardly any
money and for a while lived practically on a starvation diet. Later
on, however, he was given a scholarship, and when he entered
into an affair with a married woman who began to take a kind
of motherly interest in him, this became the "happiest period of
my life." The woman was somewhat older and seems to have supported him considerably both materially and morally. Frequently
she promised to abandon her husband and to marry *N*, but she
always tied such a promise to a condition such as graduation, completion of his studies, obtaining a Ph.D. Whenever he reached one
of these goals, she would set him a higher one, again with the
promise of marriage. Finally she broke off the relationship. This
was a considerable blow to *N*, but after a while he entered into
another affair with a ballet dancer. This relationship was considerably less happy than the previous one but in it he seemed
to play a much more masculine and assertive role. Finally *N* came
to Yale on a scholarship. Soon he felt lonely for his woman friend,
although he began to date at Yale. He says he has made the acquaintance of some rather beautiful girls but nevertheless he
always feels that they are lacking in a quality of womanliness.

At Yale he at first continued his studies in the field of economics but he became increasingly dissatisfied by the dryness
and abstractness of his subject. More and more he considered
studying social or political science. This field he felt to be more
concrete and useful, especially since he now wished to become
a kind of social missionary or reformer when going back to India.
Although he did excellent work in some courses of both subjects,

he was, however, not able to fulfill the requirements of either curriculum and finally had to leave Yale. When last seen he was planning to return to the midwestern university and to continue his study of political science there.

Although little is known about *N*'s parents, it seems that from early childhood he may have been, as were his parents, a cultural outsider in India. Furthermore, even from the very scanty descriptions which we have, it seems that he perceived his parents to be very different people. Finally we find this young man in a state of cultural transplantation; an outsider in India, he is probably even more of an outsider in the United States. His role within American society is not very clearly defined, and he has not committed himself to a specific place in it. His plans for the future are to return as a kind of reformer to India, which again implies the status of an outsider. Thus he has apparently achieved little integration of himself with any surrounding society and at present almost the only definition of his social role is that of a "foreign student."

N was an extremely polite, soft-spoken, and passive-appearing person who talked in highly abstract terms and greatly polished sentences. He seemed meek and compliant. But the clinical interviews as well as some of his history soon began to indicate that underneath this surface he considers himself an extraordinary person of great intelligence and perhaps with a mission to reform the political and economic conditions of a whole part of the world. A number of psychotherapeutic sessions, however, yielded a picture not only of lack of integration with surrounding society but also of conflicting identities within *N*. Two fairly separate identities could be discerned.

Identity A. At the bottom of this identity seems to lie an identification with the father. Connected with it seems to be a striving toward concrete, realistic, and efficient accomplishment based on intellectual effort. This goes together with an emphasis on rationality and reason which also is consistent with his use of intellectualization as a defense mechanism. Further related here seems the choice of engineering as a subject. Assertive fantasies of world improvement as expressed in his mission to reform, his activity, and his masculinity seem to be parts of this identity, which on the whole fits in with occidental traits and values.

Identity B. This identity shows quite conflicting features. At its root seems to lie an identification with the mother. Softness, sensitivity, emotionally nuanced behavior, refinement, intuitiveness, femininity, dependent clinging, a tendency to be easily hurt, passivity related to the defense mechanism of reaction formation, and an orientation toward oriental, Indian values are predominant in this second identity.

While, in identity A, *N* strove toward being the active, dominating, and independent reformer, in identity B he adopted the attitude of the lost puppy dog or the little orphan who has to be taken care of.

A psychological examination supplemented the clinical findings. In the test records again a polarity between being a powerful missionary and being a lost, clinging person became apparent, but overriding was the evidence of considerable sexual conflict. Here the polarities were male and female and, associated with them, rawness, coarseness, vulgarity, and sexual uninhibitedness vs. innocence, purity, refinement, sensitivity, and consideration. These two extremes tie in readily with identities A and B. There were indications of a fairly general rejection of the masculine identification which seemed to correspond to the finding that at the time of examination and clinical study *N* seemed to prefer identity B.

In summary, then, it appears that content and functions in all psychic areas have become aligned into one or the other of *N*'s two predominant identities. It seems reasonable to assume that the nuclei around which such crystallization occurred are probably strong, but very contradictory, identifications with both father and mother. Thus from the traditional point of view we might say that an unsolved and ambivalent oedipal conflict is present in this individual and that it has invaded a number of originally perhaps "conflict-free" psychic systems. At this point it seems relevant to state that the concepts of identity conflict and identity diffusion do not suggest new diagnostic categories or new and different kinds of psychological conflict. What we are discussing is a characteristic situation within a person's ego structure; namely, that a partisan alignment of psychological factors on all levels of the ego into two or more opposing factions has taken place.

In his paper on ego identity Erikson describes a number of

characteristic conditions related to the development of the syn-drome of identity diffusion. He states that identity diffusion tends to become manifest at times when challenges toward the handling of situations of physical intimacy, making a decisive occupational choice, entering energetic competition, and finding a psycho-social self-definition are present. Let us briefly examine these challenges in relation to *N*. We know of his affair with a married woman, which included a sexual relationship, at the time before he came to Yale. During this relationship, while initially being aggressive, he became more and more dependent on his partner's support materially and morally. Finally when she broke off with him, *N* began a new relationship with an even less suitable partner, a rather erratic girl who became pregnant. Both times, then, he chose partners with whom the likelihood of establishing a stable and satisfying intimate relationship would have seemed extremely small. When the affairs finally broke down, he experienced con-siderable feelings of emptiness, of being at a complete loss, and he wished to begin all over again. His vacillation between different subjects of study is indicative of his inability to make a decisive occupational choice. Competition with others was erratic and un-even. In some courses he excelled by very little effort; in others he failed, although having at the same time a feeling that he was really intellectually greatly superior to his competitors. *N* never maintained a consistently high level of performance. Finally *N*'s psychosocial self-definition was characterized by extreme vague-ness. We have already seen that wherever he came from and wherever he planned to go, he felt himself an outsider, and his position toward other people was usually defined as either superior or inferior, of hanging on and clinging, or of domineering and directing. Another of Erikson's criteria, namely, that of diffusion of time perspective, is perhaps somewhat less clear in this case, except that it might be represented indirectly in the fact, for in-stance, that *N* spent four years studying a subject in which he was not interested and which he did not plan to use as a basis for his career. Here might be an indication of a feeling of having un-limited time. Diffusion of industry also is manifested in our case. *N* did well in some courses which are not concerned with his primary subject, and he did badly in courses which were central to his field of interest. He used to do a great deal of research in order to win arguments on tiny points but he was often unable to concentrate on important parts of his work. Altogether, then, N shows a good number of the general characteristics attributed to cases of identity diffusion. We may hope, therefore, that his test results, also, are fairly representative of the records of such patients.

4

The preceding case description stressed N's inability to synthesize the contradictory features of identities A and B. Such an inability, it was hypothesized, may be an essential feature in cases of identity diffusion or of identity conflict. Erikson in one place refers to ego identity as a "criterion for the silent doings of *ego synthesis*" (3, p. 57). An evaluation of test records of such cases with regard to the intensity, quality, and success of synthetic functioning, then, should yield characteristic results. The criteria by which we would evaluate indices of synthetic functioning in test records depend on our theoretical conception of the nature of synthetic functioning. Current widely accepted conceptions will therefore be discussed briefly. The following paragraphs summarize some of the statements made by Kris, Nunberg, Rapaport, and Schilder (6, 7, 8, 10).

Fundamentally, that ego function which effects the elimination of contradictions within the ego is defined as the synthetic function (7, p. 124). One may specify the possible sources of contradictions within the ego: they are the demands coming from id, superego, and reality, all of them interacting with established ego institutions. From this definition, which emphasizes the "elimination of contradictions," one may deduce that in integrating various psychic elements the synthetic function follows the requirements of the secondary process by means of which alone contradictions can be perceived in the first place. Thus it is possible to distinguish the synthetic function of the ego from other functions which also establish relationships between different psychic elements but do so in nonlogical ways. In particular, one might think of phenomena such as fusion and condensation, by which different elements may be brought into very close context and may even become interchangeable in certain ways, while at the same time remaining quite contradictory in logically essential aspects. Func-

tions of binding, relating, bringing together, and organizing probably occur on various levels of organismic life, from the morpho-
logical through the physiological, the adaptational (ego level), and
the social. The term "synthetic function," however, as defined
above, is used specifically for integrative efforts discernible on
the level of the ego.

Although it is important for purposes of definition to discriminate clearly between synthetic functioning and other forces
by which psychic elements become related, it is doubtful that such
distinctions can be sharply maintained in many observations of
actual behavioral phenomena. In dreams, for instance, an inter-
play between various forms of organizing may be observed. A
certain sequence of complexly condensed images, produced under
the prominence of the primary process, may become ordered into
a "story" by means of secondary elaboration which follows, at least
to a considerable degree, the requirements of the secondary process and manifests effects of synthetic functioning. Similarly, in
some Rorschach responses, particularly those which contain besides the reaction to the given aspects of the inkblot stimulus
some fairly idiosyncratic, regressive elements, we may find con-
densations, fusions, etc., closely interwoven with attempts at logical, realistic organization. As a result we will have to investigate
any particular unit of behavior in terms of relative degrees of
various forms of organizing tendencies. It must be kept in mind,
however, that ego problems cannot be solved adaptively by such
forms of organization as condensation and fusion.

A further manifestation of synthetic functioning alluded to
by Nunberg (7, p. 126) but not included into his basic definition
of synthetic functioning seems to be the establishment of relations between unrelated but not necessarily contradictory elements within the ego. He does mention phenomena such as the
need for causal explanation, rationalization, and the establishment
of references, as in the formation of delusions, as manifestations
of synthetic functioning. Following Schilder (10, p. 579), however, one might consider its role even in much more minute and
subtle events. Thus synthetic functioning builds up perceptions
out of sensations by connecting and integrating them with already available memories; groups of perceptions are combined
into object representations from which by further synthesis (which

would have to be preceded by some differentiation) concepts evolve. On an even higher level these concepts are integrated with other factors within the personality, such as needs, affects, opinions, and convictions. While Schilder is primarily concerned with the various forms of disorder resulting from failures of synthesis at each one of the just mentioned levels, he emphasizes the importance of synthetic functioning in the development of structures within the ego. This contrasts somewhat with Nunberg's emphasis on the organization which the ego achieves with regard to contradictory demands emanating from nonego sources. Nunberg seems to elucidate primarily the role of synthetic functioning in *dynamic processes* (although he is also concerned with such matters as the introjection of the super-ego), while Schilder points out the importance of synthesis in the formation of *psychic structures*. This latter point of view is important for the present discussion because the configuration of factors which Erikson refers to in his definition of ego identity is a complex psychic structure synthesized from many different elements.

It is important to consider the economic aspect of synthetic functioning. While the ego on one hand, in the process of accumulating experience and because of processes of differentiation, continually establishes new object representations and thus cathexes, it tends at the same time to reduce cathectic expense by establishing new syntheses. Concept formation is a case in point. By subsuming a number of object representations under one concept which now becomes cathected, it becomes unnecessary to maintain the subordinate cathexes with the same intensity, while concomitantly much more ideational mobility is achieved. That this phenomenon is crucial for the theory of thinking has been shown by Rapaport (8, pp. 724 ff.). Synthetic functioning, then, is consonant with a principle which we might call that of minimal cathectic expenditure.

Some clinical observations would speak for the conclusion that this economic tendency within the ego at times may become dominant to such a degree that syntheses are attempted frantically without regard to their appropriateness. Examples may be pathological rationalizations, delusions, ideas and systems of reference, and the like.

They all seem to occur primarily when the ego is straining its

resources in an acute defensive struggle against impulses. Although the ego by such means attempts to maintain an optimal
level of adaptation, the frequently bizarre character of such phenomena not only would seem to make them unadaptive but also
would appear to contradict the previous statement that synthetic
functioning occurs under the dominance of the secondary process. Delusions, confabulations, and similar products seem more
often to be formed by means which we attribute to primary-process
functioning. Insofar as they are direct expressions of id material
this does not seem surprising. If, however, in delusions, extreme
rationalizations, confabulations, etc., we observe a return of the
repressed, we must now also expect manifestations of relatively
archaic defensive efforts on the side of the ego which had been
made at the time the now re-emerging impulses had originally
been repressed or otherwise defended against. At that time ego
functions themselves were gradually emerging from complete
domination by the primary process and became only slowly
oriented on the basis of the reality principle. Since under severe
stress from the side of previously repudiated impulses the ego
may regress and reactivate its original techniques of defense, we
must also expect regression in other areas of ego functioning to
the degree that they become invaded by conflict. Thus the previous formulation that the ego's synthetic functioning follows the
requirements of the secondary process should be specified according to the degree to which the ego developmentally has approached
the reality principle. Regression, as for instance at occasions of
defensive crises, would bring with itself a movement away from
the reality principle which would also be reflected in the formal
characteristics of the ego's synthetic functioning.

It is not necessary to assume that regression during crisis situations is equally far-reaching in all areas of the ego. In fact, clinical
observation would speak strongly against such a formulation. It
may thus happen that in part of its activity the ego may function
much more closely according to primary process criteria, while
in other parts it may be much more guided by realistic considerations. As a result, there may be opposition and mutual checking
between ego functions. Under the pressure of conflict and due
to relatively archaic, regressive efforts at defense, a particular
rationalization, for instance, may be formed, but before it is ad-

mitted to receiving full attention or expression it may fall under the censorship of relatively more mature and reality-guided ego attitudes and be consequently rejected or remodeled. Primitive synthetic efforts therefore may find opposition in the function of reality testing.

Without discussing them in much detail, two other ego functions which may oppose or modify synthetic functioning shall be mentioned briefly. These are differentiation and the defensive function. It is doubtful that they can be genuinely separated from one another; however, while they both serve the ends of adaptation, the direction in which they contribute to development may often be conceptualized as opposite. Following Hartmann (5) the gradual separation of the primitive psychological organism into ego and id is the first and perhaps most decisive differentiation; in its course an original and primitive synthesis is dissolved. On a much more advanced level an individual's ability to discriminate between perceptions and memories, between related but not identical concepts, to observe detail and variety, in fact, more basically, to form discrete and constant object relationships are all examples of differentiation. Differentiation without balancing synthesis, however, may lead to fragmentation of experience, to concreteness, and to dependence on the haphazard stimuli which may be present at any given time, or to exclusive domination by whatever psychological process is operative at any moment. Thus there is an antagonistic relationship between differentiation and synthetic functioning.

Synthetic functioning is interrupted whenever the ego resorts to defensive maneuvers in its dealing with the representations of impulses (4, 7). The common core of all defensive activity lies in the dissolution of the normally occurring connection between representations of instinctual drives and representations of their objects. In repression the instinctual drive representation becomes separated from its object but also from the function of perception. In isolation it may only be kept separate from its object while, for instance, in displacement it remains separate from its object but becomes attached to (synthesized with) a permissible object. Intersystemic synthesis between ego and id is reduced by any defensive process but particularly in the phase of repression certain object representations as well as the counter-cathexes become unavailable to synthetic processes within the ego. This, among other things, leads to reductions in capability to think abstractly, to form new concepts, or to think consequentially in persons who make very far-reaching defensive efforts.

In proceeding to the development of test criteria for synthetic functioning, at least some consideration of the test manifestations of opposing and balancing but adaptive ego functions interacting with synthetic efforts will have to be made.

5

In this section we shall attempt to construct a short catalogue of different forms in which synthetic functioning may appear in Rorschach responses. We recall the assumption that in individuals with identity conflict the ego is divided into parties which at least for the time being resist successful and harmonious synthesis but which it still attempts to integrate. Here we add the assumption that behavior in the Rorschach represents such a fairly wide sample of ego functioning that the ego's frustrated efforts at synthesis should be reflected in the test behavior. In particular, we would expect in the records of persons with identity conflict evidence of increased efforts at synthesis and evidence of failure and frustration of these efforts.

In general, we would look for evidence of synthetic functioning in responses which (a) integrate different areas of the blot into some kind of higher-order whole, (b) integrate locations and surface characteristics of the blot (color, shading, texture), and (c) establish relationships between different contents of percepts; we will also look for signs in the subject's test behavior indicating that a need for synthesis is experienced even if none is actually achieved in the responses. This approach to Rorschach interpretation is not essentially new. Concern with the degree of integratedness of responses can be found in most of the basic works on the Rorschach. Schafer, especially, draws inferences about defensive and adaptive stability and efficiency from degree of integration of responses (9).

It seems useful to discriminate between two aspects of the manifestations of synthetic functioning in test behavior, namely the degree of synthetic *effort* shown and the degree of *success* in achieving a synthesis. The latter depends on the amount of effort but is also determined by the strength of other tendencies, such as the functions of defense, differentiation, reality testing, and the general developmental level of the ego. The following list gives examples of response characteristics which we might expect as the result of various relative amounts of synthetic effort and success.

1. *Effort high and success high:*
   (a) Many appropriate, complex, well-organized, spontaneous W responses or intricate D's
   (b) Building up of combinatory, well-integrated W's from details which had at first been perceived separately, often codetermined by color, shading, or movement
   (c) Meaningful and appropriate relationships between various aspects of the blot which at first had been interpreted separately (both formally and content-wise)
   (d) Well-seen D responses combining form or movement with color or shading appropriately

2. *Effort high and success low:*
   (a) Remarks directly or indirectly expressing a need for integration
   (b) Expression of inability to achieve a more complex integration because of contradictory part aspects (outlines, movement, color, shading, or contents)
   (c) Establishment of relationships, references, and combinations of different aspects of the blot transgressing the usual or becoming bizarre; inappropriate generalizations, establishment of relationships between cards, confabulations
   (d) Need to see a complete content item even if not all parts are given in the stimulus; usually accompanied by rationalization of the response

3. *Effort low and success low:*
   (a) Obvious, unintegrated, banal responses lacking complexity
   (b) No expressed need for any larger syntheses
   (c) Concreteness, determination of the response by one single aspect or part of the blot
   (d) Many unconnected D, Dd, and Do responses

It is not intended here to provide a full scoring manual; therefore no concrete examples are given. Anyone who is familiar with the Rorschach, however, will quickly find well-known response qualities in the above categories.

As a further exploratory step the following three tables have been prepared. They describe characteristics of responses which we might expect to result from interactions between synthetic functioning and the three other functions of reality testing, ego defense in general, and differentiation. For each of the latter three functions the categories Successful and Unsuccessful have been used. There are, of course, many similar entries in the three tables. The variety of manifestations of synthetic functioning is limited,

TABLE *1*. RORSCHACH INDICES FOR VARIOUS INTERACTIONS OF REALITY TESTING AND SYNTHETIC FUNCTIONING

		Reality Testing	
		SUCCESSFUL	UNSUCCESSFUL
Synthetic Functioning	SUCCESSFUL *	Automatic, stimulus-appropriate, complex responses Specific and adequate fitting of D, Dd, color and shading into total percept Integration of various form aspects by appropriate M response	Confabulation High-order symbolism (such as "Love" for all of Card X) Inappropriate generalizations from insignificant part aspects (many DW responses) Establishment of arbitrary references between parts and aspects of blot
	UNSUCCESSFUL	Inability to decide on a desired complex response because of sharply perceived details and attributes of blot felt to be contradictory Vague but still appropriate "cheap" responses: rocks, clouds, etc., encompassing several aspects of blot	Establishment of vague and not very complex but unusual and poor references between different parts and aspects of the blot Shifting, fluid, indecisive percepts Contaminations
	MINIMAL	No indication of any subjective need for integration of percept. Good responses to part aspects but responses remain unrelated and are not complex within themselves	Responses of poor or bizarre quality to separate aspects, "concreteness," no evident need or attempt to establish contexts Confusion Organization of different aspects achieved by means of pure primary process (fusion, condensation, pars pro toto, etc.)

* "Successful" synthetic functioning implies achievement of any synthesis, but does not imply anything concerning the quality or appropriateness of the synthesis.

TABLE 2. RORSCHACH INDICES FOR VARIOUS INTERACTIONS OF DIFFERENTIATION
AND SYNTHETIC FUNCTIONING

Differentiation

		SUCCESSFUL	UNSUCCESSFUL
Synthetic Functioning	SUCCESSFUL	Beginning with spontaneous, integrated response followed by appropriate responses to part aspects which are still elaborations of and guided by total impression Appropriate integration of successive responses to part aspects into a whole Ability to give more than one response to a given area Combinations Shifting from W response to independent D responses	Automatic, complex responses in which the whole is so dominating that no responses to part aspects can come about Difficulties in shifting to new responses (not on the basis of concreteness, however), including difficulties in giving a new response to an already interpreted area
	UNSUCCESSFUL	Various sharply seen, stable and appropriate responses to part aspects but no total integration in spite of an expressed need for it Abitrary combinations of well-seen D's	Vague and relatively unwarranted responses to over-all aspects, feeling "there might be something," inability to respond explicitly to part aspects or to give more information about the response. DW responses. Physiognomic responses. Description of "feeling" evoked by blot
	MINIMAL	Enumerative sequence of responses to different aspects of blot with no implication of any possible organization Descriptions of physical properties of the blot	Perplexity Blots present insoluble problem

and one must assume relationships among the other three variables also. The general developmental level of the ego would appear as a common factor in these relationships.

TABLE 3. RORSCHACH INDICES FOR VARIOUS INTERACTIONS OF DEFENSIVE
AND SYNTHETIC FUNCTIONING

Defensive Functioning

	SUCCESSFUL	UNSUCCESSFUL
SUCCESSFUL	Well-integrated, rapidly formed, appropriate percepts disregarding some aspect of the stimulus (example: appropriate and complex WF response to colored cards without use of color. Form response on III)	Well-integrated, partly appropriate responses utilizing part aspects of a much more regressive nature, which mobilize anxiety or come up unintentionally. They may later be denied (M or C denial in inquiry, etc.)
UNSUCCESSFUL	Refusal to integrate certain aspects of blot although some need for synthesis is expressed Emphasis of impossibility of integrating certain aspects Do responses with refusal to acknowledge usual W Active refusal of M element in usual H responses, etc. Pedantry, criticism of test	Bizarre or regressive, inappropriate, and hardly integrated responses, although attempts are made at synthesis and need for it is felt
MINIMAL	Complete predominance of Dd, Do, pure form, formless movement responses, etc., only part aspects of stimuli emphasized No indication of any need for integration	Concreteness Unrelated bizarre and regressive responses

Synthetic Functioning (bracket spanning left side)

6

Let us now examine *N*'s Rorschach responses in terms of the criteria of synthetic effort and success. If our hypothesis that subjects with identity conflict will show evidence of frustrated but continued synthetic efforts holds good, we should find some manifestations of this struggle in the Rorschach record. The following discussion of the test record will be limited to those aspects which might give indications of synthetic efforts and their success. Other interpretative issues will be avoided and the conventional scores for the responses will be omitted. This would, of course, not be done in the full clinical analysis of a record. An intuitive plus or minus score for synthetic effort and for success follows "scorable" responses.

Card I.

13″ 1. "First impression is of a winged creaturelike bat." ("Had trouble recognizing this [points to wings] with the bat.") This is the usual, popular response. Some difficulty is expressed, however, in seeing the usual "wings" as an immediate part of the bat. Synthetic effort is present but it has to overcome obstacles; a successful integration is finally achieved. E+ S+

2. "Central section like a spider." ("I had some trouble finding wavy legs for the spider.") This is the usual human figure; the "wavy legs" are somewhere in the surrounding gray and contribute to the low form level of the response. Here the synthetic effort manifests itself in the need to complete the content item. E+ S—

"Can I switch to specific parts?" This remark indicates the presence of a set for the building of integrated responses which the subject now is willing to abandon if supported by the examiner.

3. "If I say this looks like a rough map of India, I can't make it consistent with the spider or the bat." (Left triangular protrusion, "complete with Himalayan range.") This is a quite accurate and self-contained response but the subject voices a feeling of frustration. The synthetic *Einstellung* is still effective. "That's all it looks like." 87″

Card II.

36″ 1. "Again very crudely this could represent two people, hands joined together, or surrealist painting of people having a toast. Bloody heads and . . ." ("The red color suggesting very roughly something like bloody heads. Reminds me of a picture of an insect or a cross, for Christ. They have sort of insectlike heads. Sort of inconsistent, feel it's more like a squirrel.") These are the frequently seen "clowns." From one point of view we may discern an element of denial in this response. Violence, blood, crucifixion are the thoughts related to the friendly gesture of "toasting." It is the red color which the subject feels needs to be integrated into the total response, but defensive processes opposed a more adequate synthesis in the first statement of the percept. This led to a feeling of "inconsistency" which we may categorize again as a frustrated tension in the direction of synthesis. E+, S from — to +

2. "At first I thought of something like a bear because they were dark and woolly, bearlike. Sort of clutching each other." ("Same as before. Have been fighting. Not too much stress on it.") Here is an appropriate synthesis of popular form and shading. E+ S+

3. "And something just struck me: just this part, like a face of a big Buddha, big heavy face." (Edge detail on the upper left outline of left black D.) This response in itself is not very remarkable for our discussion. It is fairly uncomplex in its formal aspects. Content-wise, however, it contrasts with the associations to the first response on this card in which the subject mentioned Christ. There is no attempt to relate these two topics. No synthetic effort.

4. "And this section reminds me of school; in hygiene we saw pictures of sexual parts." (Center area in bottom red: "In isolation." [sex?] "Wasn't so sure, I suppose female. The red may have menstrual significance but I didn't think of it before. I can't visualize these things in two dimensions.") For our discussion the most important element may be his remark "in isolation." Lack, or defensive avoidance, of synthesis of this last response and the previously given ones seems indicated. 182″

Card III.

10″ 1. "Here my first impression was two men standing like so, then I wanted to change it to two women because of legs and shoes and I wanted to convert these two to breasts." This response will be discussed below; it concerns the usually seen people.

2. "This looks vaguely like a butterfly." (Form only, center red)

3. "This (the center red) again from hygiene class, you see the neck and interior tubes going into lungs and stomach." (Form only)

4. "In the center these could be handbags, if I stand to my

interpretation of these being women. But I don't know how to interpret this in the center; first thought of a pot. They might want something from this pot. It's difficult to weave these into a coherent pattern." Discussion follows below.

5. "Oh, this in the center could also be an interior organ, lungs, but that's more in search of consistency." (This response was apparently based on form only but in the inquiry N said: "Now I feel they might be suffused with blood. Curious I didn't before.") The "search of consistency" (apparently with response No. 3) betrays the synthetic effort, the relatively poor form and the lack of a justified relationship to No. 3 (also lungs in part) indicates poor success. E+ S—

6. "At a loss about this little white spot here, I don't really know." (The white space in the center light gray.)

7. "This light part here, a bowl in the center, but it could be a shield; we are looking at the embellished part." N could not reconstruct this in the inquiry.

8. "But the faces are more suggestive of masculine faces, old men's, at least in their fifties. They don't have the delicacy and the refinement of a woman's face. The left one in particular seems to have a face of roughness, coarseness, vulgar as opposed to aristocratic . . . I wonder why . . . If *this* could be a rough, oldish man (left), *this* could be a woman (right)." "*This* definitely has a masculine cast with it. Trouble is its feminine leg and shoe. It's so suggestive of delicate woman's shoes. . . . Perhaps because of these protuberances one should switch back and say that these are men, because of the penis-like structure. But that's inconsistent with the legs. But this ruins any attempt to make it coherent. No, it doesn't." 9 minutes

Responses 1, 4, and 8 really contain one prolonged rumination concerning the sex of the people usually seen. The contradictory aspects of the blot are held on to by an overly strong appreciation of reality; successful synthesis would here require abandonment of some features of reality. It seems safe to say that great synthetic effort is expended here but it remains unsuccessful. E+ S—. If a weighting system were developed, one would feel tempted to give the effort shown here considerable weight.

We also make a note of the content issue involved, namely, that of sexual role identification. Another issue seemed previously indicated by the polarity of Christ and Buddha. Are these the discrepancies spurring on *N*'s synthetic efforts?

Card IV.

11″ 1. "My first impression was of something big and dark, a big animal looming down to catch you." (Usual W. "Arms, head, shoulders, lurid eyes. Big barrel-like body, feet spread akimbo. The color would be a cloak carried on his back. Reminds me of a picture of Genghis Khan.") This response contains an appropriate and automatic integration of form, movement, and shading elements. E+ S+

2. "Then, to some extent, it struck me as a cow or a bull; here are eyes and horns, tail on top. Almost like a bull turned inside out. No, it wouldn't have to be. Just turned inside out! How should I put it. The head should be on top." In the inquiry *N* specifies that he had changed his percept to that of a human being: "As if I put my head between my legs and looked at you like that." Evidence of synthetic functioning is perhaps not too clear in this response. The shifting and fluidity of perception and content due to the rejection of the first percept, however, provide some indirect indications of unsuccessful synthetic efforts.

3. "Final impression was of these two legs with big heavy boots, really heavy boots." 140″

Card V.

4″ 1. "Again some sort of creature, faintly like a bat, ears on top to hear sounds, the radar effect. And it's going in *that* direction (upward)." An automatic response which because of its usualness does not seem to indicate special synthetic accomplishments. 56″

Card VI.

7″ 1. "This again looks like a picture, an X-ray picture taken of the inside of the body, like lungs, and this part the neckish side." ("The rib cage, etc. here, then the lungs—I meant the abdomen and thorax. Roughly, from your belt upward. Both the shadiness and the configuration.") The "shadiness" was probably the primary element here, and the form elements are poor. There seems to be some attempt to identify different areas which are held together by the surface color in a weak and not very successful way. More effort here seems to be expended in attempts at differentiation. E+ S— (weak)

2. "Second impression: prehistoric animal with big body, small brain, and there are whiskers here." ("Seen from above, back, legs; or like a tigerskin laid on the ground.") Again here, an automatic, initially relatively well-integrated whole response, although its form level is quite mediocre. Then differentiation seems to occur. E+ S+ (weak) 76″

Card VII.

8″ 1. "This is pretty nearly incomprehensible and uninterpretable. But if I were to interpet it, I'd say two faces, like African Negro type leering at each other and this is the pedestal on which they are placed." ("Emphatically these are pieces of sculpture.") "I haven't given them any sex and I don't quite know how to—how to reach a decision as to how to determine it. First I thought this (left) was a woman's and this a man's but I waver. So . . . but then . . . they're either both men or both women. Both men! . . . I really don't know what to do with this here, I don't know" (the center "arms"). Already in the opening comment *N* separates "himself" from any percept he might produce on this card. The "emphatic" avoidance of any kinesthetic identification further testifies to that. In view of the fact that previously he has seen movement and of the described refusal to commit himself, especially in identifying the sex of the figures, we might state that he *refuses* to attempt a full synthesis as might be expressed in an accepted WM+ response. E— S—. Note again that sexual identification is the issue here. 176″

Card VIII.

6″ 1. "Here again for some reason I think of internal organs. In books they were always pictured like this. . . . All right, if I just stick to it, this would correspond to a backbone, these to the lungs and the stomach. But this is only a first block impression." (Whole response: backbone in center, blue is lungs, and red is stomach.) Here we have a not quite automatic, moderately appropriate whole response. E+ S+. *N*'s final comment seems indicative of a sense of an accomplished synthesis. This impression is reinforced by his introduction to the next response showing a trend toward differentiation.

2. "Breaking it down, these are two animals; I rejected a polar bear interpretation, think of something in the lion-tiger family, but didn't come to a decision. Like feline jungle creatures, legs, and tongue stuck out of its mouth. [side animals] Of course they ought to be yellow and they're red; I'm not sure what to do about that. Their legs are too long for them to be seals, although seals have the same round quality. They're brown; of course red is a little closer to brown than to yellow." Here the identification of the animals depends for the subject on a congruence of form and color. His efforts at synthesis, however, are greatly opposed by their discrepancy and his final quite inappropriate synthetic achievement is accomplished only by means of a strained rationalization. E+ S—.

3. "The upper gray blotch tends to baffle me. Same with the center grayish green one. Then I find myself surprised I didn't mention the multicoloredness although I am sensitive to colors. But they don't suggest much of anything." This response perhaps allows the interpretation that in the percept of the animals *N*'s main difficulty was one of synthesizing affect and ideation. Content-wise one might speculate on his use of opposites such as "hot" and "cold" (polar bear and seal vs. jungle animals). "I think that's about it." 312″

Card IX.

21″ 1. "First thing I thought of two fellows fishing, perhaps suggested by the previous pictures which I had to put together" (a reference to the "Little King" series in the Wechsler). "Two fellows sitting, fishing in a common pool. Here the colors only serve to differentiate the different parts. Don't think I see very much more than that. It just doesn't!" (Fellows—upper orange, pool in between them). "I wanted to make sense of the rest but couldn't. Thought of it in terms of a spout but what would that have to do in something you fish in?" (center stick). "Then thought of it in terms of a penis but then you can *always* make such an interpretation. At least it crossed my mind." Here is a fairly automatic, moderately complex detail response. It represents a fairly good synthetic achievement which is carefully preserved by a refusal to integrate any further aspects of the blot. Thus a lack of "shifting" at times might indicate a sort of defensive hanging-on to a synthesis. E+ S+ 104″

Card X.

15″ 1. "At first blush I really didn't know *what* to do with it. First I thought of this as of flowers, the color is suggestive" (center yellow).

2. "These two caterpillars" (low green).

3. "Two crabs" (center blue).

4. "Two sea shells" (lower orange).

5. "This is really surrealism. This area over here (large red) had a repellent color. I don't understand it, usually I like red. But here it is like putrefying meat, turgid. At first it was a happy picture, now it's worse than bad, it's monstrous, because now the lilies (center yellow) which are sweet and innocent are growing out of flesh. That's bad; here you have also crabs clutching on to it. Grabbing on to turgid, meaty substance. Then the idea of connection came to mind, the idea that the good lilies can be connected with something bad. It's even worse than something plain bad if something *good* is connected with this . . . horrible, decaying, putrefying. The worst is, they are not just connected but *organically* related. That revolted me."

6. "And here it's like a tube with this bluish stuff oozing out of it" (center blue).

7. "I didn't know what *these* (inner) yellow would be but I think it's what the lilies will be when they're done for, discarded, sucked dry."

8. "Afterthought: now the caterpillars are coming to eat them. In the center there's the *core* of the lilies. Now the caterpillars have been converted into evil caterpillars which are just going to eat it."

9. "I was puzzled about the little thing in the center that the caterpillars are attached to. It's faintly suggestive of fallopian tubes. And just for a second it also seemed suggestive of the head

of a goat but the impression doesn't linger" (center part of bottom green).

10. "These (center gray) are the woody and barky parts from which the beautiful lilies sprang out." 552″. These last responses, Nos. 5 to 10, show definite regressive, primary-process dominated characteristics. Themes of guilt and innocence, bloom and decay, devouring and destruction intrude in a combination which seems only minimally related to the realistic and usually perceived aspects of the stimulus. The percepts are shifting and unstable. However, there are definite strivings to synthesize, organize, and order the different aspects of the blot as well as the contents, but they are primitive, strained, and confabulative. Quite primitive ego functioning, still greatly suffused with qualities of the primary process, becomes observable. More highly developed functions of evaluation and reality testing also come into play as represented in remarks concerned with lack of understanding, puzzlement, and revulsion, but they are insufficient to stimulate more progressive integrative efforts. E+ S—

In looking over this record from the point of view of synthetic functioning only, we see considerable vacillation both in the degree of synthetic effort reflected in different responses and in the degree of its success. A count of our rough scores yields five E+ S+, six plus one doubtful E+ S—, and one E— S—. In accordance with our hypothesis we are especially interested in the responses scored E+ S—, because they are most likely to reflect the frustrated synthetic efforts discussed above. Let us summarize the contents of these responses. One is a spider, one concerns interior anatomy, emphasizing blood, then on Card III a response where *N* is unable to reconcile masculine and feminine characteristics, then another anatomy response in which the handling of the shading aspects of the blot became important. On Card VIII difficulties develop around the integration of form and color aspects leading to a lack of constancy of the resulting percept, while in Card X he finds it impossible to integrate blot characteristics as well as the contents of his percept. There the themes are guilt and innocence, bloom and decay, and destruction. The doubtfully scored response contains the elements of benevolence vs. violence as well as some alternations between percepts referring to Buddha and to Christ. The E— S— response finally represents a refusal by *N* to concern himself with the identification of the sex of the perceived figures.

Thus in the case of *N* we find recurrent and contradictory themes related to his difficulties in achieving syntheses. These themes are masculinity vs. femininity, violence and aggression vs. peacefulness and perhaps passivity, intellect vs. emotion, sordidness vs. innocence, and, perhaps, West vs. East, as suggested by the Christ-Buddha response. All these polarities, however, coincide closely with those summarized under the headings of identities A and B which had been suggested by the clinical material. Thus, at least in this one case, we find that identity conflict goes together with an inability to achieve a successful synthesis as reflected in the test record. At the same time we see the subject's ego fairly desperately at work attempting to reach such a synthesis.

Most people experienced in the use of the Rorschach probably would feel inclined to reach a diagnostic impression of schizophrenia or at least of a borderline state on the basis of even a superficial reading of *N*'s protocol. This brings us back to the initially raised question of differential diagnosis. Scrutiny of the test record suggests that the most "morbid" responses are pretty much those which were also quoted as reflecting unsuccessful synthetic functioning. Most of the remaining responses are fairly well organized and do not seem to present striking evidence of a thinking disorder. Thus it may be inferred that *N*'s "pathology" may be closely centered around his identity conflicts, while at the same time there is no over-all ego destruction or regression. To be sure, when identity problems are forced into the foreground, for instance, by environmental circumstances, we may anticipate the subject to behave in a manner closely resembling schizophrenia. This could account for at least some of the transient, adolescent schizophrenic disorders found among college students. The most marked distinguishing characteristic between acute identity crises and schizophrenic disorders with a much more pessimistic prognosis, then, would be the "topical," content-wise restricted character of the former. Many more cases on whom full clinical material as well as follow-up data are available would, however, be necessary in order to document this thesis convincingly.

REFERENCES

1. Erikson, E. H., *Childhood and Society,* New York, Norton, 1950.
2. —— Growth and crises of the "healthy personality," in C. Kluckhohn, and H. A. Murray, eds., *Personality in Nature, Society, and Culture,* 2d ed. New York, Knopf, 1953.
3. —— The problem of ego identity, *Journal of the American Psychoanalytical Association, 4*:56–121. 1956.
4. Freud, S., Splitting of the ego in the defensive process, in *Collected Papers* (London, Hogarth Press, 1950), Vol. 5.
5. Hartmann, H., Ego psychology and the problem of adaptation, in D. Rapaport, ed., *Organization and Pathology of Thought* (New York, Columbia University Press, 1951), pp. 362–96.
6. Kris, E., On preconscious mental processes, in D. Rapaport, ed., *Organization and Pathology of Thought* (New York, Columbia University Press, 1951), pp. 474–93.
7. Nunberg, H., The synthetic function of the ego, *International Journal of Psychoanalysis, 12*:123–40. 1931.
8. Rapaport, D., *Organization and Pathology of Thought,* New York, Columbia University Press, 1951.
9. Schafer, R., *Psychoanalytic Interpretation in Rorschach Testing* (New York, Grune and Stratton, 1954), pp. 180–82.
10. Schilder, P., Studies concerning the psychology and symptomatology of general paresis, in D. Rapaport, ed., *Organization and Pathology of Thought* (New York, Columbia University Press, 1951), pp. 519–80.

CHAPTER 13

The Relationship of Intellectual Achievement to the Processes of Identification

BY ALFREDO NAMNUM

In the framework of psychoanalytic ego psychology, the author presents observations of disturbance of intellectual functioning associated with other failures of synthesis. The quality of intellectual activity, certainly a prime concern of colleges, is shown to be related to unconscious ego processes and quite possibly to internal psychological structure. Still further exploration of this ego-function and its failure may be expected to provide perspective into the effects of the college experience on personality organization.

To THE PSYCHIATRIST, who is forever keenly listening to his patient's every word, insight into the psychological processes themselves—as opposed to insight into the *repressed*—is a relatively rare reward, because the change for the better that psychotherapy helps bring about goes less often with insight into psychological processes than with insight into the contents of the repressed. Although it would be wholly erroneous to assume that insight into the processes has nothing to do with therapy, nevertheless the accentuation of this contrast constitutes a whole stream in the history of psychoanalysis, because of its eminently therapeutic orientation at the beginning, with its almost exclusive interest in the drives (and conflicts), and its gradually becoming more and more a psychological science, along with its ever increasing interest in the ego. But of course even as a therapy, psychoanalysis has encompassed more and more the psychological processes (2, 6, 7).

The discrepancy above mentioned (which would, however, be equally fallacious to overestimate as to ignore) between insight into psychological processes and therapeutic change is responsible for the fact that many patients in whom for one reason or another we cannot contemplate substantial change for the better, and who

are thus therapeutically frustrating, may be otherwise quite rewarding to the psychiatrist. Such are the cases I will describe. In
them some phases of what are normally unconscious ego processes
were indirectly observable. They presented, along with disturbances in the process of identification, a fairly specific type of intellectual affliction. All of those in whom these two conditions
concurred were—and I believe by no coincidence—*graduate* students. In all of them the disturbances in the process of identification were severe, although not all of them had wound up as
"multiple personalities," or "as-if personalities," or with no character at all. Underlying their clinical picture was the fact that
that which in the ego partly makes the process of identification
possible and partly comes about as a result of it (its "synthetic"
or "organizing" function) was grossly deficient. Succinctly, the
point of this paper is that these patients, having as children failed
to go successfully through the process of identification (in all of its
phases), as grownups they lacked something in their intellectual
function in general and their intellectual creativity in particular.

It was not surprising that the most dramatic features running
through their communications were their desperate, relentless, yet
ineffectual attempts to bring about identification by intellectual
activity. These attempts to accomplish through intellectual activity
that which the ego has not accomplished in the course of normal
psychological development are not infrequently observed among
maladjusted "intellectuals." Anna Freud (2) has called attention
to the use of intellectualization in puberty. During that crisis the
ego calls on intellectualization to preserve its own integrity, its
very existence, from the onslaught of the *quantity* of instinct.
Thus Anna Freud laid the ground for the study of the function of
differentiation of the ego. She wrote (2, p. 191): "The defensive
measures which its dread of the strength of the instincts impels it
to adopt are designed to maintain this differentiation between ego
and id." Subsequently, Hartmann (10, 11) described this function
of differentiation more systematically. The clinical examples
which will follow are instances in which the ego, at a later age,
uses intellectualization for a different purpose. In these instances
the ego, through intellectualization, attempts to bring about identification, a process which is intimately connected with its syn-

thetic function just as defenses in particular (and "intellectualization" as a defense) and countercathexis in general are connected
with its function of differentiation.

One of these patients was a very gifted student of literature
who for more than five years had unsuccessfully tried to finish his
dissertation. So that when he came to treatment he was already in
his early thirties, married ten years, with two children, yet finan-
cially wholly dependent on his mother, who was a woman of rather
modest means. What seemed decisive (and I deliberately discount
the effect of increasingly exhaustive deadlines, mainly—but not
solely—because they really are interminable) in getting him on
his way to finally finishing the dissertation was one insight. This
was not a "therapeutic insight" but insight for the observer which
ultimately enhanced the therapy. It was that although ostensibly
he was writing the thesis for the purpose of getting his degree,
actually this was not at all the case. He had overburdened the task
of writing the thesis with the unconscious fantasy that with it he
would accomplish that which the ego had failed to accomplish
through the normal process of identification. (The distinction between "he" and "the ego" is due to the fact that in one instance
reference is made to a conscious action or intention and in the
other to an unconscious ego process. Actually it seems that it is the
failure of the normally unconscious process which accounts for
the consciousness and thus for its becoming available to observation.)

In this obsessive man other "insights" which were readily
available to him were, as is frequently the case, completely meaningless, therapeutically speaking. Thus the fact that he "really"
did not want to finish because he wanted forever to remain dependent on his mother, which was true enough, or that he wouldn't
finish so as to punish her, which was also true, were, with their
intricate elaborations, rather empty intellectual notions. The
"real" purpose of the thesis was revealed in fantasies. Some manifestations of his unconscious fantasies were there to see in his day-
dreams. Secretly he hoped to "arrive" with the thesis, to finally
"become somebody"; it could not get done because it had to be "a
great accomplishment." With it he would demonstrate once and
for all that he was not a "fraud," although no one other than
himself thought of him as a fraud. So that actually his fantasy

was that with the thesis he would *become* something other than the fraud he thought himself to be.

This particular form of self-beratement ("I am just a fraud") is exceedingly common among intellectuals when they are depressed, and there are numerous indications that what often underlies it is not merely a super-ego conflict, but also something of the kind of what Freud (3) called "endo-psychic perception." When scrutinized closely among these patients, it has many other derivatives, like "I am nothing intellectually," "I have acquired no knowledge" or, in the words of this particular patient, "I am no scholar, I can never have any really systematic knowledge"; in the words of other patients, "I have nothing in my memory," and so on and so forth, all of which are references to an unconscious sense of inner emptiness and have as well further specific meanings. They are intellectual reverberations of disturbed unconscious ego processes.

The student's dissertation topic was, to put it in his own words, "about a poet who looked into the past and from the past incorporated another poet." Actually, as we see it, what the living poet in question did with the dead poet was more than mere incorporation, although incorporation is the crude initial mechanism involved in the process of identification. The fact that the patient referred to the process of identification as an incorporation would have been a mere analogy, a "manner of speaking," (as he consciously meant it), were it not for the fact that it was strikingly consistent with his own oral fixation which, besides early childhood "hunger strikes" and what he later called his "enormous appetite" and his "eating bouts," had a good many manifestations.

If we compare the process of identification with the creative process of the artist following Kris' (13, 14) description of the latter, we will observe that the initial phase—introjection in one, inspiration in the other—is equally *passive* and *regressive* in both; but that from there on the ego must recollect itself; its synthetic function must take over at once in order for either creation or identification to come about. From there on it is all hard work, although in one case it is outwardly directed (communication) and in the other it is directed inwardly (building of psychological structure), as in the "work of mourning" (5, 8).

One disturbance in his own work process which had so delayed the finishing of the thesis the patient described thus: when after long waiting and looking he would come into possession of an idea—"be struck by it,"—which would surely fill the next few pages, he would suddenly stop and "then I hold on to it and dwell and dwell upon it and do nothing." "I hold on to it," he said, bringing his half-clenched fist toward his eager mouth. The gesture itself came from his deeply repressed, yet ever present, orality. A lesser fixation (anal) was obviously much more readily manifest both in the contents of his sentence ("hold on to it and dwell and dwell upon it and do nothing") and in his immediate association (it reminded him of his constipation and his childhood refusal to move his bowels). Such readily available, abundant evidence, true as his anal fixation was, was surely being used as a disguise. He wanted to devour his own ideas. Such regression reminds one of the fact that "the predecessor of thought and knowledge is the idea of the drive object" (Rapaport, 19). In this case "thought and knowledge" is approached as if it still was the drive object itself.

To summarize, in our patient, on two different levels, there existed two pathological conditions: on his libidinal development there was his oral fixation; on his ego development the process of identification was abortive because it tended to end ("stop, dwell, do nothing") in its passive, devouring, introjecting phase. The intellectual creative process has the same fate as does the process of identification ("stop, dwell, do nothing"). I have deliberately used the foregoing quotation from the patient twice because I want to stress the fact that some such productions which upon relatively superficial examination are manifestations of scarcely repressed id drives and upon further examination reveal data on deeper repressed drives, on still further examination they may give insight into disturbances of unconscious ego processes.

The patient's two fixations by their constant interaction with each other produced the intricate total clinical picture. They were both partly the result and partly the cause of deficiency in the synthetic function of the ego. On the libidinal development the synthetic (organizing) function of the ego brings about the concurrence of the pregenital drives into the genital organization and the attainment of the genital organization of the libido in turn enhances the synthetic function; and, on the process of identification, only the synthetic function makes it possible for the ego to integrate the "abandoned object cathexes" into a homogeneous ego, a character (8, 17). Insofar as the intellectual process is concerned, this failure of the process of identification (and deficit of the synthetic function) has its own expression in the "inability to acquire really synthetic knowledge" (should perhaps have said "inability to organize the acquired bits of knowledge"), or as another patient, a mathematician, with a strikingly similar clinical picture put it, "Why do I always have to look things up, why don't I ever acquire formulae and apply them to problems?" He was another "fraud" whose devouring appetite had made him gain one hundred pounds in the course of a few months following his mother's death from cancer of the breast. He came to the clinic because of "cancer phobia."

With regard to these clinical observations, nothing could be more appropriate, it seems to me, than the following quotation from Rapaport (19):

> In studying a science, to have assimilated a theory, as against "holding" isolated facts and relationships, permits a saving in cathexes. The very process of an individual's development in a field of study seems molded on a pattern similar to that of introjection, identification, and integration into the unity of the ego. Knowledge, when first acquired, remains fragments from various textbooks. It is only later that the local memories of the textbooks and of their dividing-lines recede. This recession is accompanied by a progress in the applicability of the knowledge to instances and relationships other than those given in the texts. . . . From this integration of knowledge there leads a further process of integration by which the knowledge is permeated by the organizing principles of the individual personality. . . . The fortunate development of such a synthesis is the guaranty of occupational gratification and creativeness.

Our first patient had, among other problems, very severe gastrointestinal symptoms (colitis, constipation, diarrhea). He also had bouts of depression, no history of which could be determined because they were truly lifelong. His disturbance, like that of a small child, was intimately connected with his relationship with his mother, with the neurotic interaction between them. This relationship was very much mutually possessive and mutually hostile. The mother was a cruel disciplinarian, disturbed particularly in matters of cleanliness; she had "millions" of boxes all over the place in which she kept things of all kinds, little things, old things, useless things. In childhood he countered her discipline with hunger strikes lasting days and with constipation. In recent years she had come to monopolize the symptoms and on repeated occasions her encounters with him were followed by attacks of anorexia nervosa, some very severe, lasting months. During the six months I knew him, the patient never said a word to me about his father, but I did not wonder too much about this since, from other sources, I had learned that before the patient was born the father had an encephalitis that crippled him for life. He remembered him in childhood as being asleep most of the time and in more recent years with parkinsonism and mental symptoms of organic brain pathology. One may conjecture that he had no father to identify with, just as he had no father to talk to me about. And as for his mother, one may only say that, somehow, he could not identify with her. Why the stubborn, resentful dependency had always had the upper hand could not be elucidated in the brief treatment. There was what might have been some kind of "negative" identification (or rather "negativistic"). From the hunger strikes on, the strongest motivation seemed to have become *not to be* what the mother wanted him to be (a businessman like the brother) and *not to do* what she wanted him to do. In a sense it was as if in the anal phase all matters between them had been settled once and for all, although only to that limited extent.

His intestinal dysfunction seemed to follow a familiar pattern. He talked about his bouts of eating, immediately followed by bowel movements, in his own words, "as if there was no distance between my stomach and my rectum." This had its counterpart in his complaint that he had retained nothing in his memory, that "everything seems to have gone in one ear and out the other," as if indeed there was nothing between one ear and the other. This was but one of many expressions of his sense of inner emptiness. I might say here that both the complaint of lack of memory and the sense of inner emptiness were constant features in these "intellectuals" who had failed to identify.

Again, here the voracious appetite is not merely expression of libidinal oral fixation or of deprivation of affection; the over-eating seems to want to make up for the inability to absorb. If this is carried (as so many things in this patient were thus easily interchangeable) from the physiological to the psychological, "absorption" would be the phase of the identification process which would follow the incorporating phase; there it was: in still another realm the same pattern recurred. With him there seemed to be no exception to this general pattern. He always wanted more of everything from everyone. Since I gave him no "more," the way he kept track of the minutes in our hours you would think he was going to use every one of them; but of that there was no evidence whatsoever. In many ways it was as if his organism could not use anything it was given.

It is difficult to know how much of a case to report without be-coming repetitious or irrelevant. In any case, this report would be even more incomplete than it is if I didn't say that all these conjectures in no way have begun to explain the fact that, in spite of all this pathology, there was enough intact to make it possible for him to overcome this first major hurdle in his pursuit of a career.

The second case, which I have already briefly mentioned, was that of a Japanese student in mathematics who was referred to our clinic because of fear of cancer (of the mouth, of the stomach, of the throat) and gastro-intestinal symptoms, such as diarrhea, "nervous stomach," and "hypermotility of the colon." Once the history of the illness had been established it was found to date back six years. The gastro-intestinal symptoms were the first to come into the picture; they appeared during the terminal illness of his father who died from cancer of the stomach. Three years later, after a second marriage, his mother died from metastasis of cancer of the breast, after both breasts had been amputated. Also coinciding with the mother's terminal illness, the fear of cancer made its appearance. At the same time he began to gain weight in enormous amounts and gained one hundred pounds in the course of a few months. This patient did not shed one single tear for his mother and his depression had no conscious connection with her death, but only with his physical symptoms, his cancer phobia, and his deep feelings of inadequacy. A year later, under the care of a physician, he was able to emerge from his depression and dieted so as to lose as many as fifty pounds, which he quickly regained, however, upon the birth of his daughter and only child. He had been married during his mother's illness. After his mother's death, he took his younger sister into his home where he gave her truly maternal care.

He entered the treatment ostensibly with no expectations, partly because of his own pessimism about himself and partly because he was so anxious not to make a nuisance of himself, not to be too demanding ("I don't expect any miracles"). This unobtrusiveness of his went with a somewhat indifferent affect and it was a well-rooted trait, but underlying the indifference there was a rather deep resentment for not being taken care of. He had some mannerisms worth noting. He smoked all the time and had some rather noticeable grimaces. When he was not talking, he displayed a good bit of oral activity; he pursed his lips, licked them, bit them, and swallowed. None of these gestures were really grossly inappropriate, but there they were all the time. He first approached the treatment as if it were one of his mathematical problems, which he was completely unable to meet. He was self-derogatory and frequently silent and apologetic. From the very beginning it appeared that he was going to respond quickly, if not lastingly, to my interventions. He was the kind of patient, much unlike the other one, who feels much better at the end of the session than he does at the beginning, as if a certain thirst had been quenched. To that extent he was satiable. The main task of the treatment was to establish the connections between symptoms and life events, connections which were in no way as clearly conscious as they are here reported. During this process he was forever "quitting" smoking and failing to do so, going into diets and out of them.

In spite of the fact that he once reported feelings of unreality and on occasion self-consciousness bordering on ideas of reference, his diagnosis was relatively benign compared to the other; he was diagnosed "reactive depression," although this seemed in contradiction with the indications of fairly deep oral fixation and the possible implications of such enormous gain of weight. With respect to this fixation, the difference between the two patients seemed in some respects to be a matter of degree. This one showed more of an ability to *absorb* than did the other; he could readily respond to care; he could feel happy and *satisfied,* which the other one never had; he was satiable and then again there was the fact that through eating he had become fat, while the other was a "dry," emaciated-looking man. Insofar as identification was concerned, there were indications that the process could carry all the way through to its end, as in his identification with his mother (and father) in the care of his sister, which was both constructive and satisfying.

Yet he had a great many complaints about his inability to "absorb" knowledge or to "retain" things in his memory and about his inability to acquire and possess formulae to apply to problems; of having to arrive at the formula each time, as if it didn't exist to begin with, or as if he had to go through the process each time to feel that he "really knew the stuff." He had summaries and other carefully made-out study devices which he never used. He always had to extract his knowledge out of the maze of a great deal of reading. He did such tremendous amounts of reading that even his eating was not comparable to it. Because of this he slept on an average of four hours a night; he didn't even go to classes because he had so much reading to do. In an academic atmosphere this excessive reading is not too conspicuous. But with him there never was any doubt that it could be anything but part of his general clinical picture.*

The overeating and the excessive reading were not really different. The bulimia was a direct manifestation of the libidinal oral regression following the death of the mother. The ineffective reading (always falling short of real knowledge) was evidence of the relative lack of neutralization of the drive-energy.

Summarizing, the loss of object was followed by the regression of the ego, into which the devouring drive coming from the id was set loose; its energy was not bound, it required discharge, it was therefore not at the service of the ego. The relative lack of neutralization of the libidinal oral drive was responsible for the fact that eating, which was a direct discharge of the unaltered energy of the drive, became its main expression, rather than introjection, which is an ego mechanism of defense resulting from some degree of neutralization of the energy of the oral drive.

* Excessive reading is described by Erikson (1) as a symptom of disturbance of the "sense of workmanship" in cases of "identity diffusion."

Evidence has increasingly been brought to bear, first by Freud (9) and then by Hartmann (10), to the effect that in countercathexis the ego uses the neutralized energy of the aggressive drive, but there are no indications that this necessarily applies to all ego functions. On the other hand, Nunberg (17) has described the synthetic function as a "derivative of libido." This seems to be consistent with Hartmann's (10) and Menninger's (16) later hypothesis concerning the role of aggressive energy. What seems to be of special relevance is the fact that this aggressive energy may be *more or less neutralized* (10, 11, 12, 13, 18). Pursuing Nunberg's postulate in a similar way, we could say that the libidinal energy used by the ego in its synthetic function, like the aggressive energy it uses in other functions, may be *more or less neutralized,* and that the fate of the process of identification in a given case may depend on that degree of neutralization, although different phases of the process of identification may require energies in different states of neutralization: introjection less, integration into the unity of the ego, more.

If, for the moment, we set aside two questions—the question of what energy the ego uses in other functions (reality testing) and the question of possible sources of energy originating in the ego itself (12)—we may say tentatively that for the two functions in question—differentiation and synthesis—the ego has at its disposal two different energies and that in the former it uses the neutralized energy of the aggressive drive (Freud, Hartmann) and the neutralized energy of the libidinal drive in the latter (Nunberg), although in its actual processes the ego uses not only energy in different degrees of neutralization but possibly also mixtures of energies of different origins. In a recent paper Kris (15, p. 43) writes: "Emotional deficit in child care affects specifically the capacity to neutralize"; and later (p. 45): "Not only extreme deprivation but also extreme indulgence eliminates the incentive for mental activity." Kris' statement can be paraphrased by saying that the very conditions that lead to libidinal fixation (extreme deprivation and extreme indulgence) also affect the capacity to neutralize.

If all of this is in actuality much more relative than it appears from these statements, that is because the processes are reflection of *relative degrees* of neutralization. In excessive reading, for example, the drive-energy is relatively more neutralized than in excessive eating, where it is not neutralized at all. And here one may further conjecture that reading itself (and intellectualizing in general) was the ego's attempt to bind the energy of the oral drive, by the use of some of the already neutralized energy at its disposal. This would thus be an instance of what Freud (4) once postulated and has since been shown by Hartmann (10) not always to hold, i.e. that the ego uses the neutralized energy of the same drive it regulates.

It must be stressed once more that the foregoing conjectures can at best be reflection of only partial aspects of the ego processes and the psychodynamics involved in the cases reported. Perhaps the most extreme of the many shortcomings of this approach is indicated by the fact that in both cases—and even more so in the third one which will follow—the clinical evidence suggested that the unaltered energy of the aggressive drive, whether self- or object-directed, played a major role in their respective illnesses. Yet in these cases I seem arbitrarily to have isolated the role of the libidinal drive. But this I've done in the belief that it is useful to study one aspect and then the other, even though in actual fact they occur simultaneously. This is particularly important to stress, since the destructive effect that the aggressive drive can have on the ego processes can be incalculable when its energy is not neutralized. A very fine musician told me this: "The more important the occasion the worse the performance. When there's excitement, as in an important audition, in others the energy seems to exalt their performance, to make it finer, more exquisite. With me it's different; the energy in me always seems to go to destroy that which I want to do well so badly." The self-directed aggression not only spoiled his performance but indeed threatened to destroy him altogether, for at the time he came to treatment, whenever there was a flaw in the performance, suicide was in the offing.

Some reflections in retrospect about the treatment may highlight this complexity. In the first case reported, that of the man with the thesis, if I were to characterize my attitude with the patient in one word, the word would be *firmness,* in contrast to the other case, in which the word would be *kindness.* This one word reflects only my reaction, my approach (or rather part of it), and it says nothing about the contents in the relationship.

There is much more to psychotherapy—even when it has a very limited goal—than an attitude, which does in no way begin to reflect the intricacies of the treatment. Yet it is my own personal conviction now that with these respective patients no other attitudes would have worked. Even though these attitudes were in no way consciously calculated, but spontaneous, I can clearly see in retrospect how they might have been intuitive, resulting from my preconscious awareness of the following conditions: To put it in a very schematic way, in the second case (the mathematician), at least in their more superficial manifestations, the libidinal drive seemed to a large extent object-directed and the aggressive drive to a large extent self-directed. Thus in him there was little of either clinical narcissism or outwardly directed aggression, which was much in contrast to the first case, in whom there was much more of both (he was diagnosed "narcissistic character neurosis" and he was outwardly hostile and aggressive). Thus my attitude is my own reaction *vis-à-vis* the patient's instincts.

In the development of the ego the ultimate result depends on the relative degree of neutralization of the instinctual energy. Thus in the fat man there was more "censorship," more counter-cathexis, and particularly more repression. This process in the ego of erecting a wall of countercathexis, censorship, and psychological structure in general along the frontier of the id (as well as the super-ego and the outside world) constitutes its function of differentiation; it requires the availability of neutralized aggressive energy, and it depends primarily on the ego's ability to internalize conflict. The second patient showed a better ability to internalize the object (mother) as well as the conflict. In the first case the symptoms were the result of constant interaction in actual external reality between the patient and his mother, just as is frequently the case with small children in treatment. Thus, among other things, his refusal to finish the thesis which the mother was naturally constantly urging (she was supporting him) was not unlike his refusal to move his bowels in response to her discipline in childhood. In contrast to this, in the other patient the mother had become an internal object and his main symptom—cancer phobia —was the result of a partial identification with her.

The third case I have set aside from the other two because in it the treatment has brought about no positive results so far. The reason for this I do not know with certainty, but perhaps it has something to do with the fact that in this case the super-ego conflict plays a far greater role than in the other two. Yet I have included this case because in it the attempts to substitute normally unconscious ego processes with conscious intellectual activity are particularly clear.

This is the case of a girl in her early twenties, the only child of very old parents. After an almost complete and permanent rift with them, she had left them in the Deep South and for many years maintained only superficial and formal communication with them. She was also a student of literature and, of the three, she was the most scholarly one. In common with the others, she had one distinctive characteristic of this group of patients at which I have already hinted. In their values and interests many of these patients (the ones here presented and others) have made a very sweeping departure from their own backgrounds. Most of them abandoned their religion, as had this one, even though in the depths of her depression she talked about her illness as "sin"; she did not attend church and, at least formally, she abandoned her religion. The others made a "clean break." Many had gone into graduate school very much against their parents' will or to their complete indifference. Most often the parents had no scholarly inclination or intellectual interests. For instance, none was as much of a "thinker" as any of the three patients. Only the father of the first patient had gone to graduate school; he was a dentist before his encephalitis.

I have mentioned before that in the cases here presented the self-accusation "I am a fraud," the sense of inner emptiness, and the complaint "I have retained nothing in my memory"—or a very close variation of it—all concurred, and that this is also true for other cases. Now, we come upon this other element: a sweeping departure from their backgrounds. I do not mean to include it as a constant element in the clinical picture; that would require the study of more cases with sufficient knowledge about their background. But, in any case, in the patients here reported the self-accusation "I am a fraud, I am not a scholar," takes on a new, different meaning. It is a true statement in the sense "I am not a (born) scholar" or "I am not a scholar (by birth)." In that sense the symptom is an attempt at recovery of their identification with their background—this, of course, besides the obvious implications of the symptom in terms of super-ego conflict. In those terms the accusation is directed at the internalized parent (*"you are not a scholar"*) and it is also accurate.

This young lady, up to the time of the acute breakdown that brought her to treatment, had been very proud—and rightly so—of her mind and her knowledge. But she freely conceded that without it she *was* nothing, "absolutely nothing." The breakdown occurred after, for the first time in her life, she had an episode of real intimacy with a young man, a fellow student, following which she began to doubt her mind and her knowledge and went into a panic, during which she felt empty.*

In this woman the sense of inner emptiness had literally countless expressions. She spent many hours outpouring variations of the same theme: she felt hollow, like an empty shell. On occasions she approached complete nothingness and described herself as "a vague shadow." At times this took a less malignant, more abstract, and perhaps more accurate form: "I am a person but I don't have a personality." When she referred to her thinking, the expressions were particularly abundant. She was "completely empty of ideas"; "I am a complete blank; nothing has really ever registered in my memory." And again at times this was milder: "I have read and I have known things, but real knowledge I don't have; nothing ever really came alive." This went on and on, interminably, with a dreadful richness of expressions, analogies, and near-delusions, interspersed with suicidal ideas. From time to time there were partial recoveries which she described as "feeling the ideas flowing back into me." On one occasion, in a critical essay, she had accused Hawthorne of puritanism (she was puritanical herself, and, more particularly, so were her parents) and she in

* This would correspond quite exactly to what Erikson (1, p. 79) calls a "state of acute identity diffusion," which "usually becomes manifest at a time when the young individual finds himself exposed to a combination of experiences which demand his simultaneous commitment to *physical intimacy,* to decisive occupational choice, to energetic *competition* and to *psychosocial self-definition."*

turn had been accused of missing the irony, the humor, of the writer's "puritanism." This was devastating to her because "you see, something has left me, or maybe I never had it. How can you be a person without humor?"

One day she came to tell me how, all of a sudden, she understood everything. She had arrived at some kind of strange peace with herself. From the solemn mood that accompanied it, it all sounded like a freakish substitute of a suicidal resolution. But it was a fantasy of recovery, a fantasy which reflected the ego's attempt to reintegrate itself by systematic intellectual activity. It went like this: "I now know that I have always lived frivolously; I never read seriously and carefully; I read, but didn't study. What I need is to take five years off—maybe in a mental institution—and during those five years I will go once more over every book I have read and I will learn it; I will go carefully over every character in the literature until I have really *acquired* them, and only then will I begin to be something."

On the basis of the conjectures made on the other two cases, I believe that much of the material of this one speaks for itself and I shall make no further elaborations.

Because I have focused on certain common features in these three cases, I may have made them appear similar clinically, but that was not the case at all. They were vastly different, diagnostically and otherwise. This last case had something which was very much its own. There seemed to be no visible trace of libido (object-directed, that is) anywhere, on any level of fixation. This lack of discernible libido is what at times gave her the appearance of a ghost, or a somnambulant or, to use her own words, "a vague shadow." This was puzzling in terms of the rest of the picture, although I knew that a diagnosis would have settled that matter. This would have been easy were it not for the fact that she was functioning, even though marginally, still on a high level. And actually she always functioned well, in spite of her great misery.

In conclusion, this has been an unsystematic, stereoscopic-like view of a small part of an area of psychological function which presents almost limitless possibilities for investigation. The area is that of the use of intellectualization by the ego to assist it in its essential functions. The limited part of it here touched upon is that of the relationship of intellectual activity to the process of identification.

In highly intellectualizing individuals, who use intellectualization both as a defense mechanism and as an adaptive function, some ego processes which are normally unconscious become indirectly available to observation through their more or less recognizable, intellectual derivatives.

Intellectualization being so essential a function of the ego, the fact that in the verbalizations of these individuals (and almost all are highly "verbal") the internal workings of intellectualization are sometimes recognizable is what makes this area of study so promising.

REFERENCES

1. Erikson, E. H., The problem of ego identity, *Journal of the American Psychoanalytic Association, 4:*56–121. 1956.

2. Freud, A., *The Ego and the Mechanisms of Defense* (1936), New York, International Universities Press, 1946.

3. Freud, S., Notes upon a case of obsessional neurosis (1909), in *Collected Papers* (London, Hogarth Press, 1950), *3*, 291–383.

4. ——— The unconscious (1915), in *Collected Papers, 4*, 98–136.

5. ——— Mourning and melancholia (1917), in *Collected Papers, 4*, 152–70.

6. ——— *Beyond the Pleasure Principle* (1920), London, Hogarth Press, 1948.

7. ——— *Group Psychology and the Analysis of the Ego* (1921), New York, Liveright, 1949.

8. ——— *The Ego and the Id* (1923), London, Hogarth Press, 1949.

9. ——— Analysis terminable and interminable (1937), in *Collected Papers, 5*, 316–57.

10. Hartmann, H., Comments on the psychoanalytic theory of the ego, *Psychoanalytic Study of the Child* (New York, International Universities Press, 1950), *5*, 74–96.

11. ——— The mutual influences in the development of ego and id, *Psychoanalytic Study of the Child* (New York, International Universities Press, 1952), *7*, 9–30.

12. ——— Notes on the theory of sublimation, *Psychoanalytic Study of the Child* (New York, International Universities Press, 1955), *10*, 9–29.

13. Kris, E., *Psychoanalytic Explorations in Art,* New York, International Universities Press, 1952.

14. ——— Psychoanalysis and the study of creative imagination, *Bulletin of the New York Academy of Medicine,* 29(4):334–51. 1953.

15. ——— Neutralization and sublimation, *Psychoanalytic Study of the Child* (New York, International Universities Press, 1955), *10,* 30–46.

16. Menninger, K., *Man against Himself,* New York, Harcourt, 1938.

17. Nunberg, H., *Principles of Psychoanalysis,* New York, International Universities Press, 1955.

18. Rapaport, D., On the psychoanalytic theory of thinking, *International Journal of Psychoanalysis,* 30:1–10. 1950.

19. ——— *Organization and Pathology of Thought,* New York, Columbia University Press, 1951.

CHAPTER 14

Treatment of Idiosyncratic Adaptation in College Students

BY BRYANT M. WEDGE

1

Failure to undergo adaptive change is posited as a developmental syndrome of college students. Clinical examples are used to develop a model of the mechanisms of such change in psychotherapy. It is suggested that this may be analogous to developmental processes in other college students.

SOME DEGREE of adaptive change may be assumed to occur during any student's college experience. Many students who consult a psychiatrist during college do so to get aid in modifying their own outmoded and ineffective adaptive patterns and to find new modes of expression and interaction. This chapter is an attempt to describe a brief psychotherapeutic method which has proven effective in this process.

The implications of these clinical observations for the normal college experience cannot yet be fully shown. It seems reasonable, however, to draw limited comparison between the events occurring in those patients in treatment and the developmental experience of the college student in campus life.

2

The descriptions to follow are frankly one-sided in the sense that they will deal mainly with the relation of social experience to adaptational patterns and their modification. This procedure is necessitated by the nature of the changes being described, that is, they are most apparent in the psychosocial sphere. It is well to keep in mind that concurrent shifts take place in deeper levels of the psychic apparatus even though these are not discussed.

In order to understand the alterations in adaptation taking place in college it is necessary first to outline the social origins of character in earlier life.

A child growing up in a family has to adapt himself in a variety of ways to the other family members. He has to get along comfortably with these important persons in order to have his needs from them for food, drink, and a place to sleep, for love and affection, and for interchanges of all kinds satisfied, and to avoid the punishment of their displeasure, whether expressed physically or by withdrawal of approval. In order to get along he begins to learn very quickly which impulses need to be curbed and which can be expressed, as well as the timing, manner, and intensity with which he may express himself. This process is called adaptation.

Families are on the whole remarkably consistent within themselves in the adaptational demands which they place upon their children. Consequently it soon comes about that the child does not need to deal with each new situation or impulse as unique, but is able to develop habitual patterns of impulse expression which are the nucleus of character. Each family, no matter how well integrated into a cultural or social context, is in some ways unique in the adaptational demands which it places on its children.* Consequently the habitual adaptive patterns developed within the family, unless modified by other influences, would result in idiosyncratic adaptational modes, unsuitable as a basis for appropriate response in extrafamily situations. Adelaide Johnson and several colleagues have shown in a series of papers that this is frequently the source of unsocial or maladaptive behavior in children.† In this work, children and one or more parents were taken into treatment simultaneously. The investigators were able to show with remarkable clarity that the poorly adaptive behavior

---

* For examples of recent work in family dynamics see D. Mendell and S. Fisher, "An Approach to Neurotic Behavior in Terms of a Three Generation Family Model," *Journal of Nervous and Mental Disease, 123* (2):171–80, 1956. S. Fisher and D. Mendell, "The Communication of Neurotic Patterns Over Two and Three Generations," *Psychiatry, 19*:41–46, 1956. N. W. Ackerman, "Interpersonal Disturbances in the Family," *Psychiatry, 17*:359–68, 1954.

† See, for example, Adelaide M. Johnson, "Sanctions for Superego Lacunae of Adolescents, in *Searchlights on Delinquency,* ed. K. R. Eissler, New York, International Universities Press, 1949.

of the children was often the direct counterpart of wishes or faults in the parental structure, and that the behavior was sanctioned knowingly or unconsciously by parental behavior.

Fortunately the limits of characterological development are not bounded by the idiosyncratic experience of the family environment. While it may be demonstrated regularly that basic roots of adult character structure are to be found in the experience with the family, less attention has been paid to the modifications of adaptive pattern which continue to take place to some degree throughout the lifetime of an individual. As soon as the child begins to come in contact with the wider human environment, he experiences some degree of failure of his habitual adaptive patterns in bringing about their accustomed satisfactions. The frustrations involved in these failures eventually become severe enough to force experimentation with modified adaptive modes.

The most important institutional arena for character modification is the school. The classroom presents a situation requiring a series of new adaptational acts, with some of them altering or even countering the adaptive patterns achieved in the family. It is beyond the scope of this discussion to consider the mechanisms by which new adaptive patterns are achieved but it may be mentioned that one of the more important of these is that of identification, a process of modeling one's ideals and adaptive patterns on the image of important figures in the environment. In this context, character may be said to develop and be modified through multiple partial identifications.

Successful integration of adaptational patterns developed in the family and those necessary in the wider environment depends on the ability to reconcile or compromise the adaptational demands of the two scenes. If these demands are too widely divergent, such a reconciliation does not take place and the child develops differing adaptational patterns in the various contexts of his life, with consequent weakening of the level of total integration which he may achieve. It can be seen that it is important for the flexibility of character optimum for life in a complex world that new social contexts be different in their demands from that of the family, but at the same time that they be not so different that over-all integration is sacrificed.

During all the school period, through adolescence and until leaving high school, usually at the age of sixteen to eighteen, the child continues partly under the domination of the adaptational demands of the family. He is still economically and in many ways emotionally dependent on his parents and still oriented toward them for fulfillment of his needs. Even in the case of those instances in which children spend extended periods of time away from the family, as do those who attend independent (preparatory) schools, the family remains the primary source of life orientation. Often enough the independent school represents simply an extension of the family, for the purposes of character development at least partly replacing or substituting for the parental role. With the ending of the school period there is an abrupt coming of age, which places sweeping demands on the adaptational capacity of the individual.

3

Leaving school carries with it the strongest implications of giving up dependence on the family as the continued main source of adaptational requirement. During the ensuing period, roughly from the ages of eighteen to twenty-two, there is, as Peter Blos has pointed out, an urgency to achieve a state of final commitment and stable organization of adaptational patterns which is recognizable as adult character (2). The experience of the young person at this strategic time can have extraordinary significance for the form which this final commitment takes.

Some individuals enter adult life and the responsibilities of self-sufficiency and marriage almost immediately upon leaving school. This requires the adoption of a stable adult character organization rapidly and without further opportunity for what Erikson calls "free role experimentation" (5). The characterological position assumed under these conditions is usually one which is relatively inflexible and unmodulated, with lack of rounding off and integration of adaptational patterns. The boy or girl who, however, continues with further vocational training or education delays the assumption of adulthood. Erikson, in discussing adolescence generally, has developed a view which seems to apply particularly well to this period of late adolescence. He states, "This period can be viewed as a psycho-social moratorium during which the individual, through free role experimentation, may find a niche in some section of his society" (5). This process of achieving adult character status is often recognized by educators as the process of "finding oneself."

The young person who goes to college finds himself more free than he has ever been in his life before to experiment with a range of adaptational modalities. Eventually he must choose among these alternatives or some combination of them his uniquely individual adult character pattern. Meanwhile, he has opportunity to seek his personal reorganization through processes of free role experimentation, multiple partial identification, and trial experiences with new adaptational modes. Usually by the age of twenty-two or twenty-three the person has achieved that stable integration of character necessary for a solid sense of personal identity and for a consistent adult life course. Failure to achieve this in a satisfactory way may be expressed in the characterological syndrome of prolonged adolescence (3) or alternatively in the symptom syndromes of neurosis or psychosis.

The student in college finds that his observations and experiences in this new situation challenge the idiosyncratic adaptational patterns developed within family life. These circumstances force him into experimentation with modifications of adaptation which in ideal instances lead to a modulation of manner of impulse expression, to an increased flexibility and range of responsiveness, to that "strength of character" resulting from adequate integration, together with a tolerance for new experience and a degree of continued adaptational effort necessary for satisfactory adult life.

In her discussion of the ego and the id at puberty Anna Freud points out the effects of failure of modification in these terms: "Ego institutions which have resisted the onslaught of puberty without yielding generally remain throughout life inflexible, unassailable and insusceptible of the rectification which a changing reality demands" (6). The point of yielding of these maladaptive attitudes is often only at college; in fact, it is observable that the stronger the family structure, the longer the delay.

4

Some students who come to college are unable to alter the idiosyncratic adaptational patterns developed in the family. This may be the result of the quantitative intensity of family ties or of insufficient capacity to interact outside of the family. They are invariably anxious about the meaning of growing up. As they cling to their former adaptational modes they find themselves increasingly isolated from their fellow students. Eventually they fall into such difficulties that they develop symptoms or function poorly in their work. It is then that they may consult a psychiatrist, or at least some person who can tell them how to get help.

The examples reported here are drawn from experiences in treatment of students in the above described position. The cases are chosen because of the absence of other gross psychological disturbance than that to be described, but nevertheless it must be pointed out that for purposes of demonstrating the thesis under consideration, material relating to deeper conflicts has been omitted. In short, these presentations should not be regarded as telling the whole story, only an important facet of it.

The cases which follow demonstrate the main steps in therapy of students with persistent idiosyncratic adaptation patterns in college. The major treatment phases are (a) establishing a relationship, (b) development of insight into the basis of the adaptational mode through the interpretive act of expressing surprise, (c) exploration of new adaptational modes, and (d) consolidation of alternative adaptative patterns (post-therapeutic).

Case 1. A pattern of inhibition. A, in his junior year, found himself sleeping through classes and examinations, without interest in studies and undecided on his field of future work. He was puzzled by his behavior but not much disturbed about himself. His dean, however, was disturbed and, after pointing out that *A* was on the road to failure, suggested that he consult a psychiatrist in the health department.

To the therapist *A* presented an attitude of indifferent and self-satisfied prissiness. As he spoke in his precise and almost lisping fashion, he outlined his standing in college, which he supposed would lead to his failure in spite of his previous good academic achievement. This didn't matter much to him, since he could think of nothing he wanted to do with his future. He had been interested in architecture, but this interest had dwindled as he had discovered that his next steps in the field would involve the study of actual structural problems. He didn't expect much from psychotherapy but went along with the therapist's rather indifferent suggestion that since he had come, we might as well spend some time investigating what kept him from his classes, especially since in a vague way he wanted to continue in college.

In his weekly visits *A* at first didn't present anything spontaneously but wondered what the therapist wanted him to talk about. A kind of superficial history was developed and the therapist suggested that he might tell him about his family, social life, and so on. From *A*'s standpoint all was "normal," although he had never dated a girl, had no particular friends and hadn't experienced enthusiasm since he could remember. As he described his relationships, these seemed bland and pale on all fronts and so also did his family and the people he talked about. Since any attempt to explore details of events or relationships led to even more blandness, the therapist had to be content to suggest topics and be mildly interested in *A*'s discussion. Gradually *A* came to speak more easily and discursively and a kind of low-keyed enjoyment of the interviews became apparent.

In his third interview the patient "chanced" to remark on a conversation with his sister, two years younger, which had taken place while she was taking a bath. He reported this in his usual bland way and was surprised when the therapist stopped him to ask for details about the site of the conversation. When this was clarified, the therapist showed frank astonishment that grown brother and sister should be so immodest with each other. For the first time the patient rose to the defense and in doing so was led to describe the family's mode of dress, or rather undress, within the home. His mother, father, sister, and himself never bothered to wear clothes "just for the family." This seemed to *A* to be the only natural, modern method of behavior at home and commented that he agreed with his mother that undue modesty in the family seemed unsophisticated and unnatural. He didn't recognize any special feelings about this but did recall that the family members scrupulously avoided any physical contact with each other. The therapist did not conceal his amazement at the patient's and his family's blandness about nudity and remarked that it was no wonder that the patient was so inhibited about looking closely at anything.

During the subsequent hours the patient took an objective look at his family life and his current life also, for the first time.

As he described the family now, it took on life and color, and the patient seemed astounded at every discovery. The central figure in the family was *A*'s mother. She was an excitable woman, continually tense, and for years had been maintained on sedatives and tranquilizing drugs by the family doctor. When she felt she was opposed, she would react with a tantrum of rage and weeping or else sink into physical illness. The father was a quiet, timid, and religious individual who "went along" with the mother. The patient, like his father, was afraid to oppose her for fear of her rages. The therapist reminded *A* that his mother wasn't with him now.

As this period of treatment progressed, *A* began to experiment with a number of new activities. He returned to his classes and changed his study plans to include courses which would lead to application of his aesthetic interests. He sought dates with girls and worked out in the gymnasium and was surprised at his success. On his next visit home he maintained his modesty in matters of dress and found himself uncomfortable in the presence of his mother or sister in a state of undress. As a matter of fact, they too began to be uncomfortable about it, so that before his holiday was over, a reasonable level of family modesty was being maintained. He was now concerned about his mother and said, "I'm no longer afraid of her," and spoke with the family physician, only to learn that the physician had urged psychiatric consultation on her for some years without success. His mother was upset about the change in her son, but her expostulations seemed ineffectual and, to his surprise, soon disappeared. Shortly after his return from this holiday, the patient and therapist agreed that he was quite able to carry on his own life. He had been seen for seven interviews over three months. On his return for follow-up at the therapist's request a year later, *A* had decided on a career in the production end of certain artistic work. He presented a firmer and more sharply defined personality and, although he was dissatisfied with his social gains, he thought he would be able to make progress in this area too.

Case 2. A pattern of distrust. *B*'s initial attitude was one of extraordinary guardedness, and as he outlined his difficulties in bitten-off sentences, he made it clear that although he hoped that he might be helped, he wasn't going to be taken in by false promises. *B* had been referred by a study counselor in his first college year, since he couldn't seem to concentrate on his work and was in danger of failing, in fact was considering resigning from college. His complaint, however, was that he had no friends, couldn't find any aim in life and that he felt "like a slob." That college life seemed hollow was a continuation of his feeling of the last five years.

B offered his history readily in the manner described above. He came from a small community in which his family owned the only major industry. His life was determined by the role of the Boss' Son, which involved the necessity of maintaining a front of confident competence. He had had no intimates for years, since this would involve revelations of his concern about being liked. He felt increasingly afraid of being seen through, and this had spread so that he expected shoeshine boys or hotel clerks to attack him as a "fake." He had hoped to feel differently in college but in fact had felt worse, especially as he compared the way he felt with the way his colleagues appeared, so poised and cool.

Despite *B*'s bristling and suspicious approach the therapist recognized the appeal being made to him and chose to ignore the defiance. When he commented that *B* must be desperately lonesome and really wanting help with the way he felt, there were a few moments of tears and a strong but wary affirmation of the wish to undertake treatment before *B* returned to a further exposition of his slobbishness.

The second hour with *B* proved to be the turning point of treatment. Already there was no doubt that *B* felt assured that he would be received despite his shortcomings. He told of disappointments in a girl and people he had trusted, and went on to outline his expectation of being treated as a kind of impostor and accused of dishonesty. When the therapist wondered if *B* might not feel that he was dishonest himself, he began to confess instances of hoodwinking his family, especially his father. When he or his sister wanted something, it was impossible to get it by asking directly, and they had worked out an elaborate system of hints and innuendo known as "planting the idea" that would lead to father's surprising them with a gift. On the other hand, there was no use trying to keep a bargain in the family, and *B* gave instances of broken promises by both father and sister. For example, he'd sent money home from a summer job for the sister to bank and she'd taken it for her own use, later bribing him with a gift. The father had promised him a car if he'd achieve a certain honor and then had excused himself from the bargain on grounds of unexpected expenses. As these episodes were revealed in the most innocuous terms, the therapist supplied labels to the behavior such as, "In fact your sister actually looted your bank account," or "So your father defaulted" on his agreement.

Following this, the patient began to describe interactions in the family, finally summing up the family as being governed by pretense and expediency. The sister, while living for a while in a distant city, had run up large bills and then left town. The father's business was operated by some fancy bookkeeping that involved presenting a false picture of profit and solvency, so that in fact the entire family was trained in keeping up a false front in the village while hoping for a lucky break. Actually they didn't even trust one another; the mother, for example, openly feared her son might become an alcoholic, and the father continually warned him against being a wastrel in college. After this material had been explored, it was not difficult for the patient or therapist to understand why *B* was so frightened of being "seen through" and also why he momentarily expected the support from home to drop away.

The next hour with the patient found him turning his attention to his immediate relationships, including his feelings of being exploited by his roommate, who used his equipment without asking. During the interview *B* decided he should take a stand on this instead of attempting to sabotage the roommate's activities. So it was that by the fourth interview *B* showed a striking change. He worked seriously and openly at exploring his feelings and behavior and showed the beginnings of a genuinely based self-confidence. Actually, he realized his grudging admiration for his classmates and felt less inadequate in comparison with them. The remaining five hours of this brief treatment were taken up with continued exploration of certain more basic problems and concurrently with the problems of his establishment as a functioning college man. Patient and therapist then agreed that the main attention should be directed to consolidating his experience and that the remaining problems could wait until they became resolved through his new experience or until he could take up further treatment from a position of some strength. It should be added that his feelings toward his family altered as he insisted upon definite agreements with his father (about his needs for money which he'd previously "chiseled on") and which his father kept, much to his surprise. He was certainly no closer to them than before, but less distrustful.

At the follow-up interview eight months later *B* was firmly established in a new school year. He said that he was finding himself able to study with friends for the first time in his life. He had found his father more reasonable as "I have been more unreasonable." While he was still undecided on his career, he felt he was working toward something even though he didn't know what. Finally, he said that he felt somewhat adrift because he had no one to depend on for values but guessed he was finding his own. As is common following psychotherapy of this syndrome, *B* found his recall of the treatment quite vague and couldn't say just what its effects were "since I'm still developing anyway," but he said that he had enjoyed talking with the therapist and had been pleased when he was invited to return for the follow-up interview.

Case 3. A dependent attitude. *C* was referred by an internist to whom he had persistently come with complaints of dizziness, lassitude, and pains in the knees, which he thought certainly must represent an obscure virus infection. He had an engaging boyish air of frankness about him as he talked to the therapist. He was genuinely distressed that he felt too ill to keep up with his college work, and although he enjoyed having someone to listen to him with a sympathetic ear, he had decided to withdraw from college for a time to rest and recuperate. It was only after this decision was taken that the therapist showed some surprise that the parents were so sympathetic to this action.

C's paternal grandfather had risen from obscure origins to a position of economic independence by dint of diligence, imagination, and hard work. He passed on to the patient's father the habit of hard work, and the father had not only increased the family wealth but considerably elevated its social position. The father, however, was determined that his son should not have to undergo the "struggle" which he had experienced. *C*'s mother was extremely fond of her only child, worried about his health and concerned lest he overstrain himself. She was not very pleased that he should see a psychiatrist, as he promptly did when he returned to begin his second try at college. She had the impression, she said, that psychiatrists taught children to blame and hate their mothers.

During the second period of therapy, the patient never once complained of physical ills. He was afraid that he might not be able to keep up with his classmates; he was afraid that he might give up and return home again. Almost from the first he enlisted the therapist's aid in ferreting out and withstanding the temptation of the truly astounding inducements which were offered him to give up the struggle and return home. There was, the father assured him, no necessity for him to worry about the future; in fact, if he wanted, he could right now undertake the nominal supervision of a subsidiary enterprise which would enable him to afford a very comfortable life. When he was unwise enough to flaunt the fact that he'd stayed up all night to finish a paper, his mother came to a local hotel to supervise his activities so that he wouldn't overstrain himself. Eventually as he told about these and many other events, he would smile conspiratorially and remark, "The silver platter again." Gradually as he was able to see and resist these temptations, he gained confidence in himself, but it was only after a full year that his family was able to share his pride in his accomplishment, which they now agree they had feared him incapable of.

Case 4. A constricted adaptive pattern. D, as a senior, still felt uncomfortable in the presence of girls. After he found that he became nauseated when alone with a girl, he avoided dating. He felt unsure of himself, and although he was an excellent student, he regarded himself as a failure, even academically.

D's family were unusually warm and close to each other, often picnicking and playing music together. *D*'s father was a minister, with a great deal of warmth and a sense of humor. His mother was an excellent minister's wife—sociable, conscientious, and dependable. The parents came to see the therapist together, for *D* had naturally discussed this problem with them as he did all others, and they were as puzzled and distressed about it as he. Both were proud of their son and almost vehement in their protests: they couldn't see how this had happened because they were perfectly sure that *D* was a boy who had never had anything but clean thoughts.

D was frank, friendly, intelligent, and deeply puzzled. He seemed a thoroughly capable lad. In his discussions with the therapist he conducted himself in a forthright and manly way, and it was soon evident that even his inmost conscious thoughts and dreams would pass inspection by any minister. He even avoided bull sessions, or walked out if the conversation turned to exploits with girls or "too much muck." When the therapist inquired about the nature of the "muck," *D* became quite uneasy and only with difficulty could mention bull session subjects that were surely innocuous by the standards of other boys at college. The therapist expressed his gentle astonishment that matters so usual and natural to life should cause so much pain to acknowledge. This served as a mode of introduction into *D*'s cautious exploration, both in and out of the treatment hours, of the mores of the world about him, and of the difference between thought and action. It is true that as he became a freer young man in his life, he was less intimate with his family, who were quite ready to understand and accept the change of status.

5

It is necessary to say a word about diagnostic problems before proceeding to a discussion of the treatment measures involved. As the examples have perhaps suggested, the symptom picture in the case of developmental arrest at a level of idiosyncratic family adaptation is a varied one. Although the symptoms are frequently expressed in some conflict with the environment, they also may appear in the form of inhibitions, anxiety, or other neurotic form. Differentiating this developmental syndrome from neurotic or character neurotic disturbances depends upon an appraisal of the circumstances in which the symptoms occur. These are the circumstances of having recently been separated from close family supervision and exposed to the freedom of a new situation. The symptoms are usually of relatively recent onset and often do not seem as disturbing to the patient as would seem justified by their description.* Differentiation from active or passive adolescent

* This is not surprising, since the symptoms are the outcome of adaptational distortions in the service of defense, and being ego operations can hardly be

rebellion is simple in that the symptoms in the latter circumstance are displayed in feeling or acting out toward external persons or institutions, while in this adaptive syndrome, the conflict is internal and the symptoms are of more or less clear-cut neurotic character. It is essential to the diagnosis that a therapeutic trial be made, regardless of the exact symptom picture, so long as the diagnosis is in doubt. The delayed adolescent is quick to form a relationship if he has opportunity for one acceptable on his own terms and shows a readiness to interact not characteristic of the more structured disorders. A few visits usually suffice to determine the degree to which the presenting character pattern is fixed or is open to modification.

In the experience of the writer this developmental syndrome occurs only in the narrow age range of 16–23 years and for the most part in a college situation or some rather similar life position. The time of onset of acute symptoms leading to psychiatric consultation has been observed to be mainly in the first college year with a distribution ratio during the four years of about 3, 1, 1, 2. Apparently the pressure of approaching graduation serves to mobilize acute conflict in some instances in which the maintenance of idiosyncratic adaptational patterns had not previously been incompatible with college experience. In a considerable experience this picture has never been seen in graduate students and only seldom outside of the college setting. Two clear-cut instances have been observed in high school graduates working away from home but surprisingly enough no similar cases were observed in a military outpatient service. These observations lead one to the hypothesis that this adaptive syndrome is related to the congeries of cultural and family circumstance which is associated with attendance at college.

Rather than attempting to deal with all the details of psychotherapy in the situation under discussion, this paper will concern itself with two maneuvers or techniques peculiarly applicable to the problem. It should be undertood that this discussion does not pretend to deal with the whole of the psychotherapeutic process of these cases, which would involve technical details dis-

---

ego dystonic. The discomfort which these patients do feel comes from dissatisfaction with reality—that is, the failure of the milieu to accept them as they are. Hence many students with this symptom picture come to the psychiatrist by referral, rather than spontaneously.

cussed in many other writings on dynamic psychotherapy. The technical problems to be discussed here are those concerned with the development of a relationship in the therapeutic situation and with the role of active surprise as a therapeutic tool.

The college student away from his family who retreats behind idiosyncratic adaptational patterns is a lonely person. He cannot afford relationships with his colleagues or teachers which might threaten these attitudes and cause him anxiety. Consequently in order to work psychotherapeutically with these students, it is necessary first to establish a treatment relationship within the framework of which exploration of the defensive attitudes and underlying impulses is relatively safe. These student patients are remarkably ready to form such a relationship because of their loneliness, but can do so only under the circumstances that the relationship does not too seriously threaten the established modes of adaptation. In order that such rapport may come about, then, the therapist must adapt his behavior in the therapeutic situation to the defensive needs of the patient in the initial phases.

Psychiatrists particularly talented in work with adolescents seem to be endowed with a capacity for rapport or inner sympathy with the struggle of the young person. They also possess freedom to interact without themselves being overwhelmed.

Because of the uniqueness of the defensive patterns which have been derived from the family, there can be no general formula to guide the conduct of the therapist. While a gentle, permissive, and accepting attitude may enable a therapist to relate to certain students, a strict and even authoritarian role is the only attitude which others can accept. Aichhorn was successful with delinquents, partly at least because he was able to outguess them in their deception (1). Blos speaks of the dramatic quality of some of his interviews with adolescents (4). Erikson, who pays great attention to the wider environment, speaks of the "new and honest mutuality of function which must set the patient's face toward . . . a strenuously refuted future" (5). Fry, working with college students, emphasized the importance of rapport as essential to therapeutic result (7).

One such patient may feelingly express moral strictures against smoking cigarettes, while the next may assert his right to Bohemian liberty. A frequent defensive pattern among college students is that of extraordinary intellectuality. Such students seem usually to have read more of Freud than the therapist, and they have a complete and often reasonably accurate outline of their own psychopathology. The great majority of college students who are seen when in this developmental position present some variety of inhibition, withdrawal, inability to work, excessive self-concern, or neurotic symptom formation of recent onset. Since these reactions are so individual, it would be almost impossible to attempt an exhaustive listing of the presenting situation. The point is that the therapist who seeks rapport with the student patient must accept and often even reciprocate the presenting approach on its own ground.

Up to a point, the psychotherapist in the initial phases must be able to philosophize with the intellectualizer, to discuss artistic values with the young aesthete, and to review world affairs with the junior politician. The therapist may find it necessary to complement the clinging, questioning, frightened approach of the dependent student with expressions of firmness, reassurance, and willingness to suggest solutions to immediate problems. With prissy or inhibited students, he must be able to respect the patient's reservations. Bombastic youths often can relax with the therapist only when he has shown that he can control the situation firmly.

Such patients are so ready to respond to an acceptable therapeutic climate that sufficient confidence is often established within the first one or two interviews, so that the patient can move, more or less cautiously, to the testing of the idiosyncratic family structure and, incidentally, his own defense systems. That this position is achieved so quickly in the treatment situation demonstrates how eager such students are to seek alternative solutions; that they have not been able to do so before speaks for the anxiety involved. Once this therapeutic position is arrived at, whether in two interviews or two months, the therapist is invariably given ample opportunity to exercise the therapeutic technique of active expression of surprise.

In each of the examples cited it can be noted that at some point after the patient had gained confidence in the treatment situation, he chose to reveal, as if by chance, some event of family life which was sufficiently out of context as to cause the therapist to express wonderment, astonishment, or surprise. The timing, manner, and effects of this act of intervention are issues which determine the success of treatment in facilitating healthy character modification.

The moment at which a display of active surprise is appropriate is determined by the development of the therapeutic situation and the patient's readiness to explore intimate material. During the earliest interviews an experienced psychotherapist rarely has reason to be surprised at material presented by his patients. It is only after considerable acquaintance has been gained that the therapist comes to expect a continuation of internally consistent material. If at this point the patient chooses to reveal, by whatever means, an aspect of his life which is inconsistent with the trend of the previously presented material, the therapist's spontaneous reaction is to experience the affect of surprise. Consequently the timing of an interpretative act of surprise depends on the development of a relationship in which the therapist has come to expect a certain reliability of production by the patient, followed by the revelation by the patient, from his position of security in the therapeutic situation, of material inconsistent with his previous productions.

The kind of material which may elicit surprise from the therapist is more or less unique to each case. It should be added parenthetically that although the therapist has been able to see through the material intellectually or could even predict the nature of the revelation to come, he still experiences the affect. The revelations are usually ones which concern the family environment, although they may also concern some hitherto hidden aspect of the patient's own character or behavior. It seems to be of little consequence which of these are chosen since, in the student whose adaptational patterns are still intimately connected with the family milieu, the problems of character, behavior, and family environment are practically synonymous. It is a cause for some amazement, for example, when a hitherto shy, inhibited, and blushing youth suddenly reveals the existence of a family nudist colony. When a young man, apparently the soul of uprightness, tells after several hours of the second set of books which members of the family are keeping on one another, the therapist may experience a touch of wonder; as he indeed may again when the young-man-about-campus lets him in on the fact that Mother is sending a roast chicken every Sunday and little snacks on the other days of the week. It would be detrimental to some kinds of treatment for the psychotherapist to display an open expression of this affect, particularly so early in the treatment. It is rather more easy for a careful psychotherapist to conceal rather than express this feeling which, after all, is modest in its strength. However, in the developmental circumstances being discussed and in the context of brief psychotherapy, a controlled expression of surprise may open the way to considerable adaptive modification.

The way in which the interpretation of active surprise is made depends on the character and mode of expression of the therapist as well as the tolerance and sensitivities of the patient. An expression of surprise which created fear in the patient or seemed punitive to him could only impair the therapeutic situation. With more sensitive and inhibited patients, a spontaneous raised eyebrow or an "Oh?" with a rising inflection may constitute an adequate stimulus to further questioning, exploration, and experimentation with the character pattern in question. With more complacent, rigid, or bombastic patients the therapist may find it appropriate to respond with verbal ejaculations and elaboration, as in the case of *B,* where the therapist said, "My Lord, do you mean to tell me your sister actually *looted* your bank account?" Again, while technical considerations enter into the timing and mode of expression of this kind of interpretation, the therapist, as a reasonably sensitive person engaged in a relationship, should be able to rely on his natural tact to a large degree. This constitutes the so-called intuitive response, which is subject to control as well as to rational understanding and use.

In such cases when an active interpretive expression of surprise is properly timed and expressed, the effect of the interpretation follows a regular sequence. Contrary to what might be expected when a defensive adaptational pattern is called to question, the patient's reaction is not one of increased anxiety, fear, or anger, but rather one of almost enthusiastic acceptance and confirmation. These patients now bring forth a flood of associations consisting of further examples pertaining to the idiosyncratic family patterns. The delight which is taken in this activity makes it appear as though they had for some time been most desirous of exploring aspects of life which their anxiety had hitherto prevented them from considering. This material is often expanded for the next several interviews, during which the patient experiments with new possibilities, both in the treatment hours and in everyday life. Frequently this reaction overcarries to some degree so that the previously inhibited student spends every evening on a date or stands up for his rights to an excessive degree. The formerly rigid and uncompromising young man may temporarily exercise his tolerance to the point of brief Bohemianism. This "release phenomenon" is usually short-lived and is superseded by a relatively stable and steady exploration of new modes of self-realization.

Concomitant with exploration of new modes of expression, the patient reports a growth in self-confidence and ability to get satisfaction out of his activities. There may be some expression of differences with the family, who may come to accept the patient's new modes with varying degrees of readiness. When a position of relative stability has been reached, the therapist and patient can usually agree that the immediate period of treatment has achieved its aim and that the patient is able to continue his development in normal life experience outside of the therapeutic situation. On the average, in my experience, this point is reached from two to four months after the beginning of therapy. Whether or not the patient may experience later difficulties which might require psychotherapeutic intervention can, it seems, be left an open question. In most instances in which follow-up has been possible, the new positions have been maintained, enriched, and expanded upon. Those patients who do return to psychotherapy after some interval of time present a considerably different clinical picture from that which was initially seen. This is the picture of neurotic symptom formation in persons of adult character structure. Appropriate therapy at this time is of an entirely different nature than that which has been described here and usually involves working through of the neurotic problem in the transference. This may be carried out by the same therapist but more often the vestiges of the former relationship may serve as too serious resistance to progress, so that the patient should be referred to another psychotherapist.

This brief treatment method developed directly out of some years of experience in the treatment of adolescents and especially delayed adolescents, the latter being a culturally and developmentally determined phenomenon frequently manifested in college students. The approach is based specifically on an application of psychoanalytic theories of ego development extended to the period of late adolescence. Attention has only recently been turned to changes in this period (9); consequently therapeutic method and theoretical formulation proceed side by side. In relation to treatment designed to meet the problems of a specific developmental period, the extension of techniques of psychoanalysis of children described by Anna Freud (6) can be recognized. Aichhorn's general method with acting-out adolescents is applied here to other character problems (1). This treatment shares elements with the processes of character synthesis described by Gitelson (8), the psychological counseling of Blos (4) and the therapeutic design described by Erikson (5) in the context of hospital treatment of disturbed adolescents. It is almost identical with the eclectic intuitive rapport therapy described by Fry and developed in his work with college students, the minor differences from the work of Fry residing in the somewhat more explicit statement of method and the narrowed range of application (7).

The treatment which has been described is distinctly dissimilar from psychoanalysis, although it is based on psychoanalytic theories of personality development. In the writer's experience psychoanalysis is not appropriate treatment for the developmental problems being discussed. In instances where this treatment or directly derivative psychotherapies have been applied, it appears that the immediate response of the patient is a stiffening of the idiosyncratic character defenses which may persist for long periods of time and even defeat the therapy. Even when these resistances are worked through, the treatment may become somewhat turbulent or the patient may adopt a "psychoanalytic character" out of identification with the analyst in the treatment situation, which may not necessarily represent the optimum level of integration. This is not to say that psychoanalysis ought not to be utilized in treatment of people of this age, since some of these have developed fixed neuroses, but only that it is not the treatment of choice for individuals in the developmental impasse described.

This psychotherapy also differs from strictly ego-supportive therapy with its elements of suppressive, educative, inspirational, and authoritative means of influence. While these methods of treatment, largely developed by various American "eclectic" schools, have usefulness in certain psychological disturbances, they are decidedly detrimental to the achievement of effective individual character synthesis. In instances where such supportive treatment has been used, the patient does achieve a degree of modification of the adaptational patterns developed in the family but is left with the necessity of freeing himself from the adaptational methods required in the therapy. This writer has seen, for example, instances in which patients have been *taught* to take independent and active stands during such psychotherapy but cannot achieve satisfaction in personal relationships within the framework of an artificial synthetic pattern.

6

Many of the problems of education are intimately connected with the conditions necessary for healthy personality development. These experiences with students who seek psychotherapy suggest that the conditions which make for possibilities of character revision may be important to the experience of other college students. It is expected that study of college students who do not seek treatment may show that they have been able to utilize the college scene for these purposes without special aid. If this proves to be the case, it would appear that colleges could well forward their educational objectives by paying attention to their students' needs for appropriate acceptable relatedness (to the social scene and to individuals) and for the challenge of opportunity to experiment with new modes of adaptation.* Such formulations might

* The following quotation, called to my attention by Dr. H. B. Murphy, is excerpted from *Mid-century French Poets*, ed. Wallace Fowlie (New York, Grove Press, 1956), p. 18. It exemplifies the creative restructuring of perception of the world that is an aspect of the openness to learning, creativity, and personal resynthesis which makes for a constructive college experience. "A poem is a marriage between expression and meaning. In order to compose the poem, the poet has to question everything all over again, because a successful poem is a new way of seeing and apprehending something which is familiar. . . . the poet's power of questioning the universe is essential. His capacity to be amazed at what he sees is his sign. Without it, his poem will never be the revelation it should be, the revelation to himself and to his readers of what

be taken into account in considering the many details of life in which the college as a social system impinges on the student.

REFERENCES

1. Aichhorn, August, *Wayward Youth,* New York, Viking Press, 1935; New York, Meridian Books, 1955.

2. Blos, Peter, "Observations on Late Adolescence," lecture at Division of Psychiatry and Mental Hygiene, Yale University, Nov. 1955.

3. ——— Prolonged adolescence: the formulation of a syndrome and its therapeutic implications, *American Journal of Orthopsychiatry,* 24:733–42. 1954.

4. ——— The contribution of psychoanalysis to the treatment of adolescents, in *Psychoanalysis and Social Work,* ed. Marcel Heiman, New York, International Universities Press, 1953.

5. Erikson, E. H., The problem of ego identity, *Journal of the American Psychoanalytic Association,* 4:56–121. 1956.

6. Freud, Anna, *The Ego and the Mechanisms of Defense,* New York, International Universities Press, 1946.

7. Fry, C. C., *Mental Health in College,* New York, Commonwealth Fund, 1942.

8. Gitelson, M., Character synthesis, the psychotherapeutic problem of adolescence, *American Journal of Orthopsychiatry, 18:*422–31. 1948.

9. Sanford, Nevitt, Personality development during the college years, *Personnel and Guidance Journal, 35:*74–80. 1956.

---

his questioning glance has resurrected, illuminated and understood. In order to be amazed, the poet has to practice a freedom which is unusual, because it is related to everything: the physical world, morality, mythology, God. The practice of this freedom insures what we may best call the poetic response to the world and to everything in it. This is vigilance, attentiveness, lucidity: all those disciplines which are impossible to define but which the artist needs in order to achieve his work."

INDEX

283